ORIGINS OF LIFE

ORIGINS OF LIFE
Proceedings of the First Conference

Edited by
LYNN MARGULIS

This conference was supported by the National Aeronautics and Space Administration and the Smithsonian Institution through contract with The New York Academy of Sciences. It was the first of a planned series of five yearly conferences on the *Origins of Life*. The Conference was held at Princeton, New Jersey, from May 21 to 24, 1967.

Published for
The Interdisciplinary Communication Associates, Inc.
by
GORDON AND BREACH, SCIENCE PUBLISHERS
New York • London • Paris

577
C760
89981
Oct 1974

Editorial office for Great Britain:
Gordon and Breach, Science Publishers Ltd.
12 Bloomsbury Way
London W. C. 1

Editorial office for France:
Gordon & Breach
7-9 rue Emile Dubois
Paris 14e.

Printed in the United States of America

1 3 3 2

FOREWORD

Now that studies of chimpanzees in the wild have shown them to use branches of trees as clubs, the separation of man from his anthropoid relatives by his use of tools seems to have lost validity.

I should like to propose a new criterion. Man might be described as having evolved as the first individual to speculate on the origins of life.

Thus the conference reported in this volume is in an old and honorable tradition. The impressive fact to me is the remarkable similarity of content of theory on the origin of life since earliest history.

The early Greek philosophers spoke of the combination of the "elements" to form living matter, first in the form of an amorphous mass, and later evolving function and structure.

Our present theories differ little except that we know of more than three elements. Four are required for most of our experiments, and we recognize the required participation of several others.

It is no wonder, therefore, that scientists who have turned their attention to the origin of life are attracted by the opportunities offered by space travel. Laboratory studies of recent years, sparked by the brilliantly simple experiments of Miller and Urey in 1953, have presented evidence of the plausibility of the ancient theories even though the historic facts seem still elusive.

Origin of life itself, under laboratory simulated geologic conditions, may well require a span of time that is several orders of magnitude longer in years than the span of a scientist's or of an institution's attention.

Natural origin of primordial life under terrestrial conditions, if it were to occur, would have a short life expectancy and would be most elusive of discovery. Even the fossil record on a planet as heavily populated as earth can create great confusion, though it is a rational line to pursue in search of clues to the origin. The recent ability, though still laborious, to trace evolutionary relationships in modern organisms through amino-acid sequence may provide a basis for extrapolating to more and more ancient archetypes and, therefore, is a promising line of development of confirmatory theory.

How much more satisfying it would be to find the stages in chemical evolution that we predict from laboratory experiments nicely preserved in the rocks of some unpopulated body of our solar system—or to record the chemical processes in action in the atmosphere of a Jovian planet that we now conduct in laboratory glassware—or to find a biota on another planet with a biochemical organization markedly similar or dissimilar to that of our terrestrial biota.

In 1933 Hiram Percy Maxim, designer of the "Columbia" electric car and the inventor of the "Maxim Silencer," wrote *Life's Place in the Cosmos*. The discussion in that popular book—with the exception of a few "facts"—might have been written last week. That exception, expressed by the frontispiece, shows a neatly dressed man sitting on an earth—an earth in appearance very like the earth of the Apollo VIII photographs. But the man is chained, wrist and ankle, to the earth. Mr. Maxim, for all his imagination and technical eminence only 35 years ago, did not consider space travel as an avenue to solution of this "greatest of all mysteries."

Dr. Orr E. Reynolds
Director, Biosciences Program
National Aeronautics and Space Administration
Washington, D. C.

PREFACE

The problem of "where do I come from" has plagued men throughout time. Traditional religious answers have been built on the authority of tribal and political leaders; scientific answers are somewhat more grounded in factual evidence.

"I" is always a person with a mother. We people, in spite of our protestations, are all animals evolved from primate animal forms. We are all members of the same species, one that has been on the earth for not more than 2 million years or so. Our primate species probably evolved from a relatively small group of anthropoid apes in the old world tropics. These primates most likely evolved from a primitive insectivorous group of mammals.

Students of evolution can trace the continuity among animal forms with a fair degree of certainty at least back some half a billion years. But where did life itself come from? What happened before well-developed animal fossils were deposited in the Cambrian some 600 million years ago? From what invertebrate animal stock did the primitive vertebrates come? From what flagellate form did the invertebrates evolve? From what primitive cells did the animal flagellates arise? Where did photosynthesis, the biochemical process that sustains us all, come from?

ix

As our chemical insight into biology has sharpened, so our questions have become more sophisticated: Where did the membrane-bound system of metabolic pathways recognizable as the minimal self-replicating system (that is, the cell) come from? We stumble here. From the replicating cell to man we have *organic evolution,* a process by which we can understand and document the historical continuity of related forms. But prior to the origin of a minimal self-replicating system we lack such a mechanism. Therefore, to a large extent this conference centers about the question of the origin of a self-replicating molecular process under primitive earth conditions.

It is assumed, of course, that the laws of physics and chemistry operated in the past as they do today. There is some time limit, too, on the origin of a self-replicating system—most likely it occurred between the origin of the earth and the dawn of a clear fossil record—roughly between 5000 and 2000 million years ago. From astronomy, deductions concerning the general conditions on a planet such as ours may be made, but a detailed, plausible connection between conditions on the early planet and the origin of an evolving system eludes us. Since the problem itself is composite, no one person or discipline can hope to solve it. As with any problem totally unsolved, many diverse opinions and points of view are to be entertained. Inferences can be made from experiments and observations related to the central problem. There is no better place for these inferences to appear than in these five Interdisciplinary Communications Program Conferences.

Because of the scientific training of the participants there are prevalent throughout the discussions unstated assumptions concerning the nature of the central scientific questions. Some of these might be stated: "Is the formation of an evolving system a likely event in the formation of planets in the universe?" "How, under conditions of the primitive earth, did organic compounds form and then come together to produce a self-replicating system upon which natural selection could act?" "How were the primitive living systems related to the present-day mechanisms of biological reproduction based on nucleic acid and protein?" "When did this transition from inorganic to organic occur?" "What evidence for any particular set of events can be deduced from either contemporary experimental science or historical geology?" These questions faced the participants as they proceeded to discuss the *Origins of Life*.

The publication of the proceedings of this conference has two goals. The first is to accurately capture the nature of scientific inquiry and exchange among peers by presenting essentially verbatim discussion. Presumably by including everything, the fact that scientists like humans in other activities meander, make false starts, and circuitously but often elegantly solve problems will become apparent to the reader. The second goal is to communicate the substantive scientific content of the discussions.

Thoroughly dedicated to both goals, I have found them mutually contradictory. Scientists like everyone else have their "wells," "buts," and "ahs." They say "it" whether they mean "the absorption spectrum in the infrared region of a mixture of gases" or "the two-dimensional paper chromatogram of nucleic acid residues." Thus this document is really a compromise between preserving the informal and truly communicative spirit of the sessions and preserving the reader's interest by clarifying and tightening the text. My scientific colleagues will have to forgive me if I have taken liberties with their comments or if I have erred in translating from the oral to the written. On the other hand, had I succumbed to the temptation of returning the entire manuscript to each of the participants for comments on the revisions, enough time would have elapsed to make even the revisions obsolete. As it is, I complete this note well over a year later.

Because all of the material discussed in Wednesday's (5/24/67) session on extraterrestrial life had already been published, the participants chose to present it here in synopsis form only. All references cited at the conference were retained, however, and have been included in a special bibliography at the end of the section.

Unfortunately, complete references to the literature cited throughout the conference were not submitted by all participants. Rather than further delay publication or omit them entirely I decided to retain them in their imperfect form so that interested readers might be given at least a lead to the relevant work.

I want to acknowledge the generous help of all the participants who responded to the questions that I did have a chance to ask, and

especially I acknowledge the aid of J. R. Williams who continues to
teach me the art of editing.

Dr. Lynn Margulis
Science Editor
Biology Department
Boston University
Boston, Massachusetts

CONTENTS

INTRODUCTORY REMARKS

INTRODUCTORY REMARKS

SUNDAY EVENING and *MONDAY MORNING*

May 21-22, 1967

Dr. Frank Fremont-Smith
Presiding

Fremont-Smith: Ladies and gentlemen, I am very sorry that Phil Handler's wife is ill, and therefore he will be unable to chair this meeting. He has asked that Dr. Horowitz be the Acting Chairman, and Dr. Horowitz has agreed to take on this stupendous task.

Horowitz: Thank you. No one is sorrier than I that Phil can't be here. I would like to introduce this conference by pointing out something that I think you are all aware of, namely, that the problem we are here to discuss is a most important and difficult one, probably the most important unsolved problem of biological evolution.

We realize now that past investigations into the origins of life have been futile because, until quite recently, we haven't even understood what life is. The realization that we didn't know enough about life to investigate its origin is, itself, a new realization. As you know, learned people for centuries considered the origin of life a proper subject for investigation, since they believed life originated every day in garbage. The literature of the Middle Ages abounds in recipes for making scorpions, fleas, rats, and so forth, out of mud and decaying matter. It wasn't until

1

a century ago that Pasteur demonstrated the decay seen in garbage is caused by microbes, and that even they originate only from pre-existing microbes. The problem of the origin of life was then recognized to be an historical problem.

As a consequence of Pasteur's experiments, interest in the spontaneous origin of life faded into the background, and biologists began devoting themselves to the more fruitful task of investigating the nature of living matter. As a result of the many discoveries of the past century concerning the nature and evolution of living things we have finally, in the middle of the twentieth century, arrived at the point where we think we can again discuss intelligently the origin of life. We have found that life is not one of the eternal categories of nature like energy, matter, or time, but rather a manifestation of certain molecular combinations. According to the cosmologists, not even the elements have always existed forever. They must have had an origin.

I don't want to go into the substantive matter of the conference but clearly, as the result of recent discoveries in cosmology, geo-chemistry, molecular genetics, and bio-chemistry, it is now possible to arrive at a self-consistent model for the orgin of life on the earth, making possible certain predictions regarding the origin of life on other planets. Fortunately, with the dawn of the Space Age, we may test some of these predictions on the planets nearest to the earth. The subject under discussion at this conference is a truly interdisciplinary one; various sciences have something to offer.

I think that is all I wanted to say for the introductory remarks. I should like next to introduce Dr. Henry Moss, President of the New York Academy of Sciences, which is sponsoring this meeting.

Moss: Dr. Horowitz, members of the conference: It is a pleasure to welcome you on behalf of the Scientific Council and the Board of Trustees of the New York Academy. We think the Interdisciplinary Communications Program has been a most welcome addition to the Academy Program, and since 1964 we have been fortunate to have it within the province of the Academy.

We think there is a real role for a meeting of this kind to supplement the conferences that we hold for large audiences on limited fields of investigation. Dr. Frank Fremont-Smith deserves tremendous commendation for both his pioneering efforts in making these conferences so successful and for insuring that the subsequent published monograph is a tribute to the Academy.

As the growth of science leads to greater cross-fertilization between fields, the Academy is given further opportunities to broaden its endeavors. We are indebted to individuals like yourselves who take time out from busy schedules to give your thoughts to our conferences. I am very delighted to have this opportunity to see how Dr. Frank Fremont-Smith runs his particular conference as well as the privilege, of course, to meet each of you individually.

Horowitz: Thank you, Dr. Moss. I should next like to introduce Mr. Harry Hyman of the Smithsonian Institution. The Smithsonian has had an important role in supporting this meeting.

Hyman: I bring you warm greetings from Dr. Ripley, the Secretary of the Smithsonian Institution, and from Dr. Sidney R. Galler, the Assistant Secretary for Science. They are very sorry that they cannot be here tonight.

Horowitz: Thank you, Mr. Hyman. Dr. Frank Fremont-Smith.

Fremont-Smith: I would like to open what is going to be an informal conference, very informally [taking off his jacket]. I would like to thank Dr. Moss for his words of welcome; it is the first time we have been able to capture the President of the Academy at one of our conferences.

I would also like to tell you about Orr Reynolds who has been of enormous help in sponsoring several of our conferences, including this one. We have a curious arrangement in which funds flow from one agency to another and eventually end up in our pocket; Orr, in NASA, has been very instrumental in seeing that the flow went in the right direction. More important than that, however, it was Orr who suggested that a series of conferences on the orgins of life would be particularly timely. I hope, Orr, when we come to the self-introductions, that you will tell us about the origins of your life, or any other aspects of the problem.

Reynolds: Shrouded in antiquity.

Fremont-Smith: It is a great privilege to have with us Dr. Shelesnyak, whom we are delighted to welcome not only as a participant in this conference but also, as of September 1967, Associate Director of the Interdisciplinary Communications Program.

I would like to talk a bit on the kind of communication we try to instigate here. Most conferences provide very little opportunity for any real communication. They consist of speeches; if a little discussion gets going, the chairman says, "I'm awfully sorry to interrupt this fascinating discussion but we are twenty-five minutes behind on our agenda and I must call on Professor so-and-so to make another speech at you." The most useful discussions at standard conferences take place in the corridors, in participants' rooms, and at the bar. In small bull sessions people often resolve bothersome issues or get to know others who share their interests. Even panel discussions, originally introduced to avoid coined lectures, are now just a series of short speeches. We are trying to reverse this. We want to bring into the conference room what normally takes place in the corridors.

All the different specialties are like isolated groups of people out on the ends of peninsulas of knowledge protruding into a great sea of ignorance. On the tip of each peninsula is a small group of people who have developed a special language, talk effectively to one another, but can't communicate with most people on other peninsulas. So you get progressive intellectual isolation as these peninsulas get farther and farther apart. From the history of science we know that the next breakthrough is likely to take place among several areas of specialized information, requiring coordinated activity and even genuine teamwork among people from the several disciplines. We need communication not only at conferences but also in our universities. John Gardner recognized this just before he became Secretary of Health, Education, and Welfare when he said that the educational community seems to have been playing a game of golf where each man continues to hit his own ball, rather than a game of tennis where the players hit the ball back and forth across the net to each other. Well, we are in favor of the tennis game, and we even like mixed doubles. One of the purposes of our Interdisciplinary Conference is to try to break through this pattern of isolation among the different branches of science.

We believe that the problems of communication among scientists are not really scientific. This is explored in a very nice volume by M. L. Johnson-Abercrombie, *The Anatomy of Judgement,* which contradicts our notion that first we observe phenomena and then we make a secondary step of interpreting them. She shows how observation and interpretation take place simultaneously, each person bringing to any new experience his own particular idiosyncratic past and logic.

At this conference we are free to interrupt. Just speak up. This may lead to chaos, but we prefer a little chaos to a lot of rigidity. Don't ever feel your questions are foolish; the only foolish thing to do is not to ask the question if you want to know the answer. So, too, we expect and encourage disagreements. We want challenges, and we want all of the interaction process to be made available, if possible. The published proceedings of this conference will attempt to share with a wider audience the essence of what takes place here.

I will say just one more thing. I would like to remind my friends that the one thing we can count upon is change, and change is going to come faster and faster. As a result of this, the half-life of facts is getting shorter and shorter. Thus, if we really allow ourselves to get attached to facts, we are likely to find ourselves out in left field very soon. Beginning tomorrow morning, our discussion leaders will have a special role—to keep us from making speeches, yet to evoke discussion. At this point, I will turn the meeting back to our Chairman.

Horowitz: Thank you Dr. Fremont-Smith, for your words of wisdom and advice. Dr. Fremont-Smith advised me that the best way to begin our informal self-introductions was to select one of my most distinguished and articulate friends and get him to initiate these proceedings. I can't think of anyone better than the gentleman on my right, Bill McElroy.

McElroy: John Hopkins, Baltimore.

Fremont-Smith: No, no, this won't do at all. We want to know what you are like, and how you got that way, and what you honestly believe in, and what you are going to do next week, or what you did last week that was exciting.

McElroy: Some of those things I can't tell.

Fremont-Smith: Tell us a little about yourself, how you got interested in the origin of life, if you are, and if not, what you are interested in. Who inspired you? Give!

McElroy: How far back do you want to go? Back to the frog and tadpole days in high school? I don't know how I got interested in science, frankly. I really got interested, I guess, in the origins of life when I studied with Newton Harvey right here on this campus in the 1940's.

Fremont-Smith: What was he doing at that time—when you first got excited?

McElroy: Luminescence. Harvey did practically nothing else but luminescence. My interest in energy transformation—what kinds of chemical systems were involved in the trapping of energy for useful purposes in biological systems evolved from there. This led me to the whole concept of the mechanism of oxygen activation, which is what really got me interested in the evolutionary process on the surface of the earth where presumably life originated under what was once called anaerobic conditions, but whether it was truly anaerobic is now doubtful. This led to my whole interest in how luminous organisms arose. I think luminescence is fundamentally a detoxification mechanism that arose during those periods of, let's say, very low oxygen tension on the surface of the earth. This gets us into a semantic problem of what *anaerobic* means quantitatively. Anyway, I got interested in the origin of life through the study of luminescence.

Side issues have also interested me, such as organisms going into space; aeroembolism—that is, the presence in the blood stream of obstructive air bubbles—and another topic on which we need more study—the analysis of gas mixtures, and so forth. I spent some time with Henry Eyring here at Princeton, and this carried my interest over into biochemical mechanisms and ultimately into marine biology, which has been interesting me recently. That's about it, I think.

Fremont-Smith: That's quite a lot. Thank you very much.

Horowitz: Thank you for your illuminating remarks, Bill. Going around the room, next is Phil Abelson.

Abelson: I was first trained as a nuclear physicist. After the war I looked around to see what seemed to be the most significant problem to examine and decided that it was the origin of life. However, I also noted that we didn't know very much about life, and so I turned to studies of biosynthesis in microorganisms. In 1953, I was asked to be Director of the Geophysical Laboratory in Washington and decided that I should take the job since it would give me an opportunity to become familiar with the earth and its proc-/esses. I began to look into the question of organic material in rocks and specifically organic material in fossils. I thought it would be convenient if there were some organic remains in fossils, and, sure enough, there were.

Subsequently, I became interested in some "model experiments"— that is, on chemical syntheses hopefully simulating the prebiological terrestrial environment—and from time to time have worked on those. I have felt that these model experiments are a little bit of a chancy business. If you assume wrong conditions all the work goes down the drain. Thus, it is poor policy for a person to commit himself entirely to doing model experiments. For that reason, my scientific work alternately emphasized one of two programs: Investigations of organic matter in rocks and model experiments.

For the last few months, I have been considering geological evidence about the nature of the ancient earth's surface, as early as the rocks will provide us with evidence. This is a natural program at a geophysical laboratory and, of course, relates to problems of the origin and evolution of life.

Fox: My name is Sidney Fox. Maybe it is appropriate that I follow Phil Abelson. When I think back, as I have often been asked to do, I would not have chosen to make a frontal attack upon the problem of the origin of life. In the work that we were doing in the early fifties, I wasn't even sure that we were working on the origin of life until Phil Abelson told us so and, in fact, the first symposium on the origin of life in which I participated was the one at the Brooklyn Polytechnic Institute at Phil's behest. The kind of investigation we were concerned with was an earlier interest in the evolution of protein molecules in organisms. This in turn stemmed from earlier work in the forties, pre-Sanger [Frederick Sanger, Nobel Laureate, Chemistry, 1958] work directed toward sequence studies in protein molecules. From some of the surveys of protein molecules in organisms, sequentially and compositionally, we thought we saw a clue as to how some experiments might be performed. A principal aspect of our philosophy before and after we got started in this field was attempting to discipline the concepts experimentally.

As Dr. Fremont-Smith implied, the consequence of thinking that is shaped by doing experiments; one finds a great deal of the so-called logic is, in the last analysis, illogic.

Ponnamperuma: I am Cyril Ponnamperuma of the National Aeronautics and Space Administration, Ames Research Center, Moffet Field, California. It appears that I came into this field through the back door. The first four years of my undergraduate life in India were spent studing philosophy. In Buddhist and Hindu philosophy, everything is considered to be in an evolutionary state. Unfortunately, philosophy didn't bring bread to the table so I took up chemistry. While at the University of London I had the good fortune of having Professor Bernal as a teacher in physics. One evening, instead of his usual lecture on electricity and magnetism, he spoke to us of the physical basis of life. For the first time I realized that one could really do scientific work on the problem of the origin of life. This brought me to the laboratories of Professor Melvin Calvin [Nobel Laureate, Chemistry, 1961] at the University of California, and I worked there with him for my degree. I then joined NASA where I am now, at Ames, working on chemical syntheses leading to the origin of life.

Pattee: Howard Pattee, Stanford University. I was almost trained as a nuclear physicist and, from moving too many lead bricks around, I think, I switched into something more akin to biology, x-ray microscopy, and microanalysis—that is, to instrumentation I thought might be really useful in biology.

As a young physicist, Pirie's (1952) exceedingly critical evaluation of J.D.Bernal's (1951) book irritated me a little bit. Pirie said Bernal's book was reminiscent of Schrodinger's (1944) *What Is Life?* but that it was not as bad. I didn't really see what was so bad about it. I began to think seriously about the physics of life and instruments; then three papers appeared which stimulated this line of thought. One was Von Neumann's (1951) paper on automata theory showing that self-replication was possible; another one was Philip Morrison's (1964) paper proposing a thermodynamic definition of self-replication; and the third was Eugene Wigner's (1961) paper on the quantum mechanics of self-replication in which he proved that exact self-replication was not possible. There seemed to be a certain divergence of opinion about physics and biology, without even bringing in the biologists. My interests, somewhat different from yours in chemical evolution, developed in the physics of hereditary evolution. General hereditary chemical processes (I am not talking just about DNA) are those which have some kind of memory. This leads to the question of the persistence of biological systems as opposed to non-biological systems, and that in turn leads to the idea of reliability of hereditary processes. My interest is in how the laws of physics may describe the difference between living and non-living systems in a precise way.

Moss: I am Henry Moss and I originally had no intention of participating in this conference. However, during the brief time that I have had the privilege of listening to several participants, I began to see the definite relationship between the discussion and clinical medicine. I am a member of a surgical faculty at Temple University, an attending surgeon interested in the cancer field and aspects of post-operative convalescence.

Cancer is interpreted as abnormal growth; to understand it, we need to know normal growth. This touches on the very essence of life itself. Today clinicians more than ever before face the problem of defining biological and clinical life. By the advent of new transportation techniques in trauma cases (such as in Vietnam) patients are being rescued from death by new kinds of clinical techniques. I just heard a talk last week in which it was said that 98 percent of patients who arrive alive on the Navy's hospital ship, USS Repose, actually are saved because they are removed from the battle zone in five or ten minutes. In previous wars they would never have recovered. Shock patients are now saved from the very doors of death by heroic measures such as immediately administered massive blood transfusions.

Not only in military but in civilian practice too, cardiac resuscitation restores cardiac and pulmonary functions. But are these patients really alive? Is a patient who has to have all his vital life processes performed for him alive? This represents perhaps a tangent application of some of the things we talk about when we concern ourselves with what life is, a definition of life, and perhaps ultimately to the origin of life.

The reference to bioluminescence stimulated my thinking because I, too, was a student here at Princeton, and Dr. Frank Johnson was very interested in this area. I never had the opportunity of studying under Dr. Newton Harvey, but I always held the name in great reverence, particularly because of his stature on the faculty. So I thought I might explain how, in clinical surgery, we too can see a potential application to some of the more basic sciences that will be discussed in this conference.

Schopf: My name is Bill Schopf. I am a Junior Fellow in the Society of Fellows of Harvard University. During the past four years I have worked with Professor Barghoorn on a variety of problems related to Precambrian paleobiology. Although at Harvard I am classified as a biologist, my undergraduate training at Oberlin College was in geology. My work has principally dealt with the morphology and phylogeny of Precambrian microorganisms, using both optical and electron microscopy and I have investigated several Precambrian sediments for fossil porphyrins. At present I am beginning similar work on the amino acid content of early fossiliferous deposits.

Primarily, I am interested in the geological aspects of the origin of life and the nature of the early environment. I am also interested in the biology, phylogeny, and evolutionary development of Precambrian organisms, and in the relationships between the evolving biota and the early environment.

Sulston: John Sulston. I must confess that by comparison with the previous speakers, I feel a bit of an interloper because my Ph.D. is less than a year old, and my principal reason for being here is that I was looking around a year ago for a place to go and we heard back at Cambridge, England, that Les Orgel was doing very well for himself in California, and people said, "Why don't you go? He's not a bad chap and you will get brown in the sun." So, in October, I found myself looking at the origin of life, or a small problem in it. I am very interested and honored to come and participate in this conference.

Fremont-Smith: We, too, are very interested in the evolution of Ph.D.'s. Some grow faster than others, you know.

Reynolds: I am Orr Reynolds from NASA headquarters and I have to confess that Frank Fremont-Smith is right when he accuses me of having had something to do with the stimulation of this conference. The development of my own interest in this subject is a little unusual. I was trained and worked as an animal and human physiologist and through that route became involved in Government science administration at the end of World War II.

My presumption when I joined NASA was that they were interested in me because of my background in physiology. I expected to work on the effects of the space environment on mammals, with eventual application to people. My first week at NASA, I was given a package of viewgraphs (instead of using 2X2 slides we use viewgraphs: 12X14 pieces of cardboard) and sent on a trip to make a speech! I was just barely able to shuffle through them and see the notes prepared for me when I reached my audience of five or six hundred people. Apparently it was not improper for interruptions to occur, so I was led into a brief entanglement with people on subjects I was ill-prepared to defend. Anyway, it was quite an eye opener. Soon after, I attended a two week conference chaired by Allen

Brown from the University of Pennsylvania; quite a number of people here may have been in that group. Surprising to me at the time, there was a tremendous enthusiasm in the search for extraterrestrial life. Some NASA biology people advocated throwing the other side of the program—the environmental effects on organisms—completely out of the window. I really thought this was an idle topic, not significant enough to be taken seriously. When I discovered most people at that meeting really worried about the problem of extraterrestrial life, I started to listen. I was pretty thoroughly brainwashed and began to work on it, which I have been doing ever since, in an administrative way.

For a Government science administrator to let his own scientific ideas interfere with an objective job is very dangerous, so I don't have any on our subject. I have felt that although there have been several limited symposia, we need a conference on the origins of life involving the same people over a period of several years. It will be useful also to bring in relevant segments of the scientific community that until now have not been involved. I frankly think this conference series will be fruitful for both science and the Space Administration's program.

Kramer: I am Sol Kramer. When I thought about this conference I said to myself:"Gee, the topic, *The Origins of Life,* is extremely exciting but I wonder if the conference will be as dull as all hell." Now I feel a lot more optimistic about it because Dr. Fremont-Smith mentioned something about the value of the illogical, and Dr. Fox said that a great deal of logic is illogical, and I thought, "Well, this could be a good conference if we start off that way."

Reading one of Marshall McLuhan's recent books, a sentence impressed me. "Insistence on clarity at all costs is based on sheer superstition as to the mode in which human intelligence functions." If we can only be sufficiently illogical, this may yet be a very exciting conference.

Ponnamperuma: Aristotle said, "The only intellectual quality is perspicacity."

Kramer: I am impressed, too, with the Synectics group at Cambridge, Massachusetts. They simply get six or eight people from various disciplines—biology, chemistry, physics, engineering, even some of the humanities and psychology—to sit around and solve a particular problem. They all throw out thoughts, and after about two days of this they solve the problem. Somehow, the putting together of irrelevant, analogous kinds of material catalyzes something in these individuals. I am hoping that this process will take place here as well.

I am a biologist and evolutionist, and I guess I was imprinted on the subject of evolution when I was about 13. I have involved myself with organisms from cockroaches and earwigs to the sickle fish and the pigeon, and mammals, and right now I find myself utilizing some of the concepts of ethology in relation to human behavior in mental illness. I'm working in the Department of Psychiatry at the College of Medicine at the University of Florida.

I thought to myself, " I wonder what relevancy ethology really has as far as the evolution of life is concerned, because we are mostly interested in the behavior of organisms." The word *ethology* itself derives from the term *ethos,* meaning that which is innate or characteristic of. Perhaps I will discover from this conference that there is an ethology, an innate behavior of the preorganic and organic molecules as well. Certainly molecules and atoms behave; maybe we will thus learn about the basic concepts of behavior at the molecular level which will allow us to incorporate this area into ethology, in which case I will be delighted.

Horowitz: I am beginning to get the impression, with all of these attacks on logic, that the transcript of this meeting is going to read like *Finnegan's Wake.*   Maybe Leslie Orgel will defend Aristotle.

Orgel: I am afraid I am on their side.   It is so much easier to introduce someone else, and I am inclined to give a false name.

Fremont-Smith: Which one would you choose?

Orgel: Something like Sidney Abelson.   I started off as a chemist.   When it became clear that things came apart in my hands I was directed to become a theoretician.   Later, by a series of fortunate contacts with people in biology, I got more and more interested.   When I went to Cal Tech as a post-doc, I attended a freshman biology course given by George Beadle [Nobel Laureate, Medicine and Physiology, 1958] and I thought "My goodness, what an interesting subject biology is." Of course, I should have thought, "What a good teacher George Beadle is." But I didn't realize this at the time.   That is how I got started and gradually moved away from chemistry into biology and started to work on the origins of life.

Fremont-Smith: I like very much your comment, "What I should have said," because the whole emphasis on teaching is, I think, not what is the subject but the man.

Eglinton: I was born in Wales, though my ancestry is part Scottish. I was brought up in England and have lived in Scotland.   I am now a Reader in Geochemistry at the Chemistry Department of the University of Bristol in England.   I also make temporary but frequent visits to California.

I was trained at Manchester in straight organic chemistry with Sir E. R. H. Jones, now Professor of Chemistry at Oxford University. Just prior to that time, about 1948, I used to go hill-walking with a fellow who was somewhat of an amateur geologist, and we once came across a material known as *elaterite,* and I decided then that this would be an interesting material for examination by an organic chemist.   I took it back and asked one lecturer, "Can we find out anything about this, whether it had a biological origin or not?"   I was told to get on with BSc studies and not to think of such strange things.

Fremont-Smith: And not to think!

Eglinton: Yes. I went on to Ohio State University, trained as a synthetic chemist, and learned that infrared spectroscopy was useful though expensive. I returned to Liverpool, in Britain, and had a long fight to get suitable equipment. In 1954 I went to Glasgow and there developed various applications of infrared spectroscopy. I found that I was more and more tending toward the precept that I had heard E. R. H. Jones state more than once: That the big advances in chemistry often came from advances in instrumentation. So I started work on the gas chromatography of complex mixtures of organic compounds. Then there was a very fortunate coincidence. Professor of Biochemistry, A. C. Chibnall of Cambridge University, England, who is famous for his pioneering work of the 1930's on plant waxes, saw our paper and wrote to me. In his letter he remarked on the great potential gas chromatography had as a method of studying complex mixtures such as plant waxes, and asked if I would like his whole collection of plant waxes—extracts, purified fractions, and reference compounds. This was duly handed over in the form of about fifty tin boxes (Capstan cigarettes), lovingly packed with hundreds of neatly labeled glass vials containing the precious samples. We have made frequent use of this fine collection and have constantly found that recent results substantiate Chibnall's earlier findings.

Our studies of plant waxes led us to consider the possibility of classifying organisms through the use of gas chromatography. With this technique one can be impressively definitive about the structures of compounds encountered in complex mixtures, such as the sediment *elaterite* (which interestingly enough was by now sitting in a can in the cupboard going extremely moldy).

In 1963 I applied to the British Government for a grant that would permit me to begin organic geochemical research, but nothing much happened for some months. About this time my leave of absence came up so I went over to join Professor Melvin Calvin at Berkeley. The scientific atmosphere and interest in interdisciplinary work were exciting. We started a program in organic geochemistry, thereby following in the footsteps of other gentlemen at this table. From there onward, I have changed my whole research program from synthetic organic chemistry over to the analysis of complex mixtures using whatever physical tools came to hand. This approach permits the study of biological systems, the origin of life, the sampling of planets, and so on. That is the full chronological history.

Moss: Have you continued your interest in infrared spectroscopy?

Eglinton: Yes, but by the time one starts having to incorporate other disciplines, such as mass spectrometry and most other forms of analytical tools, the portion of time one can allot to infrared diminishes. However, there is one further connection in that the work I have done in infrared has been largely concerned with hydrogen bonding, and this then leads one to a study of biological systems where hydrogen bonds are all important.

Horowitz: What is *elaterite*?

Eglinton: *Elaterite* is a horribly sticky black goo.

Siever: That is only in England, however. Everywhere else in the world it is quite different. Dr. Ponnamperuma can tell us what it looks like.

Horowitz: Is it organic goo?

Eglinton: It is a very unusual deposit, so I am assured. It consists, I believe, of polymerized olefinic hydrocarbons. Is that right?

Ponnamperuma: So they say.

Moss: I have in the last two or three years had keen interests in the application of infrared to clinical practice by the development of thermography, a technique by which heat disseminated from the body can be visualized and become a useful mechanism for the detection of cancer, particularly on superficial sites like the breast. It sounds to me that it would be extremely helpful if, at some point in time, you could dust off some of your old interests in this area and help develop more basic information and understanding of the biological aspects pertaining to infrared, because this is what thermography needs at the moment. There is a keen interest throughout the country in this diagnostic tool.

Oró: My name is Juan Oró. I have not recorded my evolutionary history in detail so what I am going to say is based upon my memory.

Fremont-Smith: Do you think the rest of us are saying what our memories do not remember?

Oró: I am not sure that my memory is the best. My mother and my father were farmers. My father eventually went to Barcelona where he became a baker. I was born in the city of Lerida, in Spain, where I learned from my father the profession of baker. I received my primary education from a Catholic school, the Brothers of Mary, and my secondary from the National Institute of Lerida. In my high school years I was influenced by Buddha, Kempis, Schopenhauer, Haeckel, and Flammarion, among others. I became interested in fundamental problems of natural philosophy and biology, and I decided at an early age to devote myself to the study of the problem of the origin of life. Toward this end I first took up chemistry at the University of Barcelona from 1942 to 1947, and then, after a pause during which I made some savings working as a baker in Lerida, I came to the U.S.A. to do graduate work in biochemistry. This I did at Baylor University College of Medicine, Houston, from 1953 to 1956, and after that accepted a faculty position as a biochemist at the University of Houston, where I started to work on the abiotic syntheses of biochemical compounds. We have continued to work in our laboratory along these lines. In addition to the work on abiotic syntheses of biochemical compounds, we have attacked also the problem of the origin of life from other angles, for example, by studying the nature of organic matter in Precambrian sediments and in meteorites.

Burlingame: My name is Al Burlingame and I am at the University of California in Berkeley, Department of Chemistry. Listening to all of these illustrious comments reminds me of several things. First, probably Juan's remark that he grew up on a farm. I grew up on a farm and thought that I would be a farmer until I got into high school and took agriculture, at least the first day of it. We spent the first day discussing how the price of eggs could be raised and lowered and so forth. Deciding this wasn't really too significant, I took a course in biology instead. Maybe the next most significant event was the opportunity I had, while a graduate student at MIT, to work for E. H. Land of the Polaroid Corporation for a summer, fall, and winter. The relevance to my presence at this conference involves his conviction that anyone who is trained in a field knows what can and what cannot be solvable problems in the field and, therefore, would never be original. So, one should have a group of well-trained people in various specialities who know how to carry out the routine techniques, and so on, but if you want to explore a new phenomenon, put somebody with a good background in another field onto the problem and have all the specialists help him with the known techniques when he gets into trouble. So, I don't really feel out of place at this particular conference, probably due to my friend, Land. Under Land, we worked on how the eye sees color. In fact, what I was supposed to do as a chemist on the project was to figure out how to print with black and red—two black inks on a red and white background—and come out with full color. This does work by the way, although I don't know what the current results are.

I got interested in mass spectrometry through Klaus Biemann at MIT and took a degree with him; then I went to Berkeley.

Since I came to Berkeley, techniques that F. W. Aston (the grand old man of mass spectroscopy, Nobel Laureate, Chemistry, 1922) used in measuring atomic masses were being applied to infer elemental compositions of molecules from direct measurements of their nuclidic masses. Thus, I got interested in double-focusing mass spectrometry (now routinely possible with commercially available instrumentation) as a sophisticated way of determining structures of organic molecules using very small amounts of material. Through Melvin Calvin, I have gotten interested in the analysis of organic molecules in Precambrian sediments as a means of tracing the evolution of biological systems through "molecular fossils." We have done a reasonable amount of work in this area.

It so happened that Geoff Eglinton and I arrived at Berkeley at about the same time, and his interests and mine just fortunately crystallized and produced some interesting results in organic geochemistry. Mass spectrometry turns out to be an excellent technique for the detection and identification of organic molecules in very small amounts, far less than microgram quantities. We are currently attempting to set up high resolution instrumentation under computer control to help NASA develop an automated technique to detect and analyze the structure of organic molecules. Combined with gas chromatography, this approach is the most feasible, I think, for a Martian lander or any search for extraterrestrial life. The advantage is that one will be able to see any kind of small organic molecules and not be limited to any preconceived ideas about what kind of molecules they are, as long as they can be broken down either pyrolytically or chemically. I think I have talked long enough.

Shelesnyak: I believe my introduction by Frank points out the fact that I am here in a somewhat different category. In fact, I am concerned not only with the subject of the conference but also with the technique and technology of interdisciplinary communication. There is a bridge that I will come to in a moment.

In the past few years, most of my interest in the laboratory has been related to some study of experimental investigations of reproductive processes in the mammal. With good fortune and a certain amount of skill in grantsmanship, I managed to get the Ford Foundation to give me enough money to set up an interdisciplinary research group in the study of reproduction. In my own laboratory we attempt to explore the mechanism of certain reproductive processes (specifically, progestation) from every aspect except the ecological one, which is in the draft of the proposal but a stage that we have not as yet reached. Even within my small group, where each member is primarily a biologist with special conceptual and technical skills in some field such as biochemistry, pharmacology, or immunology, communication was not always as fluid as it should be, and communication with other groups in the Weizman Institute, particularly those concerned with molecular biology, was even more remote and more difficult.

When the opportunity presented itself to join Frank's (Fremont-Smith) group, it struck me as a challenge, perhaps in a sort of illogical way not having been entirely successful in a small operation, to try to see whether I could be successful in a larger one. In a sense, what intrigues me most about the problems of the origin of life is the transitional stage, what I like to think of as from *life* to *living* not in a social sense but in the sense we are concerned with—the organism or component parts of the organism. My own feeling is that this is probably going to be one of the toughest nuts to crack, but as I see it, it is one that we should attempt while we are wrestling with the more basic subject, which is the one of this conference.

I might close this by saying that I am here primarily as an observer. I think it was good of Frank, perhaps for administrative purposes, to designate me as a consultant.

Fremont-Smith: We don't permit observers, only participants.

Shelesnyak: Then, I am going to be an observant consultant.

Barghoorn: Elso Barghoorn. My first interest in science was in astronomy; my next, in chemistry. During later high school years I became fascinated with living organisms, especially plants. I suppose there is no rational sequence in the development of one's intellectual center of interest. In fact, I think all of us develop several systems of interest—science, literature, or history, for example. Various sciences impinge on certain few fundamental questions, and it is fortunate that this conference is to be, because the origin of life is the focus of interest of nearly all aspects of science. Perhaps one reason for this is the fact that life processes are so inscrutable, and that we have to borrow from every direction in an approach to understanding them and their origins. Personally, I thought, and I still think, the origin of life is a philosophical rather than a scientific problem, and I risk rousing some antagonism with my statement. Even if we can produce life, the question is still beyond resolution because the origin of life was a sort of diffuse event in the history of the earth or some other planetary body, and even if we can make life in the laboratory, we still haven't resolved the problem of the origin of life in the cosmic sense. It is a scientific gamble to go into such research. One of the fundamental wedges that has been driven into the problem is the development of geochronology. If one looks back on the history of the concepts of measuring time, one quickly realizes that time is a sort of skeleton that we can hang our facts on. The improvement in geochronology plus a far more comprehensive elucidation of geologic processes and the geologic record in general—that is, historic geology—and the incorporation of concepts of organic evolution in the Darwinian sense into this dimension have given us a real comprehension of the problem.

Miller: I am Stanley Miller, Department of Chemistry at the University of California, San Diego. I am primarily a chemist with an interest in a great many things, such as clay mineralogy, some applications of chemical techniques to astronomical problems, water relations, and the negative pressures in the xylem of plants. I have been interested in the mechanism of organic reactions of certain types; I am also interested in general anesthesia and the mechanisms of nerve action. I would say that my primary interest is in the origin of life and in attempting to reconstruct, insofar as possible, the steps that led up to the spontaneous formation of life. My work, as you know, started with the chemist Harold Urey (Nobel Laureate, Chemistry, 1934), my professor when I was a graduate student at the University of Chicago.

Although we think about finding one path for the formation of life, it may be that there will be several plausible reconstructions of how life started on the earth. I would be most content if we could have even one plausible, detailed, and complete explanation of how life started. I am primarily interested in the origin of life from an experimental standpoint: How does one make various types of organic compounds? How could these plausibly have been made under primitive earth conditions? How do these various organic compounds combine to form the more complex organic molecules? And so on. I find this a very fascinating although perhaps a peculiar sort of science because it attempts an historical reconstruction. Most science deals with facts as they are today. Nevertheless, this is an interesting topic and my principal interest.

Bada: My name is Jeffrey Bada. I am also at the University of California at San Diego. I am a graduate student with about one year left on my thesis. It is on the kinetics and geochemical implications of the deamination of aspartic acid.

I originally was interested in liquid structure and, primarily, the structure of aqueous solutions, but through conversations with Dr. Miller I became interested in the origin of life. Recently I have become interested in the geochemistry of clay minerals and of sediments.

Margulis: My name is Lynn Margulis, but it used to be Lynn Sagan. I am basically a geneticist and cytologist, trained at the Universities of Chicago, Wisconsin, and California (Berkeley). I am presently in the Biology Department at Boston University. I have always been very interested in the evolutionary relationships between prokaryotic microbes (bacteria and blue-green algae) and eukaryotic cells (those of animals and plants and other higher organisms). I have spent a lot of time working out a relationship between these two cellular forms and I have some very strong opinions (Sagan, L. 1967). If anyone asks, I will be very happy to tell him about these opinions.

Until Dr. Barghoorn and Bill Schopf showed me how to hang my thoughts on the geochronological framework, I never realized the implications these ideas could have for the early terrestrial atmos--phere and the discontinuity in the fossil record at the base of the Cambrian. Mostly, my ideas involve events occurring from about

3.4 billion to about 6.2 million years ago. Earlier times I leave up to you people. I'm very grateful to Phil Morrison for inviting me here.

Fremont-Smith: We are pleased to have you.

Morrison: Phil Morrison, MIT, Physics. Even visitors to Cambridge (Massachusetts) are very likely to go out (from Harvard Square) into the hinterlands a few miles to the center of oriental philosophy known as Joyce Chen's (a popular Chinese restaurant). There, a couple of months ago, I received one of those cryptic messages that comes in a little cookie at the end of the meal and it said: "Indulge in untried ideas at the risk of reputation." I think this is perhaps the kind of stimulus that brought many of us here to this interdisciplinary exchange.

I am a theoretical physicist and for a good many years have been interested in the edge between nuclear physics and astronomy. During the war, I came into contact with the radiologists K. C. Cole and Henry Quastler and others, and began to think about many of their problems. Since I was a rather undistinguished student under the virologist Mark Adams many years ago, I know a little bit of primitive biology. I think that my interest in the origin of life is essentially a statistical one. I am happy to see that the originators of this conference included this notion by adding that terminal *s* to the title. *(Origins of Life)*.

Siever: I'm Ray Siever, in Geology at Harvard, and I am a very recent convert to work on the origins of life. I started out being interested in science sort of as fun and games and I haven't really much changed my attitude. I couldn't make up my mind between chemistry and geology and possibly history, but finally, after having seen the Grand Canyon and deciding that it was much more fun than the interior of the chemistry lab at the University of Chicago, I went into geology.

I then went into high temperature things, uninterested in anything cooler than the region between 400 and 600° C. The result of World War II was that I had to go to work in coal and oil fields.

My interest in coal led to an interest in organic chemistry, which had bored me to tears in college. Sedimentary rocks continued to be my interest, getting me into marine biology and oceanography after a while. I have been sort of running around within the field. At the International Oceanographic Congress in 1959, Lars Gunnar Sillen, physical chemist from Stockholm, was asked to put his mind to what the chemical system that we call the oceans was, and how it was controlled, and how it might have started. Sillen, of course, made a very wonderful kind of synthesis of how the oceans might look to an equilibrium chemist.

More recently, a group of us in geology have become more and more concerned with the question of just how the oceans were formed, and that is what has led me into this. When one starts worrying about the steady-state systems, or things that appear to be in steady state—or, rather, should we say we hope are in steady state so that we can handle them a little bit—one then starts thinking about what happened earlier. You can't discuss the oceans without discussing the atmosphere; and as soon as I started discussing the atmosphere I discovered I was running afoul of all sorts of people who were discussing what the early atmosphere of the earth was like. The study of geology or, rather, what concrete evidence we have in the rocks, is probably the only way we can set boundary values on these problems of the origin and evolution of the atmosphere, oceans, and life, other than the general boundaries that apply to all such physical problems. So that is my interest here.

Horowitz: I am Norman Horowitz. I spend half of my time at Cal Tech teaching and doing research in chemical genetics, the other half at the Jet Propulsion Laboratory trying to design experiments to land on and explore the surface of Mars.

I wasn't seriously interested in the origin of life until I became a post-doctoral fellow in Professor George Beadle's laboratory at Stanford in the early forties. Before then, I felt that the problem of the origin of life was philosophically interesting but impenetrable. I think my attitude is best illustrated by a conversation I once heard between one of the physicists at Cal Tech, where I was a graduate student, and the geneticist T. H. Morgan, (Nobel Laureate, Medicine and Physiology, 1933), who was Chairman of the Biology Department at the time. The physicists asked Morgan what his ideas were on the origin of life and Morgan thought for a moment and said, "The origin of life? That's something for you physicists to worry about. We biologists take life for granted."

In Beadle's laboratory, exciting discoveries were being made about the relation between genes and enzymes, and it soon became apparent that there were also some interesting evolutionary problems. It turned out that the pathways of biosynthesis were governed by constellations of genes, and you had to have the whole constellation for the pathway to operate. It didn't do the organism any good to have one or two or three of these genes and enzymes, but the whole pathway had to come into existence at once, it seemed. I thought about this problem and happened to pick up a book entitled *The Origin of Life* by a Russian named Oparin(1938) that had recently been translated into English. While reading this book it occured to me that it was possible, starting with Oparin's notions about the origins of life on the earth, to arrive at a plausible solution to the problem of the origin of biosynthetic pathways. I published my idea in a short paper (Horowitz, (1945) and have had an interest in the origin of life ever since.

Fremont-Smith: I am Frank Fremont-Smith, a physician whose father was a physician, whose great uncle was a physician, whose older brother is a physician, and whose two oldest sons are physicians; so I am sort of immersed. While in medical school, Dr. Harvey Cushing demonstrated a hydrocephalous child and I then fell in love with the cerebrospinal fluid and have been swimming in it for quite a while; but after working for a good many years in the chemistry of body fluids, including the amniotic fluid, I became more and more interested in emotion factors and the influence they have on physiological processes, and from there I moved from psychosomatic medicine into psychiatry, but I quickly tell my friends that I am only a half-baked psychiatrist. That reassures them a little, but they want to know, "What do you mean by a half-baked psychiatrist?" I explain that to be fully baked, you have to lie quite flat on the couch during your analysis and I was in a semi-reclining position all the time, so I am only half-baked.

The late Dr. Fred Keppel, who was the President of the Carnegie Corporation, said that foundation executives — poor, lonely creatures that they are — deserve a special appelation, and he suggested they should be called *philanthropoids*. Why? Because, he said, they acted like philanthropists but with somebody else's money. So, I was in the Josiah Macy, Jr. Foundation as a philanthropoid for some twenty-four years, but when I first came to the Foundation, I had to be looked over by the trustees, and one of them looked me over very closely; he sat me down in a chair and he sat opposite, looking at me, and after a long silence he said, "Dr. Fremont-Smith, do you believe in conferences?" Well, I had practically never attended a conference. I didn't know whether I believed in them or not and I thought: What do I say? Yes? No? It has to be yes, and so I said, "Yes, sir, yes, sir, I do." And then I felt, well, I've got to say something more than that and I couldn't think what in the world to say, but then I added, "Yes, sir, I do if they last long enough." So, I have been with conferences ever since, trying to help them last long enough.

As we have listened to the wonderful remarks that, fortunately, are all recorded, we are beginning to get pictures of each other. I think that some of you who have known some of the others will find you got points of view from these self-introductions that you hadn't heard previously. In any case, this kind of self-introduction does really serve a purpose — it gives the participants some picture of the resources in the group, and our job during the next three days is to tap these resources as fully as we can. I think it is quite a challenge, and I don't believe we would tap them fully even if we could spend several months together.

We thank you all very much indeed. I am very happy that we got started and especially happy that we have our President Dr. Henry Moss with us, as well as his lovely lady.

Monday Morning

Horowitz: We have three members this morning who weren't present last night and I am going to ask them to introduce themselves, tell where they are from, and what their special connection is with the origins of life problem.

Fremont-Smith: Give a little of yourself. Don't be reticent. The rest of us had cocktails last night, you see, and now you have to pay the penalty for being late.

Horowitz: After dinner and cocktails, the subject people are most interested in is themselves.

Sagan: My name is Carl Sagan. I'm at Harvard University and the Smithsonian Astrophysical Observatory in Cambridge, Massachusetts. I'm primarily interested in planetary astronomy, but one aspect of the planets, it seems to me, is the question of possible life on them; so I have for some time been interested in the problem of the origin of life as the only problem reasonably accessible at the present time that is relevant to life on other planets. My first published paper was on this subject. While I spend most of my time on planetary physics, I do some laboratory and theoretical work along these lines.

Horowitz: Thank you. Alex, would you introduce yourself, please?

Rich: Yes, I am Alex Rich. I am at MIT in Biophysics. I'm interested in the nucleic acids. My feeling about the origin of life is that it is a problem with a large number of experimentally possible solutions. We will not know which one to choose from in terms of how the whole system started to operate. The nucleic acids occupy a central position in living systems today, but it is not necessarily evident that they occupied such a position years ago. My pursuing questions on the origin of life is just a consequence, as it were, of continuing study of the nucleic acids today.

Woese: I am Carl Woese, University of Illinois, Department of Microbiology. I have been sort of forced into the field because of my interest in the genetic code. When you spend enough time wondering about the code as it presently exists, you come to the conclusion that you don't understand it until you understand how it arose and what it might have been in earlier days. I guess most of you come at it from the opposite direction, starting with nothing biological and working up toward the intermediate state. That is essentially my reason for being here. Other than that, I was invited.

ORGANIC CHEMISTRY

The Fossil Record

ORGANIC CHEMISTRY
THE FOSSIL RECORD

May 22, 1967

Dr. Stanley Miller
Discussion Initiator

Horowitz: The discussion initiator this morning, as I am sure you all know, is the gentleman who more than anyone else is responsible for transforming the origins of life problem from a speculative one to an experimental one (Miller, 1953), Dr. Stanley Miller.

Age of the Earth

Miller: This morning we are scheduled to discuss what, from an experimental standpoint, seems to be a central issue: Just what were conditions on the primitive earth? If you don't have some idea of what the primitive earth conditions were, it is difficult to do a model experiment. There has arisen in this area a series of dogmas, rightly questioned from time to time, particularly by some of the participants here. I think one has to look very critically at the assumptions upon which adoption of any set of particular conditions for the primitive earth are based. I think this would make an excellent topic for discussion.

It seems to me that there is some confusion as to which period is being talked about. When the primitive earth is discussed, it is well established, or at least generally accepted, that the earth is 4.5 billion years old—4.55 billion is the latest figure. For those who aren't familiar with it, this comes from the age of meteorites. The age of the meteorites is taken as the age of the earth, and this seems well established, as depicted in Figure 1.

Abelson: This is an arbitrary assumption. Just because a meteorite coming from elsewhere arrived on earth a few hundred thousand years ago doesn't necessarily say it tags the age of the earth.

Sagan: The fundamental assumption, I think, is that all the bodies in the solar system were formed roughly at the same time, and in all models of the solar system that I know about, this is in fact very difficult to get away from. Even in modern versions of the cosmogony of Kant and LaPlace, which had the planets form from the outside in, the age difference among planets is quite small. In most modern planetary cosmogonies it is also small. It seems reasonable to assume the earth is 4.5 billion years old, if we are talking about plus or minus a few hundred million years.

Morrison: This data is not so much an assumption as a physical statement, namely, that all the processes for forming planets out of something more gaseous take a short time compared to 5 billion years. If you find things like meteorites becoming solid out of gas roughly 5 billion years ago, it doesn't at all exclude two phases.

Abelson: Isn't it also true that they get some other dates besides 4.5 billion years for the ages of some of the meteorites?

Morrison: Yes, I think so, but you have to look for the oldest date.

Miller: At present, except for meteorites, we have no rock samples that have any possibility of being equal to the age of the earth. Thus we are somewhat stuck with a minimum age of the earth of about 4.5 billion years. Nobody, so far as I know, really questions this.

31

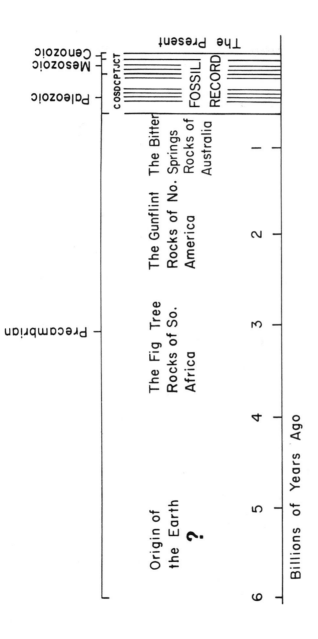

Figure 1. Simplified geochronology

Morrison: I think the other date we have is the age of the sun.

Miller: Yes, but how valid are the measurements?

Morrison: Better than those of the meteorites.

Sagan: The age of the sun is a number that depends on one's model of stellar evolution. The assumptions involved in models of stellar evolution are an entirely different set than those used in dating the meteorites. If you get two quite totally independent methods to converge on a figure of 5 billion years, let's say, that tends to substantiate each method.

Morrison: It is worthwhile, though, to look at the source of the models. I think you are quite right in saying that strictures on cosmology are very unsettled, but nuclear physics and stellar interiors are relatively more subtle. I would say it would be quite surprising if, conservatively, you could stretch the age of the sun to more than 10 billion years. All the experts say 7.4, but I wouldn't believe that. With modest errors, we might assess the age as somewhat older, but don't you agree that between 10 and 5 billion is about what we've got?

Sagan: Yes. I might also point out that it was the lack of concordance between the cosmological and geological ages that led to a careful reassessment of the methods of dating the earth. There was this awkward period when the earth was older than the universe!

Fremont-Smith: That was awkward!

Morrison: And both changed.

Sagan: Yes, both changed substantially. But I think we can have some confidence that after some very careful study, both ages converge. I remember that the velocity of light was determined precisely by a great many methods and supposedly known with great precision twenty-five years ago, and now we find that the present accepted value of the velocity of light has changed by ten times the probable error of what was considered to be firmly established at that time.

Morrison: But that problem was one in the hundred thousands. If you are going to believe precision in figures like that (for astronomical processes), you are going to be surprised very often.

Fremont-Smith: It will be awfully interesting to reread this discussion in the future. I hope twelve years from now we can set up another conference on the origins of life that will start with a rereading of some of this discussion. One thing I can be quite sure of is that many of the things we are sure of now we will no longer hang on— which is good.

Miller: To get back to the age of the earth, although there may be some uncertainty, and the numbers may change in twelve years, we will discuss the geological aspects of the origin and evolution of life within the framework of 4.5 billion. There are some fixed ages. The first fixed age is that of the Earth. The second is the base of the Cambrian, where the first hard-shelled animal fossils appear. It is dated at something like 700 million, or 0.7 billion years.

Siever: I will object. I would rather have it 0.6 billion years.

Miller: All right, somewhere between 0.6 and 0.8 billion. This has no effect on the discussion. At about 2.5 billion years, as has been shown by several of the participants [Barghoorn and Schopf], a substantial number of rocks appear to have fossil microorganisms in them, and more recently somewhere between 3.0 and 3.5 billion—I think this is the Fig Tree Series, South Africa—there are apparently fossil microorganisms. Without right now entering into a discussion of whether these inclusions in sedimentary rocks are or are not fossil microorganisms, we see that there was roughly a billion years between the origin of the earth and the formation of life.

Sagan: That doesn't follow, does it? It is actually about a billion years between the origin of the earth and the fossilization of microorganisms of the complexity reported.

Miller: Yes, of course.

Sagan: The origin of life itself probably involved much simpler organisms.

Miller: There is no way of saying how long it took.

Abelson: I will remind you also that no rock on earth older than 3.5 billion years has ever been found.

Morrison: Doesn't it mean that no older rocks have been dated? If you look at the geology, don't you find a history in these most ancient rocks even if you can't date them?

Abelson: If they were really there 4.0 billion years ago, you would be able to date them at 4.0 billion.

Morrison: You might, and you might not.

Siever: There is a point here. Both some kind of life and the rock cycle were established by 3.5 billion years ago. That is, 3.5 billion years ago essentially the whole cycle on the earth's surface was operating in some fashion similar to that of today. This means it got well started before that time.

Abelson: It is true that if you heat rock sufficiently you can wipe out the former clock. If you are going to assume that the earth was formed 4.5 billion years ago, then you have to further assume that every trace of this at the earth's surface was wiped out by processes occurring not further back than 3.5 billion years ago. We can find relatively unaltered rocks, such as the Fig Tree formation, sitting there quietly for 3.5 billion years with little metamorphism. Why didn't other rocks sit for 3.7 billion years and not be affected?

Miller: The problem is that there are dynamic processes in geology, and the older the rock the more likely it is that it has been buried and heated; you would expect that some sort of exponential loss of rock———

Abelson: On all the continents there are rocks of the order of 3.5 billion years.

Horowitz: Some worldwide cataclysm.

Abelson: A real-for-sure cataclysm would have had to have occurred 3.5 billion years ago.

Siever: A plot of estimates of the age of the oldest rock versus chronological time since the fifth century gives a straight line. In other words, the longer we work on dating rocks and the earth, the older the rocks we discover.

Abelson: I would buy that if there hadn't been about five to ten thousand datings of rocks from all over the world and an effort to be the champion dater of the oldest rock.

Siever: Yes, but we have pushed the dates back roughly a billion, from about 2.5 to 3.5 billion years ago in the last ten years.

Abelson: No, not a billion in the last ten years, because new dates came all of a sudden. There hasn't been any marked change in the date of the oldest rock in the last five years. At the same time there have been many thousands of additional dates.

Orgel: But how many of the new observations have been made on rocks 3.5 billion years old? One hundred examples of rocks 3.5 billion years old and not one example of something 3.6 billion years old might imply a cataclysm. If, on the other hand, you found ten examples at 3.2 billion years, seven at 3.3 billion years, and so on, down to one example, at 3.5 billion years, you would have a statistical distribution. Which way is it?

Abelson: There is a little bit of fuzziness here because you never measure precisely 3.50. The date has a probability error of perhaps 0.20 billion—that is, 200 million years.

Orgel: It is somewhat like the fossil distribution for———

Abelson: No, it is not. It is as if there is really cutoff here and, as I say, there are dates on all the continents. Any kind of analysis of various models for the weathering of a primordial crust says, regardless of what its composition may be, there will be such a small amount of primary crust remaining that the probability of finding it, although finite, is very small. Radiometric daters go after the oldest dates; this results in a terribly asymmetrical distribution, skewed strongly in favor of the number of older rocks that have been dated versus the number of younger rocks that have been dated. Therefore, my guess is that in a few years we will go to something like 3.5 as the oldest date and then somebody will find something a little older, maybe 3.6 if he is lucky. It is extremely unlikely, however, in view of the vast areas of the earth that are inaccessible, that we will ever find something much older.

Schopf: I have some data with me which may be of interest at this point. About two years ago, a paper appeared in the GSA (Geological Society of America) bulletin in which many of the oldest dates were summarized. I don't recall the author's name.

Ponnamperuma: Donn, Donn, and Valentine (1965).

Schopf: Thank you. I have here their tabulation of these very old rock dates, and there are at least two items of particular interest. In the first place, according to my notes, many of the oldest dates, those in the 3.4 billion-year-old category, are minimum ages, for example, micas in a pegmatic-argon age of 3.44 billion years. This is a minimum age. It indicates that the Sebakwian is older than 3.44 billion years.

Similarly, Donn et al (1965) list a potassium-argon date on metamorphic rocks of the Kola Series of the Kola Peninsula (USSR) as being 3.44 to 3.45 billion years. Again, this is a minimum age.

Sagan: Physically, why are these minimum ages? Because of argon diffusion?

Schopf: Partially, but they are also minimum because they are dates on intrusive or metamorphic rocks; they date the time of intrusion or metamorphism rather than the time of original sedimentary deposition.

In addition, there are a couple of older dates of particular interest. A potassium-argon of 3.6 billion years, which may be somewhat unreliable because of low potassium content, has been reported on a charnokite granite from nothern Tanganyika. Also, there is a date of 3.93 billion years on a migmatite from French Guiana. However, the authors state that this age is not yet firmly accepted.

Although open to question, then, some dates older than 3.5 billion years have been reported. And it seems significant that several of the determinations in the 3.4 to 3.5 billion-year-old range appear to be minimum ages, implying that geologic processes were taking place prior to that time.

Barghoorn: Are these all potassium-argon dates?

Schopf: Yes, except of course for the Swaziland system (of which the Fig Tree Series is a member) which has a lead-lead date of 3.4 billion years, a rubidium-strontonium tentative age of 3.4 ± 0.3 billion years, and a rubidium-strontium whole rock date giving a minimum age of 3.1 billion years.

Barghoorn: A number of these people do not agree with the validity of the procedure. L. D. Nicolaysen and H. L. Allsoppe (1965, personal communication) of the University of Witwatersrand, South Africa, hesitate to accept any potassium-argon dates. The best date so far as the rubidium-strontium people are concerned, are in the Swaziland system and they are minimally about 3.1 billion years.

Miller: In general, if you do not use three dating methods, at least two of which are concordant, you do not accept the age. The potassium-argon method, while it has its place, can give very peculiar results. Wasserburg (Lanphere, et al, 1964) found some really anomalous things in migration of ions in the Panniment Range in Death Valley. Just to summarize, if you do not have a rubidium-strontium, a potassium-argon, and possibly a lead date, the age cannot be accepted as firm. Even those that seem to be firm sometimes prove to be incorrect, so that you have to be very careful on these ages. I think the only one of the very old ones that is generally accepted is the 3.4 billion years of the Swaziland system and the various Precambrian dates of the Canadian shield. Again, I am not an expert on this but this is my understanding of the status at the present time.

Primitive Atmosphere

Miller: Thus, we have discussed the whole problem of ages, and we come back to the original time scale. We will accept 4.5 billion as the age of the earth. The question is, what were the conditions on the earth at the beginning and up to the present? What is the time course of the evolution of the atmosphere and the evolution of life?

The dogmas state that in the beginning there was an atmosphere consisting of methane (CH_4), ammonia (NH_3), and hydrogen (H_2), which in time became more and more oxidizing. At present we have an atmosphere consisting of carbon dioxide (CO_2), nitrogen (N_2), oxygen (O_2), and water (H_2O). What was the time course of this transition? The dogmas further state that the first organisms were heterotrophic, that they did not carry out photosynthesis. Photosynthesis was a later development. This implies that large quantities of organic compounds must have been synthesized before life began. The organisms were not only made up of these compounds, but initially used them for food until they exhausted this food supply.

If we confine our attention period from 4.5 to 3.5 billion years ago, one question is, did the atmosphere turn oxidizing by 3.5 billion years? In my opinion, it is not clear from the fossil evidence of the Fig Tree Series whether the atmosphere was oxidizing or reducing.

Fremont-Smith: What is this Fig Tree?

Miller: The Fig Tree is very funny. It is one of these geological terms. It refers to a certain group of Precambrian rocks in South Africa, and it is part of the so-called South African shield.

Fremont-Smith: Why Fig Tree?

Barghoorn: It has nothing to do with the Garden of Eden.

Fremont-Smith: That is what I was reaching for.

Barghoorn: It is a small village in the eastern Transvaal in South Africa. It is the type locality for these rocks—the town of Fig Tree.

Miller: I would ask those who have thought about this much more that I have, is there any way of saying anything about the nature of the atmosphere at the time these organisms were laid down in the Fig Tree rocks?

Siever: Some carbonate is there.

Barghoorn: Very little.

Siever: Well, there is some carbonate in the Fig Tree Series, so we have some limits on the partial pressure of carbon dioxide at that point. The question is, was enough carbon dioxide present to serve photosynthetic organisms as a carbon source.

Horowitz: What else is there? Are there reducing substances? Is there reduced iron?

Siever: I don't know.

Barghoorn: There is very little carbonate in the Fig Tree, and what there is is almost inconspicuous; just the fact that it is there is important. (That is, atmospheric CO_2 itself would not limit the potential for photosynthesis had such a potential evolved.)

Fremont-Smith: If there is any, doesn't that mean something?

Barghoorn: The bulk of the Fig Tree Series is reduced rocks; reduced carbon is abundant in the Fig Tree.

Horowitz: Organic carbon? That is, is the reduced carbon the result of microbial metabolism or is it primitive prebiotic organic matter?

Barghoorn: Yes.

Horowitz: Is ferrous iron present?

Barghoorn: There is ferric iron; there is banded iron formation.

Horowitz: Banded iron? What does that mean?

Siever: They are oxidized iron ores. It is Fe_2O_3 (ferric oxide) with or without water, it doesn't make much difference. The less oxidized ferrous iron detectable in these sediments is probably of secondary origin, that is, ferrous sulfides. Ferrous sulfide deposits probably come as a result of bacterial activity; it is known that sulfate reduction is an extraordinarily difficult process in the absence of bacteria. The whole argument that everybody has been using on the oxidation state of the atmosphere at these times has been the evidence of reduced metals in the few famous Precambrian uranium ore localities of the world, chiefly the Blind River and the Rand deposits (South Africa). That evidence is not conclusive. It is a peculiar kind of association in a few places in the world, and it is not at all clear what the kinetics of iron oxygen systems are with and without benefit of bacteria.

Let us put it this way: There is a great deal of doubt as to the fundamental thermodynamic quantities involved in the oxidation of ferrous iron; that is, depending on whose numbers you pick, you can arrive at different equilibrium constants for whatever reaction you want to write.

Miller: At what temperature?

Siever: At 25°C.

Miller: You mean there is great uncertainty?

Siever: If you want to take all the figures and the data, Sillen (1965) makes the statement that from various equilibrium constants, he can predict oxygen pressures that can vary from 10^{-117} to $10^{-0.7}$ (atmosphere). He uses this in his recent argument (Sillen, 1967) that it is conceivable that the present oxgen atmosphere of the earth is buffered by the iron oxygen system rather than by any photosynthesis-respiration system. The thermochemical quantities are in doubt for the entire iron-oxygen-water system at low temperatures.

McElroy: What you are saying here is that with oxygen you don't even know what the flux looks like.

Siever: That is right. What we don't know is the rapidity of oxidation of a ferrous metal in a sterile environment, depending on the partial pressure of oxygen.

McElroy: What is the best guess, though?

Siever: We are now estimating 10^{-4} atmospheres of oxygen as the equilibrium pressure, in equilibrium with the ferrous-ferric couple. Carl, have you thought about this one at all?

Sagan: I've been worrying about the hydration more than the oxidation.

Siever: We don't know very much about even the hydration that Carl has been worried about. The equilibrium between solids and liquids is at issue; one cannot demonstrate equilibrium. Furthermore, low temperature calorimetric results are in doubt.

Miller: This is easily rectified. The thermodynamics can be worked out; you get your entropies from applying the third law of thermodynamics.

Siever: The problem is that this is a refractory system with respect to getting accurately known quantities. People have been working at it for a good long time. For example, a young man at our school who has been studying the oxidation of ferrous iron in siderite finds that if he sterilized the solution, the reaction is extraordinarily sluggish. It turns out that this reaction is very bacteria-dependent. Perhaps most of the oxidation we see today is the result of life and has nothing to do with the conditions for life.

Miller: You also run into the problem of attempting to extrapolate back with chemical kinetics. There are many reactions that become important on the long time scale but are minor on the short time scale. This is the problem with the growth of manganese nodules, which is a very slow process. If you try to do kinetics under a set of conditions and then extrapolate to other conditions, there will be many uncertainties in the extrapolation.

Siever: We don't know what the equilibrium state is precisely, although we don't think we are very far off on a good many of these reactions. If we just take equilibrium, then I think all the previous estimates for urananite, pyrite, and all the other reduced metal minerals, which one finds in these close to 2-billion-year-old rocks, indicate an oxygen pressure of somewhere less that 10^{-4} atmosphere.

Abelson: This is an extremely difficult problem. If pH is high, it is easy to oxidize ferrous to ferric iron. So many events may have occurred on the earth that the geologists cannot agree about when the oxygen in the atmosphere originated. They have fought it out for years. We are not going to be able to settle it here today.

Miller: There is also the problem of sampling. You may have a sample, but if you examine certain present-day samples of the earth and ask whether the atmosphere is oxidizing or reducing, you come up with the wrong answer. So if you have the wrong rock—a nonrepresentative rock that is 2.5 or 3.5 billion years old—the conclusions may be incorrect. Even a liquid inclusion in which everything is preserved may be skewed.

Sagan: I wonder if we could spend just another minute pursuing Dr. Barghoorn's point about the high relative abundance of organic to inorganic carbon.

Barghoorn: We don't have any real good quantitation, but there is an abundance of reduced carbon in these very old Precambrian rocks, which it seems to me on thermodynamic grounds couldn't possibly be explained by non-biological synthesis. You must rely on photosynthetic reduction to explain the presence of such large amounts of organic carbon.

Sagan: You say it could not be explained abiologically?

Barghoorn : Yes.

Sagan: Why do you say that?

Barghoorn: Just quantitatively, I think it is unreasonable.

Sagan: How much is it? How many grams per square centimeter column?

Barghoorn: I don't know. The last comprehensive inventory of the carbon budget I think is in Rubey's (1951) paper. This is expressed as CO_2 in grams $X\ 10^{18}$. I think his figure was about 92,000 $X\ 10^{18}$ grams, of which the atmosphere was 2.3 $X\ 10^{18}$ grams. The point I am getting at is that it is 25,000 $X\ 10^{18}$ average grams per square centimeter column carbon in all geological sediments, and a very large percentage of it is Precambrian.

Sagan: Why do you say that much organic carbon couldn't be abiological?

Barghoorn: Because all living and soil organic matter on Rubey's scale represents only 14 $X\ 10^{18}$ grams per square centimeter. (That is, only about 0.06 percent of the organic carbon on the earth is in living organisms and soil; the remainder is in sedimentary rocks. Somewhat less than half of all sedimentary rocks are Precambrian, according to Schopf and Barghoorn. To argue that the Precambrian organic matter is abiogenic in origin implies that the abiogenic production was a process quantitatively competitive with the biogenic production of organic matter during the history of the earth.)
A large part of western Australia, for example, contains rocks in which thick black shales are common. These are 2,500 million years in age. In the Fig Tree Series of the Swaziland system, perhaps 10,000 feet thick and covering

thousands of square miles, there are thick black shale members. The same is true in other Precambrian shield areas. Unfortunately we do not have any good quantitation of carbon in the Precambrian systems.

Horowitz: What is your interpretation?

Barghoorn: That this is organically produced; in other words, the organic carbon is a product of photosynthetic reduction.

Abelson: The reason I would say the reduced carbon is biogenic is because the isotope ratios say so.

Barghoorn: This is another argument, of course; all these isotope ratios—stable isotopes of carbon—would be indicative of photosynthesis. I don't think there are any inconsistencies.

Margulis: In the Fig Tree, at 3.4 billion years ago, there is even morphological evidence for microfossils.

Barghoorn: Well, we can come to that later, but I think on the basis of gross chemical evidence alone one would assume there must have been some biological photosynthetic system.

Margulis: How much reduced sulfur is there in these rocks?

Barghoorn: It is fairly variable and, again, whether it is primary (that is, the ferrous sulfide has been deposited directly) or secondary (that is, the ferrous sulfide is a product of bacterial metabolism) is a problem.

Margulis: Why can't it just have been formed by anaerobic heterotrophs—organisms that reduce sulfate like, for example, *Desulfovibrio*?

Barghoorn: They have to have a carbon source.

Margulis: They may eat some of the abiologically produced or photosynthetically fixed carbon you referred to. It is not inconsistent; the presence of carbonates implies that CO_2 for photosynthesis was available. Some of these anaerobic respirers can even use CO_2 and hydrogen gas directly in their "lithotrophic" metabolism. All they need are a few salts in the medium.

Barghoorn: In sedimentary processes, organic matter is preserved only under conditions of the right redox potential. Most black sediments, whether they are Pleistocene (one million years old) or Precambrian (more than 600 million years old) were accumulated under anaerobic conditions, underwater.

Margulis: All I am saying is that anaerobic heterotrophs could have reduced the sulfate; the sulfur may even be a product of anaerobic bacterial photosynthesis. The explanations for Precambrian reduced organic matter may be strictly biological.

Barghoorn: Anaerobic heterotrophs aren't very efficient.

Abelson: Tom Hoering (1967) has looked at isotopes, both of sulfur and carbon, in many of the oldest sedimentary rocks. Obviously, you can't say he has looked at everything, but everything he has looked at has shown the reduced carbon to be enriched in the light isotope fraction by an amount that is characteristic of the organically derived carbon today. While he hasn't looked at many of the pyrites associated with the reduced carbon, all the pyrites he has looked at had sulfur isotope ratios characteristic of having been produced biologically.

Barghoorn: I think it is also significant that the oxidized carbonates show a very different isotope fractionation from the reduced carbon in the same rock.

Abelson: That is what Hoering always tried to do—compare the carbonate to the reduced carbon.

Sagan: It is clear that there could not be any abiological processes that fractionate the isotopes and give you these ratios?

Abelson: One can't say that it is clear. I was just saying that insofar as Hoering has measured it, the ratios are characteristic of biological formation.

Miller: There are two points I would like to make relative to this. It is not clear to me how you can exclude nonbiological synthesis of the organic compounds in the Fig Tree just on the basis of amount. Some of us envision enormous amounts of organic compounds on the earth prior to the formation of life. I think there are various mechanisms for accumulating these in rocks. I don't doubt your conclusion, but I would not base it on just the quantitative amounts.

Barghoorn: I don't think what I said can be defended. We don't have the data, but if you add up the concatenation of the evidence—reduced carbon in such quantities—the presence of morphology indicative of organisms and the isotopic ratios of the stable isotopes of carbon—they all point in one direction (that is, toward the presence of microorganisms).

Miller: Yes, I said I don't doubt the conclusion; I just don't think it's a good argument to say that quantitatively there is a lot of carbon there and, therefore, it cannot have been abiological. Also on the matter of the C^{13} to C^{12} ratios, whenever you make these comparisons, you have one ratio and you assume you have a standard source material being fractionated. There may have been a drift in the ratio of C^{13} and C^{12} with time over the last three billion years, and then you get———

Abelson: There are many dated carbonates to measure and many instances where you can measure carbonate in association with reduced carbon. There has been a drift in the carbon isotope ratio. The base value has shifted a bit, but that shift does not interfere. You are able to measure the oxidized and reduced carbon in association with each other—often in the same rock.

Miller: Has it been demonstrated that the same shift between the reduced and oxidized carbon cannot be obtained by nonbiological means?

Abelson: It is not at all excluded, but in these particular instances you get a characteristic deposition of sediment that obviously has been formed under relatively low temperature conditions, and it's pretty hard to assume extreme conditions.

Sagan: If it is true that this huge amount of carbon is of biological origin, then presumably it is produced photosynthetically.

Barghoorn: I think you might call this conclusion the geological syndrome of symptoms. It is very difficult to explain all the evidence except by photosynthetic reduction.

Burlingame: One other point indicates that the molecules in those rocks were produced photosynthetically: You don't find all compound structural types. (That is, the range of structure you would expect on chemical grounds alone is not present).

Horowitz: Do you find pristane and phytane?

Burlingame: You can find isoprenoid alkanes, for one thing.

Barghoorn: Alkane hydrocarbons.

Miller: May I please digress, perhaps, to the assertion that the pristane and phytane imply photosynthesis? It is my understanding that the halophiles, organisms that live in high concentrations of salt, have isoprenoid-type lipids.

Margulis: Pristane and phytane may have been derived from carotenoids or membranous isoprenoid derivatives. Almost every organism that is growing, except for some strictly anaerobic fermenters, contain these compounds. You don't need a photosynthetic system to get carotenoid derivatives.

Orgel: What is the argument that biological materials have to be photosynthetic?

Miller: As I understand the argument, the presence of the pristane and phytane in rocks derives from the phytol group on chlorophyll.

Ponnamperuma: This is a suggestion made by Bendoraitis (1962). Nobody has proved it experimentally. The phytol chain is considered to break into two fractions.

Miller: Is it, Juan (Oró), correct to say that when you find pristane or phytane, it was photosynthetic in origin—that pristane and phytane come from the phytol side chain of the chlorophyll after reduction?

Orgel: May we ask the biologists if it is true that you don't get this particular structure anywhere else?

Margulis: I think you can get it from carotenoids (and even coenzyme Q, vitamins E and K, and perhaps some membranous components in general); all but a very few organisms have some type of carotenoids and these few are obligate anaerobic fermenters.

Schopf: The work of Konrad Bloch on the distribution of isoprene derivatives in nature seems pertinent here. In a recent paper (Bloch, 1964) he notes that isoprene derivatives have been found in all organisms with the exception of some nonphotosynthetic anaerobic bacteria. Based on this distribution, perhaps the minimum inference one can draw from the presence of fossil isoprenoids is that if they are of biological origin, they have been produced by organisms different from, and I should think higher than—more evolved than—nonphotosynthetic anaerobes.

Sagan: Even that needn't necessarily follow, because you are assuming that the distinctions existing today apply to many billions of years ago.

Oró: The finding of saturated polyisoprenoid hydrocarbons may not necessarily be an absolute indication of photosynthesis since, in principle, it is possible for phytol to be synthesized in nonphotosynthetic microorganisms (Kates, et al, 1965).

Ponnamperuma: Haven't Blumer and Thomas (1965) recently found free pristane and phytane in some marine organisms?

Burlingame: Is that of primary origin or as a metabolite of ingested food?

Ponnamperuma: I don't know that.

Oró: Actually the discovery of these isoprenoid hydrocarbons was made by Japanese investigators of sharks and other fishes. Basking sharks feed on copepods and other zooplanktonic organisms which in turn feed on blue-green algae and other phytoplanktonic organisms. These plants are presumed to be the primary sources of phytol biosynthesis.

Ponnamperuma: It is also significant that if one takes isoprene and irradiates it with gamma rays, the cyclic compounds are produced—the dimer, trimer, and so on. If, however, the irradiation is done in the presence of vermiculite, for example, which is known to have catalytic properties in producing straight chain hydrocarbons, you get acyclic compounds (Munday et al, 1967). So, one can conceive of certain abiogenic processes by which isoprenoids could arise. This is an interesting observation. One must be cautious in using pristane or phytane as an indicator of photosynthesis.

Sagan: Apart from the arguments about isoprenoids and morphology, you did agree, Dr. Barghoorn, that if all this organic matter is produced biologically it must have been photosynthetic? It seems difficult to get around that.

Barghoorn: It is more reasonable of the two alternatives.

Sagan: In that case, may I ask, need this photosynthesis be green plant photosynthesis, that is, oxygen-eliminating, or might it have been a nonoxygen-eliminating photosynthesis? If the former is the case, we in fact have a handle on the oxidation state in the environment at that time.

Barghoorn: You mean bacterial photosynthesis that does not lead to the elimination of molecular oxygen?

Sagan: For example.

Horowitz: In the fossil evidence, I guess, you have algae present (all of which are green plant, oxygen-eliminating photosynthesizers).

Sagan: Maybe those are the most visible members of the biological population but they make an insignificant contribution to the photosynthesis.

Morrison: I still don't see why the organic carbon has to be due to photosynthesis.

Sagan: How would you get organic matter laid down?

Morrison: There must be a free energy source of some sort, that you can surely say; but it doesn't have to be———

Sagan: We didn't specify———

Morrison: It doesn't have to be light.

Fox: I don't think that is so hard to visualize. A lot of these reactions studied in general terms have been found to have internally directed forces, which we didn't recognize until we looked at them with sufficient thoroughness. If you come at this problem from a purely theoretical or random basis, you can say that all the isomers might be formed, but when you understand the reactions sufficiently, it turns out that in many cases there occurs a selective line of synthesis for steric or other reasons.

Orgel: It seems to me that there are two points at issue. One is, is the stuff biological? The second is, is it photosynthetic? Arguments that say it is biological don't necessarily say it is photosynthetic. It is, I suppose, clear that there must be an energy source, but in biophotosynthesis we have had in mind not only that the energy comes from the sun but also that it is utilized in a way somewhat related to contemporary photosynthesis. What I haven't heard yet is the evidence that the sun's energy was utilized directly by these organisms in a way related to contemporary photosynthesis.

Miller: Does "contemporary" mean oxygen-eliminating?

Orgel: The implication seems to be that if the phytol side chains are really critical, something like chlorophyll was involved.

Miller: All photosynthesis involves chlorophyll, so far as I know, even anaerobic photosynthesis. Isn't the issue more whether it is oxygen-eliminating versus anaerobic photosynthesis?

Orgel: That is one issue. But it might also be that the photosynthesis is a completely different type, namely, the production of energetic materials outside an organism and their subsequent utilization. You might imagine a short ultraviolet wavelength producing something in the atmosphere that was used by the organisms.

Horowitz: You could have chemosynthetic reduction of CO_2.

Orgel: Based ultimately on sunlight, certainly, but not necessarily anything like contemporary photosynthesis.

Abelson: We know that in the fixation of carbon in photosynthesis, the carbon dioxide is fixed to ribulose diphosphate. Other studies have shown that there is an isotope separation factor in that process. It has also been shown that there is a small further isotope fractionation in the conversion of sugars into fats. Taken together, those two processes can make a delta of about 25—that is, 25 parts in a thousand—and this coincides with the sort of deltas one finds in nature between carbonates and organic carbon produced by photosynthesis. Of course it might be that sometime in the past, sometime between now and 3.4 billion years ago, there was a different process that had just the same isotopic fractionation, and we could be fooled by this.

McElroy: Such pathways, which use reduced ferrodoxin as the electron donor, are already well known.

Abelson: Having the same isotope fractionation?

McElroy: That is what it looks like, namely, the phosphyl-pyruvate-CO_2 system. It gives exactly the same product.

Abelson: With the same delta?

McElroy: Yes, within an experimental error of 20 percent, probably.

Morrison: What is the origin of the delta? Is it the free energy differences between the particular fundamentally original reactants? Does it involve the number of steps in the chain? Does it depend mainly on what you start with? And where does it come from?

Miller: I would think the isotope separation comes from the kinetics.

McElroy: Kinetics and rate process are involved.

Miller: All of these have relatively large kinetic isotope fractionations.

Morrison: And they don't depend on actual differences?

Miller: These photosynthetic fractionation factors depend on the particular organisms. I understand it involves rates of diffusion and reaction as well as metabolic pools and rates of turnover, so the net fractionation can vary from organism to organism, depending on the details of this process.

Orgel: Is it or is it not true, Dr. Abelson, that the carbon isotope fractionation rules out other explanations of these things?

Abelson: I wouldn't say it necessarily rules them out. McElroy has shaken me here.   However, I do happen to know, having studied fixation of carbon by photosynthetic organisms, that, for instance, the incorporation of CO_2 into aspartic acid gives a fixed carbon that doesn't have the delta———

McElroy: Right.

Abelson: ———and the fixation of carbon, for instance, into the amidine carbon of arginine has no isotope fraction whatsoever. So there are processes of fixation by biological material that have no fractionation; it's not automatic that fixation of CO_2 by an organism is going to produce an isotope fractionation.

Orgel: On the other hand, photosynthesis might not be unique in this respect.

McElroy: You are talking about making aspartic acid by CO_2 fixation of pyruvic acid.   That is the reductive amination of oxaloacetic acid.   I am talking about the Calvin cycle in which you have at least seven steps of fractionation taking place.   If you reverse that cycle and go in through succinate and so forth, you can get seven steps just like in the citric acid cycle, and that will give you fractionation of carbon.

Photochemically, I could see any number of ways of doing this, and I think the strongest argument, and one that Fox countered by saying that if you got long-chain hydrocarbons with definite stereochemical problems coming in, then, if it isn't biological, you have to propose that it is some other surface on which you can make these long-chain hydrocarbons with a given stereochemistry; I can't argue that that couldn't be nonbiological.   It could very well be.

Horowitz: Still, you are way out on the tail of the probability curve when you argue that way.   There are fossils. There is no nonbiological method for making fossils.   Isn't that sufficient?

Sagan: I don't see why. Why couldn't you have some biological and some abiological production of organic matter; the fossils get sequestered, and there you have fossils among organic molecules produced abiologically. Certainly, in fact, that must have happened; at the very early stages of the origin of life, there must have been abiological organic matter around.

Horowitz: Except these are photosynthetic fossils. They are algae.

Orgel: Is that clear?

Barghoorn: We are going around in circles. One thing though, Carl, if you make biological organic matter that is a substrate for an organism, you can't sequester the fossil from the nonfossil organic mixture because, as everyone knows, with cultured organism the rate of reproduction and food consumption goes up so steeply that the substrate is completely depleted.

Fox: But your fossils aren't cultured organisms.

Barghoorn: They are essentially growing in a natural culture broth. You may start out with an abiological soup, if you wish.

Sagan: That depends on how good is the replication of these very primitive organisms and on the statistics of the distribution of abiological organic matter. It is not at all clear to me that there would be an exponential takeoff, and organisms would eat up all the food. I would imagine the replication rates would be very slow, keeping pace with the production rates of organic molecules.

Horowitz: What is the percentage of organic matter in these Precambrian deposits?

Barghoorn: It commonly may run up to one percent carbon of the total rock.

Horowitz: Over a percent? Then it is very high for non-biological deposit.

Sagan: But at the time of the origin of life———

Morrison: There was a time when the nonbiological carbon had to be 100 percent.

Sagan: Right.

Ponnamperuma: That is a very high figure, I think, for the Fig Tree.

Burlingame: You have to distinguish between the extractable and the nonextractable organic matter. I think Hoering (1967) has found that the extractables are of the order of tens to hundreds of parts per million, but the nonextractable material might be 5 percent or it might be 50 percent.

Fox: We are arguing on the basis of the contemporary situation, and we are pretty blind about what the situation was earlier.

Sagan: Dr. Miller has already mentioned that some of us think there is a very efficient production of organic molecules in early times, and that one percent of the rocks may be made of abiological organic matter. I don't see how one can exclude that.

Sulston: It doesn't mean it has to be one percent of all rocks, does it? In light of concentration processes, one immediately postulates: Is it possible that these rocks were in a special situation?

Barghoorn: No, the situation indicated by the field relations in the general geological setting is that you are dealing with normal sedimentary processes, incorporation of organic material into fine grain sediments actually depositing rather rapidly, in terms of the processes that Carl mentions, so that there is nothing in the situation that you can see—in the geological setting—that is out of line with what we know of modern processes in sediments.

Burlingame: We don't know of a large source—a high concentration source—of abiologically produced matter anywhere on earth.

Siever: It seems to me if you are contrasting efficiencies, which is really what you are saying, that as soon as you develop something having greater efficiency, it is going to take over, as far as the time scale we are worried about.

Fox: That's right, you don't know where it came from. You don't know that it wasn't abiological. I believe we have to keep our books open on that point.

Burlingame: On the other hand, we don't have a well-defined source of abiological material in terrestrial rocks.

Sagan: How do you mean, well defined? Just to give you a number, if you had a quantum yield of 10^{-5} (molecules produced per photon absorbed) for the production of simple organic molecules by ultraviolet photons with wavelengths less than 2500 Å and you let this process operate on the earth for a billion years, you would produce roughly a kilogram of organic matter per square centimeter column, assuming no loss of organic matter.

Burlingame: So, where is the organic matter resulting from such an abiological process?

Sagan: You just said you couldn't conceive of a process that would produce this much. I'm pointing out that there may be such a process.

Horowitz: It comes out to one percent of the ocean.

Sagan: About one percent of the ocean by mass.

Horowitz: You have one percent in rocks, and you are postulating that this was nonbiological. This seems very unlikely to me. If one percent was the maximum concentration in the primitive seas, and several billions years later you find one percent of the mass of rocks is organic, I think Professor Barghoorn's hypothesis seems more likely.

Sagan: Again, I don't understand. The total amount of carbon in the sedimentary column—both as organic material and as carbonates—isn't that of the order of 10 kilograms per square centimeter column?

McElroy: Particularly if you have a template of a hydrocarbon laid down, this would immediately move very rapidly, and the rate process we are talking about would go up very fast in terms of just making multiple layers.

Sagan: Putting it another way, is it possible that all the carbon we have around today once was layered down as abiological organic matter? I don't see any argument against that.

Abelson: I don't see any strong argument for it.

Siever: That depends on when your carbon became available.

Fox: On the basis of the fact that microbes are nearly ubiquitous on the surface of the earth today, organic compounds would tend to be consumed except for those too far beyond the metabolic or catabolic capability of the microbe. In fact, this can be related to concepts of the origin of petroleum deposits (Fox & Maier, 1959).

Sagan: Another consideration is the high organic matter contained in carbonaceous chondrites, which does run up to several percent. There is at least a major school of thought that these molecules are produced abiologically and in an environment that is probably less conducive to the production of organic molecules than the primitive earth.

Burlingame: Is there anything other than theoretical calculations to support that contention, that it is abiological in origin?

Fox: There is no rigorous evidence. It is just a matter of keeping the books open among the various possibilities.

Burlingame: That's true, but if you put it that way, there are so little data on the composition of the organic matter from any terrestrial geologic source that you just really can't draw any conclusions about whether it is totally biological or abiological.

Sagan: The conclusion of all of this may be that we are very ignorant.

Fox: Let's not start any new dogma.

Burlingame: No, no, particularly experimentally; even if you have one percent organic matter in Precambrian sediments, so little is known about the total composition that our knowledge is almost trivial now. We should bear that in mind. In Clarke's paper (1924), he says that the average amount of reduced carbon in fine grain sediments is 0.85 percent, and others who have studied this make the observation that while there are great variations locally—as in coal deposits and so on—on the average there has been no marked change with time.

Siever: That 0.85 percent reduced carbon figure of Clarke's may be a bit low, and that is pertinent. There may be a little more permanently trapped in the sedimentary part of the crust if you include all extractables and nonextractables in all rocks and fluids. The thing that bothers me about the Fig Tree is that back to the time of the Fig Tree there is absolutely no indication of any change in the abundance of organic carbon, granted that it is very heterogeneous from one rock to another.

Morrison: But the trouble is that if you include the chondrites, then the abundance of organic carbon goes up if anything. The conditions are by now so completely heterogeneous that it looks as though there is no "signal-to-noise" ratio going. If you didn't have that, I think the indication would be that there should be a change someplace, a change in process. I grant that there should be, but what about the meteorites? You can agree that the meteorites were made under the sea somewhere, but this is unlikely.

The trouble seems to be this: Here is a normal set of geological conditions giving you a certain percent carbon in sediments; yet you use a global figure like this one for carbon and then throw in a chondrite (which has nothing to do with terrestrial sedimentary rocks) and still get roughly the same answer for percentage reduced carbon. This looks to me as though you have noise, terrible noise.

Horowitz: It seems to me that respectable people have proposed that meteorites were made under the sea.

Morrison: Some people even propose meteorites have ragweed pollen in them.

Horowitz: In fact, ragweed pollen has been demonstrated in meteorites. (See, for example Sullivan, 1964).

Morrison: There is interstellar chlorophyll, too, according to some experts.

Oró: I am not sure that the meteorites can be related to the Precambrian sediments. I don't think we should cloud the issue of the Precambrian organic matter by bringing the meteorites in.

Sagan: Except, Juan, that it does suggest that there are very effective mechanisms for the abiogenic production of organic molecules.

Oró: I favor your proposal on the major question; that is to say, the fact that there is a large amount of carbon in the chert is not necessarily a justification for saying that it is biological in origin, although this may be highly probable. I understand Professors Barghoorn and Schopf (1966) thought that some of the less organized fibrous materials in the chert could be of abiological origin.

Morrison: Are the hydrogens in any way helpful—hydrogen labeling?

Horowitz: It should be a tremendous fractionation, I should imagine.

Morrison: It should be enormous. Can't you get enough sample?

Horowitz: There isn't much deuterium around, I guess.

Miller: The deuterium is easily measured at the 0.015 percent natural abundance.

Horowitz: Could you find a fractionation in these sediments?

Miller: This could be determined. There are people who have mass spectrometers for hydrogen. I think that the deuterium in organic molecules has not been worked on as much as the C^{12} and C^{13}, but you do get peculiar fractionations.

Horowitz: It does seem unlikely that if there are fossils—such as photosynthetic algae which are really advanced organisms—that there would still be so much primordial organic material around. You would think that most of it would have been consumed in the production of living forms, especially these highly evolved forms. In the presence of abundant primordial organic matter, the ability to perform photosynthesis would have conferred no selective advantage. It therefore seems highly improbable that photosynthesis would have evolved before this material was exhausted.

Margulis: What is the frequency of morphologically preserved fossils in these cherts?

Barghoorn: Pretty low in the Fig Tree.

Margulis: What is the total number?

Barghoorn: I don't know. Do you want to make a guess on this?

Schopf: When we first reported the bacterium-like fossils from the Fig Tree chert (Barghoorn & Schopf, 1966) we had seen about thirty cells. I would guess that since that time I have found about twenty-five or thirty more. The algal-like spheroids are somewhat more common. In our paper published a few weeks ago (Schopf & Barghoorn, 1967), there is a diagram showing the size distribution of twenty eight of these organic microfossils, and thus far I have seen a total of about two hundred cells. They are not ubiquitous, of course; one finds them in some thin sections and not in others.

Morrison: Is there a comparison of Gunflint and Fig Tree in terms of numbers?

Barghoorn: There is a world of difference here. In contrast to the Fig Tree, one of the problems in studying the Gunflint is that there are too many fossils.

Morrison: That is not something to leave out. It is extremely important.

Barghoorn: But it is so much younger than the Fig Tree, another billion years.

Morrison: That is exactly the point.

Sagan: Let's imagine some early epoch where, according to what is now being called the standard dogma, there is lots of organic matter around and organisms that are heterotrophically consuming it. Let's suppose that we freeze some cubic meter of this stuff and then examine it today; what would we find? We would find a distribution of abiologically synthesized organic molecules, and if we are lucky, some fossilized heterotrophs. It is not at all clear that your bacterial and algal-like organisms are photosynthetic. It is possible that they may be heterotrophs.

Schopf: There are several types of information which bear on this problem. First, one wonders whether the reactants for photosynthesis were available in Fig Tree time. Carbonates—dolomitic limestones—have been reported from the

lower Swaziland system immediately underlying the Fig Tree
Series (Ramsay, 1967). They are apparently not widespread,
but their presence suggests that at this time, at least, part of
the atmospheric carbon was present as CO_2 rather than as
methane. Liquid water was present. There is ample evidence
for this: Cross-bedding; ripple marks; mud-cracks; pillow lavas;
and so forth. It seems clear that the reactants for photosynthesis were available at least as early as 3.1 billion years ago.

The presence of ferric oxides in the Fig Tree Series seems
to indicate that at least small amounts of free oxygen were
present in the environment. Whether this oxygen reflects
photosynthetic activity or is merely the product of ultra-
violet-induced photodissociation of water vapor is uncertain.
Organic matter, possibly of photosynthetic origin, varies from
about one-half percent by weight of the Fig Tree cherts to
something over one percent for the shales. Juan Oró has reported pristane and phytane from the Fig Tree sediments
(Oró & Nooner, 1967), and Tom Hoering (1962) has reported
that the reduced carbon in the Fig Tree rocks has a C^{12} to
C^{13} ratio comparable to that measured in photosynthetically
produced organic matter of younger geologic age. Our interpretation, based on these data and the fact that algal-like
microfossils are present in the Fig Tree cherts, is that green-
plant photosynthesis had already evolved by Fig Tree time.
This conclusion seems to be consistent with all the available
information.

Barghoorn: When you add it all up, you come up with this
conclusion.

Morrison: Suppose you said the same thing for Gunflint.

Fox: One of your supports, though, is morphological. I
would point out that experiments have demonstrated, I think
most emphatically, that if you had a pool of organic matter
that included polyamino acids and permitted water to enter

and leave the scene, there would form vast numbers of what Dr. Schopf calls bacterium-like spheroids. These units have double walls, demonstrated by electron microscopy in the laboratory. So I think that in this case to use the morphology as part of your concatenation is to base the argument on a not very firm pillar.

Horowitz: But if there were no morphology, the argument would be much weaker.

Fox: I think we come also to the point where we have to decide whether we are coming or going with respect to an organism.

Fremont-Smith: Dr. Morrison, you wanted to get in and got submerged.

Morrison: I wanted to ask a question. Suppose you made the same rough capsule count of the Gunflint, what would the differences be?

Barghoorn: The differences in the total amount of organic matter are negligible. I am speaking of the cherts. With respect to the relative abundance of recognizable and unquestionable fossils, it is far greater in Gunflint. This could in part be due simply to geologic partial metamorphism—destruction of form in the older rocks—but I don't think this is really the answer.

Horowitz: This metazoan-like object that was reported in *Science* a few weeks ago by Hoffman (1967), how old is that? Was that Gunflint, and do you believe it?

Barghoorn: It is older than Gunflint.

Schopf: It is from the Huronian.

Horowitz: I would love to hear the experts discuss the primitive ocean and the related primitive earth conditions after coffee.

Miller: Now that we have had coffee, I think we should
get back to the primitive atmosphere and discuss consequences
for the primitive oceans in a little more detail before continuing
with the geological evidence.   As I mentioned, the dogmas
state, with greater or lesser merit, that at the beginning———

Fremont-Smith: Greater or lesser emotion is the way to
put it, not merit.

Miller: ———there was methane, ammonia, hydrogen, and water
in the atmosphere.   As you all know, the really logical basis
for believing this was given by Urey (1952 a&b).   The original
argument was made in a qualitative way by Oparin (1938).   Urey
made the reducing atmosphere very plausible, and I think it was
the basis for all subsequent work, especially experimental work,
in this area.

When you argue that the primitive atmosphere was CH_4 and
NH_3, it is clear (as Urey certainly realized) that this is an
abstraction of what you are really trying to say.   Ammonia is
very soluble in water so there would not be much ammonia in
the atmosphere.   There would probably have been a substantial amount of molecular nitrogen in the atmosphere.

I would like to take a few minutes to discuss some thoughts
Jeff Bada and I (Bada & Miller, 1968) have had on how one
can establish some limits on the concentration of ammonium
ion in the primitive ocean.   The basic assumptions are that
there was an aqueous environment and things were more or
less in equilibrium.   We ask, "What was the ammonium ion
concentration?"   The first thing we have to settle is, "What
was the pH of the ocean?"

The pH, which as Sillen pointed out (1961, 1965, 1967)
is determined mainly by clay minerals, affects the ratio of
ammonia (NH_3) to ammonium (NH_4^+) in the ocean.   Although
the carbonate, bicarbonate, calcium carbonate, and carbon
dioxide equilibrium play their roles, the pH of the oceans
is mainly determined by the clay minerals.   In particular, you
can write a set of equilibria for the exchange of H+, Na+.

and NH_4^+ ions (Fig. 2). The equilibrium constants are such that 0.5 M Na^+ is in equilibrium with approximately 10^{-8} M H^+, or a pH of 8. The H^+ in equilibrium with 0.01 M K^+ is also approximately 10^{-8} M.

Infortunately, these reactions are quite complicated, and all the equilibria have not been worked out. Apparently more than a single clay mineral is involved, for example, illite and chlorite; montmorillonite apparently plays a minor role. But it is very hard to write a chemical reaction as the chemists ordinarily do. Nevertheless, this is apparently the principle by which the various ions are regulated in the ocean. When you consider the process in detail—a Garrels (1965) and others (Mackenzie & Garrels, 1965; Holland, 1965; Mackenzie & Garrels, 1966) have done in terms of the material that comes in from the rivers, is deposited, and goes through all the chemical mass balances—a plausible story is formed. I think this explanation will turn out to be correct.

If the same process occurred on the primitive earth and the dominant ionic regulation was by the clay minerals, we can expect a similar pH of the ocean. Those of us who work with laboratory models of prebiological synthesis think that a pH of 8 is just about right. For some reactions, you might want the ocean a little more acid, sometimes a little more basic, but a pH of 8 is a nice figure. Is that fair enough?

Orgel: I would say 8.5.

Fox: I raise an objection to that. I think I detect the assumption (correct me if I am wrong) that life began in the ocean, in a general sense. I think you have to consider also the possibility that life began in more restricted locales. Darwin, for instance, mentioned "a warm little pond."

Miller: Well, in reply to your objection, we should not exclude any possibilities, although I don't think a statement by Darwin is evidence for one set of conditions or another. I think the various restricted locales versus the ocean as a

$$H^+ + clay \cdot Na^+ = Na^+ + clay \cdot H^+$$

$$H^+ + clay \cdot K^+ = K^+ + clay \cdot H^+$$

$$H^+ + clay \cdot NH_4^+ = NH_4^+ + clay \cdot H^+$$

$$NH_4^+ + clay \cdot Na^+ = Na^+ + clay \cdot NH_4^+$$

$$K = \frac{(Na^+) \, N_{NH_4^+}}{(NH_4^+) \, N_{Na^+}}$$

$$NH_4^+ + clay \cdot K^+ = K^+ + clay \cdot NH_4^+$$

$$K = \frac{(K^+) \, N_{NH_4^+}}{(NH_4^+) \, N_{K^+}}$$

Figure 2. Equilibrium equations for positive ions and clay minerals

whole has to be considered on its merits, and I am discussing the ocean as a whole in attempting to set some boundary conditions.

Horowitz: He is only discussing the ammonia equilibrium between the atmosphere and the ocean, not the origin of life.

Fremont-Smith: But every sentence doesn't mean origin of life. When we say "coffee break," it doesn't mean origin of life.

Abelson: I will raise a different objection, and this is a qualitative one. The kinds of silicates that are in the earth's crust, or even in the earliest rocks at the bottom of the geological column—the volcanics—when exposed to water, give a pH of about 9.6 to 9.8 What has brought the present pH down to 8.1 is the neutralizing effect of carbon dioxide. If, as in your model, the atmosphere were methane and ammonia, there would be no CO_2 to neutralize the alkalinity of the rocks. What is more, you would have a contribution from ammonia which, as you know, would drive the pH higher, so that you would be talking about an ocean with a pH above rather than below 9.6 to 9.8.

Miller: What is the pH of a present clay mineral when dissolved in water?

Abelson: We are not talking about clay minerals, because clay minerals are small in comparison with the volume of weathered igneous rocks. This is what you have to talk about.

Siever: This is a big subject and I personally would like to hear about the ammonium, but I think we ought to reserve a little time to talk about this question of the pH of the oceans. Essentially what happens is that you get a high pH for the whole process, which is the result of an over-titration; then a back-titration produces the oceans. The real fundamental question is the assumption that these processes are operating in the quasi-equilibrium fashion. That is really what you are saying, too.

Abelson: All I am saying right now is that if you put methane and ammonia and the earth's crust together, you will have a pH of 10 and above.

Miller: If I may continue the argument, I should mention that the presence of methane early in the earth's history, at the very beginning or subsequently, really does not exclude the presence of CO_2. If the CO_2 was regulated in the same way as is done today, the CO_2 pressure would be approximately 10^{-3} to 10^{-4} atmosphere. This is by no means excluded by the Urey model. An atmosphere very rich in methane does not exclude the presence of CO_2.

Abelson: At the same time you will agree that the outgassing of the earth was proceeding at those very primitive times, because you wouldn't have any CO_2 in the atmosphere for very long, not with the alkaline crusts around. In order to have CO_2 in the atmosphere, you must have a continuous flow from the interior of the earth.

Miller: I don't exclude the outgassing, certainly. That is probably the way the atmosphere was formed. I don't see any reason why you can't have limestones deposited nonbiologically, by outgassing CO_2, dissolving this CO_2 in the ocean as a bicarbonate $(HCO_3{}^-)$ which is then in rapid equilibrium with the atmosphere and precipitating as carbonate $(CO_3{}^=)$. There is no problem there. We will accept a pH of approximately 8 for the ocean, and the argument is not changed if you raise the pH to 9. The only way the argument is changed by a pH of 9 is if the clay minerals are made unstable because of the pH.

Ponnamperuma: Was the outgassing also CO_2?

Miller: One does not know. That is a separate question. The argument I wish to make is that the ammonium ion concentration cannot rise substantially above .01 M, and I will later discuss a lower limit on the concentration of ammonium ion. The equilibrium constant for the exchange of Na^+ and NH_4^+ is 5 in the case of montmorillonite and about one for the NH_4^+ and K^+ exchange. I am told by my colleagues in geology that ammonium ion would be very similar to potassium under geological conditions. There could be differences of a factor of two, but this would not affect the argument.

Fox: Would you state the temperatures, Stanley, for these K's?

Miller: These K's are given for 25°C. However, the heats of reaction are known. They are of the order of 1 or 2 kilocalories. Therefore, the temperature coefficient is low. Whether the temperature was zero or twenty-five doesn't affect this discussion.

Siever: The only time that temperature is important is when you get up to 200°C, 250°C, or something like that.

Miller: What are the boundary conditions on the amount of nitrogen available? If we were to take all the atmospheric nitrogen and put it into the ocean as ammonium ion or ammonium, what would the concentration be? There are 755 grams per square centimeter of nitrogen in the atmosphere, and 280 liters per square centimeter of water. If we put all this nitrogen as ammonia into the present ocean, we get 0.19 *M*. A smaller ocean would give a correspondingly higher NH_4 concentration.

Horowitz: If you put all the nitrogen and living material and fossils, and so on———

Miller: That is very small. I think there is considerable nitrogen in the rocks.

Oró: About twenty times the amount of nitrogen present in the atmosphere is in the rocks in the form of ammonium ion. However, the rocks also contain a large amount of water, so I don't know whether or not including the nitrogen bound in rocks would modify the picture.

Miller: We are not going to include the nitrogen in the rocks. Suppose, for some reason, the ammonium ion concentration got higher than 0.01 M. The complicated clay mineral equilibria regulate potassium ion concentration at 0.01 M according to present ideas. Let's assume it was regulated in the primitive earth in the same way. If the ammonium ion concentration got substantially above 0.01 M, what would happen? The ammonium ion would be taken up by the clay minerals and the potassium and sodium would be released. The K^+ and Na^+ in the ocean would increase and NH_4^+ would decrease until the NH_4 and the K^+ were approximately equal. There is a large exchange capacity of the oceanic sediments, apparently enough to buffer the ions in the ocean.

Abelson: One of the things that is wrong with your argument is that you are talking about clays that are forming today. The reason clays are formed today is because of the action of carbon dioxide, which is breathed out by rootlets, so that the carbon dioxide content in the soil zone is a hundred times as much or more than it is in the atmosphere. The silicates in soil are facing a pH of about 4 to 5 and hence are being converted into clay. In the early earth, without such action of plants, the weathering process was entirely different and, what is more likely, there was not even as much carbon dioxide in the atmosphere as now. You just wouldn't have available the amounts of these clay minerals that you are talking about. There would be several orders of magnitude difference in the reduction rates.

Miller: Are you saying that it is inescapable that the rate of weathering was slower on the primitive earth?

Abelson: Oh, quite inescapable.

Miller: I wonder if this would be quite so inescapable. I don't think we are really in a position to say what the weathering processes were on the primitive earth.

Abelson: I have conducted some experiments on weathering with silicates in distilled water and in the presence of CO_2, and I know that the weathering process would have been different.

Kramer: Is the formation of clay really a physical process, or is it a physical and chemical process combined?

Abelson: It is, first of all, a chemical process. You can have water exposed to the silicates and then only the very outside layers react; but in the presence of CO_2 to carry away calcium and other soluble ions, a reorganization of the surface occurs that makes more surface available. It is true that there is a mechanical aspect but nothing happens unless there is something like carbonic acid to carry away the solubilized divalent cations.

Siever: I think you can look at weathering in very much the same way that Miller has shown. If you substitute any silicate for the clay-Na, then you see the reaction of weathering to be simply the absorption of hydrogen ion onto a silicate.
There are only three acids, really, that are important. You can either have water, which is not very strong; or carbonic acid; or you can have hydrochloric acid. What really always is at issue is, what is the ratio of H_2CO_3 (carbonic acid) to HCl (hydrochloric acid) coming out of the interior at any given moment. That depends on whether you want to assume that there was a lot of outgassing at the beginning or whether it came at unequal rates; whether at the beginning more CO_2 came out or more HCl came out; and whether this was later followed by different amounts of CO_2.

Abelson: As you well know, over the period of the earth's history, CO_2 has been quantitatively the largest and most important source of acid.

Siever: That is right, and you can get this by making the total ratio of chloride present on the surface to the total carbonate plus total carbon on the earth's surface, and the ratios are skewed far in favor of carbonic acid.

I do differ on the idea of the weathering, because I think that the geological experience differs from the experimental results on the rapidity of weathering or, rather, the results of weathering. If you look at the later Precambrian rocks—those rocks younger than about 2 billion years—one sees no obvious evidence of slower weathering rates. As far as we can tell, the very massive sedimentary sections in the Huronian of the Lake Superior region (and even somewhat older rocks than that) show us, for example, some sandstones which are almost entirely made of quartz. Those sandstones imply a disappearance of all silicates other than quartz, which is simply the result of weathering. Everything we see, with the possible exception of the very oldest rocks, says that weathering was going on, but we haven't got the time scale. I don't know just how long these thick quartz-like sections represent. I assume they represent the same time as we have at present because the physical processes of sedimentation would not have changed. It may have been a slower process and have taken longer.

Sagan: How is it known that HCl rather than H_2CO_3 was not the dominant acid at the time Stanley (Miller) is talking about?

Siever: This is what Phil (Abelson) was implying: HCl might have outgassed quickly at first. Isn't that your idea?

Abelson: Yes, but HCl reacts with alkaline silicates and that is the end of the line. HCl doesn't recirculate as CO_2 does.

Sagan: Isn't it curious that HCl is present in the atmosphere of Venus, then?

Abelson: There is a different situation on Venus than on the earth.

Sagan: It is probably not as reducing as the primitive earth.

Miller: Phil (Abelson), I think your point is that if you don't have enough clay minerals on the primitive earth to get equilibrium with this ion exchange, then this argument is not valid.

Oró: Do we have an estimate of the amount of clay on the primitive earth?

Abelson: It is not well known. The most authoritative assessment of the oldest rocks that we have available is Pettijohn's (1943) paper. In the products of weathering, the fine-grain sediments of clays were not nearly as abundant as they are today.

Miller: Are these rocks 4.5 billion years old?

Abelson: This is one of the oldest dated rocks.

Siever: About 3.5 billion years.

Miller: There is always the question of skewed sample.

Siever: There is something interesting here, and that is why I mentioned the quartz sandstones. The very oldest rocks are not quartzitic; they do not contain limestone. They have chert in them sometimes, but they are igneous-looking rocks (graywackes) or derived from igneous rocks; so when we discuss the very oldest sediments in the Precambrian shield, there is some question about the nature of weathering.

I think the vital question at issue is how much clay you need to buffer the amount of nitrogen. Even though there is less clay in Precambrian, I think there is still such an overwhelming amount that I would guess there was enough then to buffer the ammonia.

Miller: I don't think anybody including myself knows how much clay there was. The assumption is that there was enough clay, and if that assumption is invalid, then the argument is invalid.

Oró: Type I carbonaceous chondrites are presumed to be closely related to primordial matter out of which the earth was formed. These chondrites are composed mainly of hydrated magnesium iron silicates which, even though deficient in aluminum and other elements, are somewhat similar to clays.

Abelson: They are not clays.

Siever: They are not clay; they are deficient in hydrogen.

Oró: The pH that has been measured in the case of the carbonaceous chondrites is from 8 to 10 for Type I and pH 6 to 8 for the remainder of the chondrites investigated (Du Fresne, & Anders, 1962).

Abelson: Insofar as the composition of the chondrites is similar to the composition of the earth, the pH of the unweathered chondrite is going to be on the order of 9.5.

Miller: This argument is not affected at all by pH, except if the pH becomes too low or too high, such that clay minerals become unstable.

Siever: That is one of the wonderful things about clay minerals, there is such a range; different ones are stable at varying pH's and you don't have to worry about that.

Miller: At high pH's, the zeolites become stable. At low pH, the muscovites are stable.

The next question I would like to discuss is: Can we set a lower limit on the concentration of ammonium ion? We have to make one general assumption, that aspartic acid [an amino acid found in the proteins of all living organisms] is necessary for the origin of life. We assume that substantial amounts of aspartic acid were available. You can say that this assumption may not be valid, but it is the basis of the argument. Dr.

Abelson who has conducted a substantial amount of work on the decomposition of amino acids, extrapolated to 25°C. The principal mechanism of amino acid decomposition is decarboxylation. For example, alanine irreversibly decarboxylates to ethylamine and carbon dioxide. Aspartic acid is unique in these decompositions in that it does not decompose by decarboxylation. Although it can be decarboxylated, it principally decomposes to fumaric acid and ammonia (aspartic acid = fumaric acid + NH_4^+). The reason it is different is that aspartic acid is both a beta and alpha amino acid, and this is really a beta decomposition. We can write this reaction,

$$^-OO-CH_2-CH_2(NH_3^+)COO^- = {}^-OOC-CH\!\!=\!\!CH-COO^- + NH_4^+$$
$$\text{(aspartic)} \qquad\qquad\qquad \text{(fumaric)} \qquad\quad \text{(amonia)}$$

$$K = \frac{(NH_4^+)(fum^=)}{(asp^{-+-})}$$

This decomposition of aspartic acid is reversible. You can go back to the aspartic acid from the fumaric acid simply by increasing the concentration of ammonium. One can write an equilibrium constant for this reaction.

$$\tfrac{1}{2}N_2 + \tfrac{3}{2}H_2 = NH_3$$

We have determined the equilibrium constant nonenzymatically from 118°C to 135°C. The equilibrium constant can be determined at 25°C by the enzyme, aspartase. At 0°C the equilibrium constant is 1×10^{-3}, and at 25°C it is about 2.7×10^{-3}. At 100°C it is 1.5×10^{-2}. At 100°C it is about 67. I will show later that this reaction is relatively fast. We will assume that it was necessary for the ratio of aspartic acid to fumaric acid to be at least 1.0. If we accept this assumption, then the NH_4^+ must be at least $1\times10^{-3}\,M$ if the temperature is 0°C, and $2.7\times10^{-3}\,M$ if the temperature is 25°C. If the ammonium concentration falls substantially below $1\times10^{-3}\,M$ at 0°C, and this is the most favorable temperature; the aspartic will decompose to fumaric and NH_4^+.

Therefore, if we accept the assumption that we need substantial amounts of aspartic acid for the origin of life, we have to have the ammonium concentration at least as high as 0.001 *M*. The assumption that the aspartic to fumaric ratio was at least 1.0 may be too restrictive; a smaller ratio may have been possible.

It remains to be shown that this reaction is fast. Jeff Bada has worked on this reaction, carried out the kinetics of the decomposition at high temperatures, and extrapolated to lower temperatures. Figure 3 shows the rate of decomposition as a function of pH. It is clear that there are at least two reactions: One that is occurring in base and another in neutral and weakly acid solutions. The rate is nearly independent of pH in the regions from about 4 to 8, and from 10 to 14.

It turns out that there are really three reactions going on, one in base, one in neutral, and one slightly acid, but I will not take the time to discuss the mechanism of this deamination. The Arrhenius activation energies are 28.6 Kcal. at pH 12 and 36.8 Kcal. at pH 7.0.—almost 36 kilocalories. The half-life for the neutral raction is 96,000 years at 25°C and 28 million years at 0°C. The half-life for the basic reaction is 4100 years at 25°C and 360,000 years at 0°C. I will leave you to judge whether this is rapid compared to geological time. To me 96,000 years is quite rapid on the geological time scale; 28 million years is still fairly rapid. These data show that no matter how the aspartic acid is made, whether it is made from cyanide or an aldehyde, it will deaminate to fumaric acid unless the NH_4^+ concentration is high enough.

Fox: I would add a footnote. There are other possibilities. Once you form aspartic acid, if your temperature is high enough, you can get polymers or co-polymers of aspartic acid, and the chemical behavior of those co-polymers cannot be expected to be the same as aspartic acid under the conditions specified here.

Miller: Yes, if you have a peptide bond with aspartic acid, this elimination reaction of ammonia won't take place. However, there is then the question of whether the lifetime of

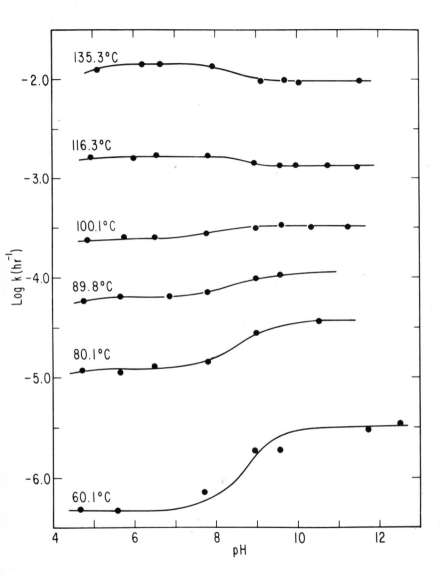

Figure 3. Rate of decomposition from aspartic to fumaric acid as a function of pH

hydrolysis of the aspartic acid polymers is large or small compared to the geological time scale.

I should mention that there are a number of other primitive earth synthetic reactions that require ammonia. There are insufficient data to make as detailed an argument as in the case of aspartic acid. However, I think that a NH_4^+ concentration of 10^{-3} or $10^{-3} M$ will be needed for efficient syntheses by these pathways.

Morrison: What is it now?

Miller: It is extremely low.

Horowitz: What could the pH of the oceans have been and still allow you to have 0.01 M of ammonium ion? Could it have been 9?

Miller: At a pH of 9.2, you have half ammonium and half ammonia. If you change the pH to 11———

Horowitz: You have to get it very high?

Miller: Yes, it affects these equilibria. In the basic solution, aspartic acid becomes less stable, but I don't know whether it is worth taking the time to write out the complete equation.

Horowitz: I was just wondering if we could still cover Phil Abelson's objection.

Miller: With a pH of 9, there would be a factor of 2 in the aspartic acid concentration. This is not going to affect the argument.

McElroy: Would you say a word about the possibility of having reductive amination rather than going through this aspartase reaction?

Miller: The aspartic acid could be made by reductive amination, but this is not a very good reaction because the oxaloacetic acid decarboxylates at a substantial rate. However, if the aspartic acid were made somehow by reductive amination, it would still deaminate to fumaric acid over this time scale.

Abelson: Stan, I think that you have put up a very good argument and one that I buy 100 percent, for the moment at least. There is one difficulty about the ammonia. Have you considered the problem of ultraviolet degradation of ammonia?

Miller: I have not considered this problem in detail. I think Rasool (1966) has.

Abelson: There is a threshold for degradation of ammonia at about 2250 Å. This makes ammonium one of the really sensitive substances. If all the nitrogen now in the atmosphere were present as ammonia, it would take only about 30,000 years for it all to be destroyed.

Sagan: That is assuming no shielding (of the ammonia from the ultraviolet light).

Miller: Assuming no shielding and assuming no resynthesis.

Abelson: The re-formation is slow.

Ponnamperuma: You get some re-formation from methane and nitrogen.

Abelson: You get some re-formation, but remember the way that the number of quanta per wavelength is dropping off; there are very few quanta at 1500 Å in comparison with those at 2250 Å.

Miller: There are certain implications about the atmosphere, if you accept the ammonia argument. We will assume a pH of 8 and a N_2 pressure of one atmosphere. We will consider two cases. The first is the ammonium ion concentration being fixed at 0.01 M by the clay minerals. The second case is the ammonium ion concentration when the aspartic acid concentration equals the fumaric acid. In Table 1, these figures are calculated from the ionization constant of NH_4^+, the volatility of ammonia, and the equilibrium constant for the reaction.

Table I

Equilibrium Concentrations of Ammonia and Hydrogen

| | Upper Limit from Clay Mineral Equilibrium | | |
	$0°C$	$25°C$	$50°C$
$NH_4 + (M)$	0.01	0.01	0.01
NH_3 (M)	6.0×10^{-5}	4.1×10^{-4}	2.1×10^{-3}
pNH_3 (atm)	2.9×10^{-7}	6.9×10^{-6}	1.0×10^{-4}
pH_2 (atm)	1.6×10^{-7}	4.2×10^{-6}	6.4×10^{-5}

| | Lower Limit from Aspartic Acid Equilibrium | | |
	$0°C$	$25°C$	$50°C$
$NH_4^+ (M)$	1.0×10^{-3}	2.7×10^{-3}	5.7×10^{-3}
NH_3 (M)	6.0×10^{-6}	1.1×10^{-4}	1.2×10^{-3}
pNH_3 (atm)	2.9×10^{-8}	1.9×10^{-6}	5.9×10^{-5}
pH_2 (atm)	3.5×10^{-8}	1.8×10^{-6}	4.5×10^{-5}

Key
   M (molar)
   atm (atmospheres)

All these equilibria are temperature dependent. The pNH_3 (partial pressure of ammonia) would be quite low—between 3×10^{-8} to 1×10^{-4} atm depending on the assumed temperature. The hydrogen pressures are also low—from 4×10^{-8} to 5×10^{-5} atmospheres depending on the assumed temperature, and assuming equilibrium for these reactions.

Abelson: But you can't use equilibrium here.

Miller: Quite so. However, if ammonia is placed in a vessel at 25°C and ultraviolet light is used, a steady state mixture of N_2, H_2, and NH_3 is formed. This mixture has an apparent equilibrium which would be a true equilibrium at a substantially higher temperature. Although light decomposes ammonia, it does re-form.

Abelson: Ammonia re-forms very, very slowly and requires quanta of such wavelengths that these quanta are not abundant in comparison to the number present at 2250Å to degrade the ammonia. Once you make N_2, which is an inert substance, there are very few things that can activate this N_2.

Miller: I think there are ways around this. If there is no way that results in ammonia, and you accept that only 30,000 years is needed to destroy it, there will be difficulty in synthesizing amino acids on the primitive earth.

Sagan: If you imagine an atmosphere initially of ammonia, methane, water, and hydrogen, and then ask which molecules are going to be produced in some low yield in that atmosphere, you find there are many that start absorbing below 2400Å . It may very well be that much ammonia was shielded by such molecules.

Abelson: The problem is that many of the shielded molecules would be knocked out by the cold trap. There is inevitably going to be a cold trap in the atmosphere.

Sagan: This is a very difficult calculation even for the contemporary atmosphere. To do it for primitive atmosphere seems to me to be extremely difficult.

Abelson: All I am saying is that there was both the cold trap and rain to sweep out the complex molecules from the atmosphere. It takes some doing to have a shield for the ammonia.

Sagan: It depends on what wavelength. You might very well have, for example, a window at wavelengths longer than 2400 Å and a substantial amount of opacity above the mesopause at wavelengths shorter than 2400 Å. Also, it is possible that the ultraviolet absorbing gases are produced above the mesopause, so there is no question of penetrating through it. There are quite respectable rates of reaction that can occur at high altitudes.

McElroy: Phil, can't you imagine a mechanism for reducing molecular nitrogen, much the way organisms do it today, without such high energy requirements? What if you have a molybdenum clay complex that is capable of absorbing molecular nitrogen; all you need now is reduced ferrodoxin.

Abelson: I only raised this point to indicate that there is a substantial problem with respect to retaining ammonia in the primitive atmosphere, one which requires some ingenuity for its solution. In this question of origin of life I think we have to look out for these key problems, because in the end they might drive us into Sid Fox's camp. That is, my own preference is to find an origin of life that occurs in the ocean, under the most probable conditions with the most probable energy source, and so on. I would like to see it that way and would like to keep working at it until I find some kind of barrier that says: "No, you have got to look for some special condition in order to get around the problem."

Fox: These conditions that you are imputing to Sid Fox's model are not at all special, but the support of my statement requires time for a connected presentation.

Morrison: How sensitive are these to infrequent, unusual components of solar radiations from solar activity—bursts of ultraviolet, in particular?

Abelson: The big bursts from the sun amount to the black body radiation. For instance, there are several hundred calories per square centimeter per year (I forget the exact number) radiated at about 250 Å. These other bursts from the sun are less—in the vicinity of a tenth or so calories per square centimeter.

Sagan: That's right. For example, in hydrogen Lyman series the amount is 10,000 ergs per square centimeter per second during solar activity.

Morrison: Averaged over a few———

Sagan: Over the two decades we have been looking at.

Morrison: Ten thousand ergs is a hell of a burst.

Sagan: If it is 10,000 ergs per centimeter per second, then it would start getting competitive with black body radiation. But that's a difference of four orders of magnitude.

Morrison: Before this SID (sudden ionic disturbance) was noticed, I am sure nobody believed that strong ionization peaks existed.

Sagan: In fact, this whole subject has the objection to it that an extraordinarily unusual event may have played a critical role, either energetically or as far as abundance or reaction rates are concerned. No one is ever going to guess that event because we are not going to be around long enough to see it recur.

Morrison: It isn't all that unusual. In terms of the time of geologic history, it wouldn't occur to me to be particularly unusual. We still wouldn't know it.

The less energetic radiation is extremely interesting for just what Phil (Abelson) said: Is there a sensitive reaction that might be mediated by an occasional lower energy burst with a high quantum yield? It would be very useful to look for it, to try to block it out. You probably can't make extremes, because once you start ionizing, then you are going to have nice shielding below, as we do have in unusual flips.

Fox: Would the discussion initiator please repeat what he said about getting into undue trouble ove a period of 20,000 years?

Miller: If the concentration of ammonium ion is too low, the aspartic acid will decompose with a half-life that depends on the temperature.

Fox: By 30,000 years after the aspartic acid is formed?

Miller: Yes, if the temperature is 25°C or higher. However, if the ammonium ion concentration is high enough, then the aspartic acid is stable, because any that does deaminate will react with the ammonium ion to re-form aspartic acid.

Fox: What about the possibility that the aspartic acid could form polymers promptly? These polymers would form organized units when an astonishing array of properties of the contemporary cell, as our experiments have shown (Fox, 1965b), and these then sink below the surface of the pond or the ocean, whichever it may be. It has been demonstrated that this can occur in a matter of less than 24 hours. What do you have to say about that as against the 30,000 years?

Miller: It is a question of whether and under what conditions polyaspartic acid will form on the primitive earth, as well as its rate of hydrolysis on the long geological time scale.

Fox: But I am taking it out of that context, to emphasize the possibility of other contexts.

Miller: That is the context that we are dealing with.

Fox: Not the experiments I am talking about. These experiments are carried through in less than 24 hours.

Miller: Under primitive earth conditions?

Fox: Under even contemporary earth conditions.

Miller: The rate of synthesis in your laboratory in 24 hours is not the rate of the synthesis over the earth as a whole under primitive earth conditions. You have not taken into account the rate of hydrolysis under these conditions.

Fox: But these conditions exist on the earth right now in a widespread way.

Miller: I think the extent to which they do occur is something we might discuss later on.

Fox: I don't see the need for an assumption of a long period of time like 30,000 years. The point is that natural experiments could have occurred in various ways. The repeatedly-voiced objection to stability of amino acids and their polymers is not germane to some of the alternative possibilities. Seems to me I have heard this 30,000 year argument before.

Miller: The kinetics of the situation are that as long as the aspartic acid is in peptides, the deamination reaction time I am talking about will not take place.

Horowitz: I think his point is, Sidney, that you will not get enough aspartic acid to have polypeptides unless the ammonia concentration is kept high. To build up the concentration of aspartic acid takes time.

Miller: Correct. Once polymerized, they are stable with respect to this deamination reaction. I don't have data on this, but this would be predicted from organic chemistry.

Fox: Other alternatives for the synthesis of the aspartic acid are known from experiments. When aspartic acid is synthesized by heat it immediately polymerizes to polyaspartic acid and must be recovered by hydrolysis. The experiments thus show that, contrary to Dr. Horowitz's assumption, the accumulation of amino acids prior to polymerization is not required, in some cases is not possible.

Sagan: The ammonia atmospheric mixing ratios that you get are certainly not excessive except at the high temperature end. The contemporary atmosphere has a mixing ratio of 2×10^{-8}, and that is sort of the range you are talking about. Of course, the contemporary value represents a disequilibrium state. The Jovian planets have a mixing ratio of about 10^{-3} under conditions probably more reducing than that of primitive earth, so an intermediate value for the early earth is very plausible.

Miller: I think ammonia concentration in the atmosphere is quite reasonable for the low temperatures. If the whole earth were at 100°C, then the NH_3 and H_2 would probably be a little too high.

Sagan: That is only because you assume one atmosphere of pressure.

Miller: These numbers are not affected much by changing the nitrogen pressure.

Sagan: They may be a little too high because you assume only one atmosphere of pressure; in some early time the pressure may have been much larger. Everyone assumes one atmosphere pressure is somehow fixed for all of geological time. The basis for this assumption, particularly in the first billion years of earth history, seems to me very obscure.

Miller: There is a question of the partial pressure of hydrogen and the rate of its escape.

Sagan: The escape rate is proportional to the hydrogen mixing ratio at the base of the exosphere; if you have more stuff up there it escapes faster.

Miller: Yes, and you may get into difficulties there. It is a very complicated thing. I just want to present the numbers, and everyone can draw his own conclusion. A key assumption is whether aspartic acid is really needed. I am not convinced this is a valid assumption, but at least it is a basis for discussion. You notice (Table 1) that the calculated rate between the upper limit and the lower limit is only about a factor of 10. This sets at least a definite concentration of ammonia in moles per liter, which one can take into account when doing laboratory model experiments.

Siever: Is this calculation also insensitive to the total amount of nitrogen?

Miller: Yes, the atmospheric N_2 doesn't affect equilibrium very much. You could get a factor of two or so difference, but this would not affect the argument.

I have presented what I have to say. Does anybody have any other ideas about primitive earth conditions or the chemical aspects of this?

Siever: I want to pick up a little bit of what Carl said about this question of what the density of the primitive atmosphere was or, rather, what the total pressure was. Essentially we have been working with an idea about the accumulation of the atmosphere based on a continuous outgassing of the interior. A number of us have been re-examining this question to see how likely it is that the carbon dioxide, nitrogen, water, and all the rest were outgassed and accumulated gradually, in this neat orderly way.

Just from considerations of the accretion of the earth and how unstable conditions must have been at that time and also during the formation of the core by sedimenting of heavy metals, it seems likely that there may have been a rather early and rather large outgassing episode. I call it the "Big Burp" hypothesis. It is not inconceivable that this whole surface cycle based on a dense primitive atmosphere was set in motion rather early. Originally we thought we couldn't have a dense primitive atmosphere because this would give rise to such extreme weathering conditions that we would have a very acid ocean. In fact, one can make a good case for the very opposite. I think this is what is interesting about the pH of the oceans.

One can ask, "What if there was a great big belch of the gases that are now characteristic of the atmosphere and sediments?" Immediately there would have been a back reaction between those gases and the igneous rocks of the crust—the volcanic rocks—which would have given rise very early to an ocean with sediment in it. This back reaction would probably be very rapid because of the very great concentration of the gases, and we might have been left with a complete obliteration of the original volcanic crust. Instead we'd have a sort of primitive sedimentary crust and an ocean that would be very much like it is today. The question of a pH in that ocean would only be controlled by how fast there would be reconstitution reactions that would back-titrate to an end point of around 8 or thereabouts. In other words, the whole weathering reaction is one in which you absorb hydrogen ion from acids that are available. In most cases, pH would rise to somewhere around 8, 9, or even higher, and then the back-titration to the end point would come in the ocean over a period of time.

Apparently, a steady state would be established by silicate reconstitution reactions of one sort or another, carbonate precipitation and other more minor reactions. If very rapid sedimentation in this very early dense primitive atmosphere is assumed, it is entirely possible that the back-titration reactions were slowed up by the rapidity of the forward process. We then end up with an ocean—which I guess a lot of people would be happy about—in which the pH is around 8.5 to 9, and gradually lowers. But the question is, "What is the time scale?" I would imagine the time scale here is something like the order of about 10^8 years, maybe long enough to give us a period in which to grow some life. I would be interested in any reactions to this.

Abelson: I have a different working hypothesis. My working hypothesis is that the earth accumulated from small pieces, since the noble gases were lost. Other substances like nitrogen were also lost. Thus, in the beginning there was no atmosphere. Then, after a period of time and heating, about 3.4 to 3.5 billion years ago, the earth began to outgas.

Naturally various components won't outgas at the same rate. Some silicates contain water, which is bound quite loosely. My working hypothesis is that water came out preferentially, ahead of some of the other gases. Silicates containing ammonia must be heated very hot in order to break down the NH_4^+ and drive the nitrogen out of the rock. I feel that nitrogen arrived relatively late.

Miller: When did this volcanic activity start—3.5 billion years ago?

Abelson: That is the oldest we can date.

Miller: How long would it take to heat up the interior of the earth?

Sagan: Models of the evolution of the earth have as a feature that it takes time for radioactive heating to heat up the earth.

Miller: But you also have the gravitational heating.

Abelson: Sure, you can have some gravitational heating, but it will depend on how fast the earth accumulated, from what size pieces, and how much heat could be dissipated in each stage of the game. If the earth were formed from small pieces, the gravitational heat could be largely dissipated by radiation.

Orgel: Do you picture the nitrogen as having been trapped as ammonia?

Abelson: Yes. Since noble gases went, nitrogen went. Ammonia ion does proxy, as Stan (Miller) said, for potassium in silicates.

Orgel: What happens if you heat ammonium silicate—what comes out?

Abelson: All that I know is that much of the nitrogen that arrives at the surface of the earth today arrives in the form of nitrogen gas.

Orgel: I thought ammonium silicates pyrolyze to give ammonia. Stanley, do you know if ammonium silicates give ammonia on heating?

Abelson: Remember, there would be iron silicates and so on, so that it would not be pure ammonium silicate compounds being caused to pyrolyze.

Miller: A paper in *Science* a year ago by Eugster and Munox of the Johns Hopkins Geology Department showed that the ammonia in ammonium muscovite is oxidized very easily into nitrogen in the presence of oxygen. However, if there were no oxygen around, the ammonium muscovite would be more stable. If you washed out instead of pyrolyzed out, it will come as ammonia or ammonium ion.

Sagan: Isn't that the main point? If we extrapolate from the products of contemporary volcanism, we are of course going to get more oxidizing gases out than must have been outgassed in the primitive environment.

Abelson: Not very much. People have looked at the very earliest magmas, and it turns out that the ratio of ferrous to ferric iron in those magmas is surprisingly constant.

Sagan: That is not early enough. We talked this morning about how the conditions three-point /something-or-other-billion years ago may have been barely oxidizing. It may be that in the billion years before that, where there is no available geological evidence———

Abelson: When you argue that, you argue about an inaccessible subject.

Sagan: But there are arguments that can be made anyway. For example, I think that the main starting point is that the universe is already reducing and, therefore, any typical cosmically abundant material is going to be reducing. This implies that all materials occluded, precipitated, or chemically bound during the formation of the earth were reduced.

When, for whatever cause—gravitational accretion or radioactive heating—the earth heats up and the sequestered stuff comes out, it must be reducing. Subsequent events must have changed the earth from reducing to oxidizing. Even if there is no free hydrogen at all left during the origin of the earth, the compounds layered down then must have been reduced. I don't see how one can reasonably extrapolate———

Abelson: We don't have to. There is really no evidence for these things in the old rocks. There is no evidence, for instance, in the salts or in the granites, that the earliest rocks encountered any more highly reducing situation than they are encountering today.

Sagan: But if I may say so, those earliest rocks are not the earliest rocks.

Abelson: Then, I say you are talking about something for which there is no hard evidence. You might as well be speculating about the origin of life 35,000 light years away.

Horowitz: What about evidence from the meteorites? They are largely reduced, are they not?

Abelson: Well, people talk about the carbonaceous chondrites, and they are just one of many meteorite types. It is true that, in general, they are reduced.

Sagan: But, in fact, iron is sometimes present in oxidized form, isn't it?

Miller: The iron meteorites contain metallic iron.

Orgel: Are there nitrides in the meteorites?

Miller: I believe so; also iron phosphide.

Fox: But mostly meteorites are metallic. Aren't they just iron?

Miller: By weight, the meteorites are mostly iron. But remember they are mostly stones. The iron weighs more than the stones on the average. There is also a correction for the probability of finding a stone versus an iron.

Sagan: My understanding was that the iron in the carbonaceous chondrites goes through a wide range of oxidation states.

Miller: It is hard to know what came in with the meteorite and what was oxidized while sitting in the Paris Museum for one hundred years.

Abelson: Let me finish describing my working hypothesis. You can have yours. There is plenty of room for individual dogmas.

Fremont-Smith: Thank goodness for this.

Abelson: In the outgassing of the earth the nitrogen tended to come somewhat slower than H_2O. There was also a relative lag in the appearance of carbon dioxide in the atmosphere of the primitive earth. Some carbon dioxide was present, but the proportion of carbonates in the very oldest sediments was not nearly as great as in those two billion years later. The early atmosphere then was thin. The nitrogen took a long time to come. And if there was nitrogen at the beginning of the earth, then the pressures were considerably lower than those today. The nitrogen in the atmosphere slowly increased.

Reynolds. Does your model include already having a lot of reduced carbon lying around in solid material, not in gas?

Abelson: I see no evidence for a lot of reduced carbon on the surface of the earth.

Sagan: I understood we just heard from Dr. Barghoorn that there were huge amounts of reduced carbon.

Abelson: Dr. Barghoorn and I are in disagreement on that point. Incidentally this illustrates the state of the art, and the fact that the geochemical balance sheets are none too good.

Reynolds: In contemporary volcano outgassing, what amount of carbon dioxide is hot?

Abelson: The biggest component of volcanic gas is water, and the next is CO_2. The composition is very difficult to measure because the temperature can range as high as $1200°C$. It is very difficult to catch and to be sure that samples of volcanic acid aren't contaminated. Roughly, volcanic gas is in the neighborhood of a few percent of CO to every 100 parts of CO_2.

Reynolds: And very little methane and hydrogen?

Abelson: Again, about one part of hydrogen to every 100 parts of water.

Horowitz: But this isn't supposed to be juvenile gas [original gas, never outgassed before in the history of the earth].

Abelson: No. There is a big argument about that, too. But it is possible to get some samples where we can argue from the nature of the trapped argon that the gas is juvenile.

Horowitz: With this composition [H_2O, CO_2, N_2, H_2, CO]?

Abelson: Yes.

Fox: An additional difficulty, I think, in drawing inferences is that the analyses from one locale to another are not the same. Even during a single eruption, Naughton (Heald, Naughton & Barnes, 1963) at the University of Hawaii showed that there were wide variations in composition of gases.

Ponnamperuma: In Iceland, where they have analyzed the gases from hot springs, they found 50 percent hydrogen in some cases.

Sagan: Is there any reason to think that figure is too high?

Ponnamperuma: No. They don't know. They haven't done enough analyses. The hydrogen might be from the dissociation of water.

Barghoorn: Are these volcanic?

Ponnamperuma: Yes, in some instances. As regards nitrogen, is it possible that during the accretion of the earth the nitrogen could have been held as nitrodes and, by the action of water on the nitrides, nitrogen was released in its reduced form?

Miller: You would expect that if a large part of the nitrogen was held as nitride, you would find this in the meteorites. Only small amounts of nitrogen are found in the iron meteorites. However, nitrides are not excluded as a source of nitrogen because there may have been more in the material that formed the earth. Dr. Abelson, I am worried about the timing of your model. If you accept Dr. Barghoorn's material as genuine biological fossils 3.5 or so billion years old in your model, was your atmosphere present at that time?

Abelson: I didn't make it clear that to get a magma requires temperatures of the order of 1100°C, but to drive water off from many hydrous silicates only requires a few hundred degrees. The outgassing process began long before a magma formed.

Miller: But then mostly water and very little carbon and nitrogen would outgas.

Abelson: Water would predominate. The earth is so variable in composition, that one could expect there would be local hot spots stemming from unusual concentrations of radioactivity. It is unlikely that all of the water came out first and then something else. There would be some of each volatile with a preference for water to come out ahead of ammonia and carbon dioxide.

Siever: Would you rank order it as water, and then going up in the temperature scale: Chloride, carbon dioxide, and then the rest—nitrogen and so on.

Abelson: I rank the order of first, water, and then I start getting vague.

Sagan: Does anyone know what would happen if you took a carbonaceous chondrite and pyrolyzed it—what atmosphere would you produce from it?

Miller: That's an expensive experiment!

Orgel: I would like to ask Dr. Abelson if any useful simple experiments have been done in which well-defined materials are heated to see what comes out?

Abelson: I think such experiments would be worth doing.

Orgel: What ones would you like to see heated?

Abelson: I would want to think about that.

Siever: There have been many experiments heating up and degassing rocks, rather inclusive as to rock types. Very small amounts of gas come out.

Abelson: The Russians have done a bit of this.

Siever: There are some data but very sketchy.

Orgel: If the geologists are able to decide which are the relevant rocks, that would answer the difficult question. Then finding out what happens when they are heated should be easy.

Siever: One would want to pick a basalt—certainly a typical rock.

Ponnamperuma: Assuming there was no change.

Abelson: I would think one could take some range of likely compositions and perhaps establish some general principles, like water coming off first or coming off as vapor. The first "off" gas would tend to be relatively rich in water, for instance, in comparison to chloride. If carbon dioxide were present as calcium carbonate, the CO_2 would tend to remain behind while every single hydrous silicate would decompose, since they have a vapor pressure of at least one atmosphere of water at temperatures much lower than 960°C—the temperature at which the dissociation pressure of $CaCO_3$ is one atmosphere.

Orgel: What seems to me to be really interesting is if there is some reasonably short experimental program that would give significant results. It would be pointless to heat 100 rocks.

Abelson: Not 100, but with a chosen range of - - -

Orgel: Do you think there is some small set of rocks that could be heated and would give significant results in this context?

Horowitz: Lunar rock!

Orgel: That is what everyone is after.

Sagan: Carbonaceous chondrites.

Fox: You want rock, don't you, that hasn't been heated?

Orgel: I want Dr. Abelson to tell me what sort of rock.

Abelson: You are asking me to be God Almighty, and I decline the role.

Horowitz: Carbonaceous chondrites are subject to contamination.

Sagan: The contamination would be a very small fraction.

Horowitz: But they are detecting very small amounts.

Sagan: What one would like to know is the overall composition: Is it ammonia or nitrogen? Is it CO_2 or methane? Certainly contaminants wouldn't affect such questions.

Siever: Do you know whether the chondrites have been outgassed?

Sagan: They are porous. They have been in space for a long time. They probably have been outgassed.

Burlingame: Why do you think that they are relatively uncontaminated?

Sagan: The organic content is a few percent by mass. To the best of my knowledge, no one is suggesting, except for *Junkus conglomeratus* and a few other ghastly cases, that this few percent by mass is mostly contamination. People are talking about contamination by vanadylporphyrins, assuming it is there, as one part in 10^{10} or something. Isn't that right? Am I mistaken about this?

Oró: Not necessarily. The percentage you are referring to corresponds to a highly insoluble material that is very difficult to characterize. If you are talking about extractable material, then some of the claims that have been made are difficult to accept. For instance, the little bit that has been done on amino acids checks reasonably well with human fingertip amino acids (Hamilton, 1965).

Sagan: On the other hand, the fraction of amino acids was very low, wasn't it?

Oró: Yes, and so it is with the majority of the extractable substances.

Miller: It is the nonextractables that you might want to pyrolyze. Nobody even questions that they are indigenous in the carbonaceous chondrites.

Sagan: That is my understanding.

Oró: Some of this work on pyrolysis has been done. Unfortunately, the components were not measured, but George Mueller (Mueller, et al, 1965) has heated the chondrites up to 1000° C, and he arrived at some conclusions on the rate of degasification. These experiments should be done again, checking which components come out at different times. Hayes and Biemann (1967) heated chondrites up to temperatures of close to 500° C (or at least to around 350° C) and measured some of the organic components. I don't think they paid any attention to the water, inorganic components, CO_2, or sulfur and things like this. By the way, the sulfur has been measured.

Burlingame: Sulfur has been measured?

Oró: The different polymers of sulfur have been measured.

Horowitz: What are the general results of the pyrolysis—just organic compounds?

Oró: They were looking specifically for organic compounds—sulfur components, nitrogen components, and so forth. We cannot say what is the meaning of the results unless we can assert that these components are indigenous. Today there is no proof that the extractable components are indigenous.

Burlingame: The only indication that they might be indigenous is that the apparent degree of oxidation increases as you go out from the center of - - -

Horowitz: If you extracted a meteorite so that you had left only a nonextractable fraction and then pyrolyzed that, would that be a proper experiment?

Burlingame: I think so.

Oró: I am going to put it this way. I think it is a fair experiment if the amount of carbonaceous chondrite is available and you want to waste it in this way, so to speak; it is a fair experiment because even if there is contamination, I think it will be minor in relation to the major results. However, I think it would be awfully difficult to arrive at conclusions in terms of water content, the reason being that some minerals for instance have been found with different degrees of deterioration, depending on whether they come from a New York museum or from a Chicago museum. You must assume an equilibrium with the atmosphere, and at this moment you could say very little about the water content. Yet, in terms of the overall mineral composition, I think it is an ideal sample to work on.

Sagan: On the question of expense, detection techniques are now so sophisticated that I think you could do quite well with a combined gas chromatography and mass spectrographic technique, couldn't you? It seems like a very feasible thing to do.

Abelson: Another approach is that having analyzed some of these carbonaceous chrondites, one would not then have to use actual carbonaceous chondrite material but could use a facsimile.

Orgel: If carbonaceous chondrites were pyrolyzed and the results were brought to a meeting like this, would people accept their relevance to the primitive earth, or would we have a long discussion?

Fox: We would have a long discussion.

Orgel: Then would it be useful to do the experiment?

Oró: Certainly on lunar samples, as Dr. Horowitz said; or better yet, if available, rocks that were on earth 4.5 billion years ago, should yield useful results.

Orgel: The question is, would experiments on any more recent rocks produce relevant theories about outgassing on the primitive earth?

Abelson: One thing you can do is to see what is now at the crust of the earth. There are certain amounts of water and other volatiles. Then you stuff them back in the rock.

Siever: A simple thing to do is to take sediment, put it together with salty water, blow some carbon dioxide into it, heat it up, and make yourself a rock—we don't really much care what that rock is like—and then outgas it.

Sagan: How about hydrogen?

Siever: Put in some hydrogen—I don't really much care.

Sagan: But that's going to make a great difference.

Siever: What you care about is the order in which things come out.

Sagan: That's not the only thing you're interested in.

Abelson: It might turn out that on adjusting the amount of hydrogen over some orders of magnitude one would find that the variable was irrelevant.

Sagan: If that were the result, it would be a good experiment.

Orgel: My contention would be that all of these things, if they are true, could be demonstrated easily, provided one knows what sample one has to work with. If you say water vapor comes off first from hydrated silicate, you can take twenty hydrated silicates, and see if it is true. If it is claimed that CO_2 comes off with ammonia, or that ammonia is released as nitrogen in the presence of iron, all of these things can be tested very easily.

Let's take one problem: What comes off when you heat a silicate containing ferric iron—ammonia or nitrogen? That seems to be relevant to what we were talking about earlier. That is a very easy thing to find out.

Fremont-Smith: After quite a lot of discussion, one of the things that comes out of this kind of conference is some idea of the experiments that can and should be done. Getting this on the record will be of great worth afterwards.

Precambrian Microfossils

Reynolds: This is sharp discontinuity, I am afraid, but I was intrigued by reading about the comparison between Professor Barghoorn's umbrella-shaped fossil *Kakabekia* (Schopf et al, 1965) and Dr. Siegel's (Siegel & Giumarro, 1966) castle wall isolate which required ammonia to grow. Yours was from Gunflint chert, wasn't it, 2.7 billion years ago?

Barghoorn: About 2 billion years old.

Reynolds: One implication might be that if, in fact, anything like the same organism is involved there was much ammonia in that environment. Morphologically, it looks as though it might be. I wonder if I could get you to comment on this.

Barghoorn: This was a suggestion that Siegel made. I don't think the physiological comparison of the fossil to the alleged living representative is necessarily valid. The morphological comparison is quite striking.

Sagan: Would the same remark apply to the identification of algae, namely, that it may be morphologically similar but, physiologically, you would not be too sure?

Barghoorn: Yes, I think one would have to admit that could be the case. The environment from which Siegel's organism came is a highly unusual one but, nevertheless, there are many unusual environments in terrestrial ecological niches. Since he published his first paper he has done a great deal more. There is a current paper (Siegel, *et al,* 1967) describing the parameters of the physiological experiments.

In addition to this peculiar organism, which looks like that in the Gunflint, he has also a number of other organisms—such as an *Oscillatoria,* a blue-green alga—growing in the same unusual atmosphere, ammonia of pH 10 or more. It is an intriguing thought but I don't think that the context of the rest of the presumed environmental conditions of Gunflint chert formation would indicate that the environment was atmospherically comparable. In other words, if such were the case, we would have a reflection in the mineral complexes of the Gunflint formation—evidences that would be indicative of extraordinarily high pH conditions. These are not to be found.

Oró: Would it be too wild an hypothesis to assume that the water contained ammonium silicate, and that there was displacement of the equilibrium—the ammonia was evaporated as gas into the atmosphere and the silicate precipitated as silica gel, trapping the microorganisms?

Barghoorn: It is a little difficult to visualize this. I don't know. What do you think, Ray?

Siever: I think it suggests an experiment. We ought to take some of the Gunflint, outgas it, and see how much ammonia there is. Because the internal surface area of this chert originally must have been very high. There would have been a great deal of the gas absorbed and trapped I expect.

Barghoorn: This was done. John Hunt (Chairman of the Department of Chemistry, Woods Hole Oceanographic Institute) did this.

Miller: Does this umbrella-like organism show up anywhere else besides in Gunflint chert fossils and in Siegel's soil samples?

Barghoorn: No. So far as the fossil record is concerned, the situation is unique. Siegel has also tried soil from various sources. As far as the soil source is concerned, the *Kakabekia*-like living organism is microbiologically unique.

Sagan: Has any further work been done on characterizing the metabolic processes of this organism Siegel has isolated?

Barghoorn: Yes, and this is going to be published. It is a very difficult organism to work with because it appears to require ammonia. As soon as you get it into the atmospheric conditions of the laboratory, you lose the very special requirement that it seems to favor for growth. The Feulgen staining (cytological stain specific for chromosomal DNA) apparently indicates there is no (typical eukaryote) nucleus. It appears as though it were a prokaryotic organism. It lacks chlorophyll; it is heterotrophic. Its source of nutrients has been described in detail (Siegel et al, 1967). Another interesting feature is the number of different forms he has seen, quite similar to the microfossil forms we've observed in the Gunflint. The morphological comparisons are quite intriguing (see Fig. 9).

Morrison: Dr. Barghoorn, are you saying not only that Siegel's organism is positively correlated with the fossil you've seen in Gunflint chert but also that it is anticorrelated with any other known contemporary organism?

Barghoorn: Exactly. The organism that Siegel has in culture is unique among living organisms.

Morrison: That is a strong a priori argument for going beyond the morphological similarities.

Barghoorn: I am inclined in this direction.

Horowitz: Has he examined the nucleic acids and the proteins in this beast?

Barghoorn: I can't remember. I'm sorry I didn't bring a copy of the manuscript.

Reynolds: As I recall, though, the optimal growth occurs when there is somewhere between 30 and 60 percent ammonia in the atmosphere.

Barghoorn: That is right.

Horowitz: It has an umbrella shape, too. From the place (behind the castle wall) where he got it, that would be expected! I think it is lunchtime.

End of Morning Session

Miller: I thought this afternoon we would start out discussing recent work on Precambrian fossils. The earliest fossil evidence is one of the most important boundary conditions for which we have an upper time limit for the origin of life. I would like to call on Dr. Barghoorn to show us some of his work in this area, so that we can get a real feeling for what is being done.

Barghoorn: First, I think it would be interesting to look at the distribution of Precambrian rocks. They are found primarily in South Africa, western Australia, and northern Michigan and Ontario in North America. Bear in mind that Precambrian rocks, even though they go under the name of basement complex, are not necessarily volcanic, igneus, nor metamorphic; nor are the sediments necessarily highly altered diagenetically (sediment hardened by chemical changes caused by deposition of minerals dissolved in percolating water).

I would like to talk a few minutes about a North American Precambrian formation which, for its age, is remarkably unaltered: The Gunflint* (Tyler & Barghoorn, 1954). The chert itself is a very minor portion of the Gunflint formation and in no place is more than 18 inches thick. It occurs in two zones in a formation separated by about 200 feet of black shale.

Fremont-Smith: Do you want to tell us just where it is?

Barghoorn: It is right along the north shore of Lake Superior. On examination, the rock surface is found to be very peculiar. These algal cherts, as they are called, are no recent discovery. Only the investigation of them is recent. The algal cherts have a very peculiar appearance of concentricities which is in part the result of the deposition of the chert on the tops of boulders. The chert, as we visualize it, was formed when silica came out of solution—or at least out of a gel or a supersaturated solution—and deposited directly on the surface that was weathering before the encroachment of the water in Gunflint time. The environ-

---

*The author gratefully acknowledges support for this research from the National Science Foundation and the National Aeronautics and Space Administration to Harvard University.

ment of deposition must have been a normal aquatic environment of relatively shallow water in which there were clastic particles (fragments of older rocks) percolating in suspension, depositing with the algal mats as these mats grew on the boulders. You have here a situation probably comparable to that of a shallow lake or at least a shallow lagoonal depositional environment.

This is a thin slice of the rock itself. It is not a photograph. You notice in the thinner section that the organic matter is brown; it is not graphitized. Chert looks black, like a piece of bituminous coal, when you see it *en masse*. If you grind a piece of bituminous coal down to 15 or 20 microns, it also has all shades of brown, amber, and yellow.

Horowitz: Is the black material organic?

Barghoorn: Yes. The black effect has to do with the organic matter. It depends on the samples, but the organic matter in Gunflint is as high as 0.75 or 0.80 percent by weight of the rock. The predominant cause of this black color is the organic matter. Because there are small amounts of other minerals—hematite, pyrite, et cetera—you get different colors and gradations of color.

Morrison: Is the calcium carbonate thought to be an algal secretion?

Barghoorn: I don't think so, but this involves some arguments. Was the organism biologically responsible for the carbonate or did changes in pH cause carbonate deposition to take place at times of maximum CO_2 extrusion? It is not clear.

Morrison: You call it an algal chert out of this classic view?

Barghoorn: Yes. These algal cherts are widely scattered throughout the Precambrian. I'm showing you now a thin slice of a siliceous Sinter from Yellowstone. As you know, thermophilic blue-green algae are notoriously abundant and widely speciated in these thermal waters, growing at temperatures ranging up to perhaps 75°C. I think there are statements in the literature of algae growing at temperatures up to 90°C, but I believe these are erroneous. The silicate, which may run up to 800 parts per million (wtg/wtg) in these extremely supersaturated solutions, precipitates. It essentially forms an embedding matrix for the algal colonies. The blue-green algae continue to grow at the upper surface as the silicate encases and imprisons the algal column below. This forms the curious thimble-like arrangement and the development of pillars. The extant phenomenon at Yellowstone, I think, is a remarkable counterpart in an existing situation to what we see in the Gunflint rocks.

Miller: Are there organisms that grow nonthermally within a similar deposition?

Barghoorn: Yes. Some interesting studies have been made in the Great Salt Lake (Utah) where many square miles are covered by blue-green algal clumps. Their growth habit is very similar, although silica is not currently deposited on these as far as I'm aware.

Siever: There are some recent descriptions of modern cherts swarming with algal matter. One, in South Australia, is very small, but it is associated with carbonate precipitation, algal mats, pH values up around 9.5 or 10, and a great amount of photosynthesis. The other, Lake Magadi in East Africa, about which Hans Eugster (1967) has written, apparently has close affinity to a soda lake, which is quite a different thing.

Barghoorn: In the thermal areas of New Zealand, on the North Island, I couldn't find any evidence that primary deposition of opaline silica is going on currently—either in basins or even fair sized bodies of water.

Siever: The only thing we have in the column are the classic large beds of cherts which are definitely marine and are attributable to causes that are quite different. There is one other thing I think I ought to insert here, this is the question about the relation of carbon dioxide to this whole matter. The Gunflint occurs in a rock series that contains a lot of dolomite. One would expect to find hydrous magnesium silicates associated with marine-deposited cherts, since they are just the product of a reaction of seawater or any electrolyte solution that contains much magnesium with dissolved silica. That is, if you get somewhere over about 25 milligrams per liter of silica associated with much magnesium, hydrous magnesium silicate—the mineral sepiolite—is soon precipitated. The perplexing question has been that in a good many of these apparently marine-deposited cherts, these magnesium silicates are not associated with the chert;   they should be if the silica simply came out of solution without benefit of biology. In all the later (Paleozoic and younger) cherts, we can ascribe this lack to the fact that there are organisms we know have been removing the silicate (and even now at Yellowstone there is some question as to the role the thermophilic algae play). One can pose a question about the Gunflint: "Is it possible that there was a higher CO_2 pressure in the atmosphere at that time?"   If CO_2 were higher, the magnesium would have been precipitated as dolomite and, therefore, would not have been available for magnesium silicate. This would explain why we get relatively pure chert in association with dolomite.

Miller: Has dolomite ever been formed directly?

Siever: Dolomite is a rather peculiar mineral and, kinetically, takes a rather high supersaturation with respect to carbon dioxide precipitated directly as magnesium.

Miller: But it will precipitate as such?

Siever: Yes, but most of the dolomites we see now seem to be immediately secondary; that is, the first precipitate is calcium carbonate which then quickly double-salts. It becomes the mineral dolomite.

Barghoorn: There is some evidence that dolomite has been made in the laboratory.

Siever: Oh yes, but the classic, quick way to make dolomite is to increase CO_2 pressure to high levels. Dick Holland (Professor H.D. Holland, Department of Geology, Princeton University) for example (and I am sorry he can't be here) speculates, in fact, that this indicates a CO_2 pressure as high as 10 ^{2}, which would correlate with what Phil Abelson was talking about—acid levels you get in soils now.

Barghoorn: Of course, an abundant source of silica in solution is essential to the initial formation of chert. In the Gunflint, the cherts are featured by pyroclastics (rock material fragmented by volcanic action); there must have been active volcanism, so there seems no doubt that there was an abundance of silica around the basins of deposition.

The question of whether organisms actually are active biologically in silica precipitation is not wholly answered. There is no doubt the diatoms and some higher plants are active in precipitating silica, but in the case of the blue-green algae in the thermal environment, I don't believe this is clear. Silica comes out of solution and where there is enough light and CO_2 to permit growth, the algae are passively trapped.

This (Fig. 4) is from a thin section (of Gunflint chert) 30 microns thick. The round bodies are on the order of 10 microns—and you notice the great abundance of these spheroidal objects. They vary in size and intermesh with long filaments. The variety of form and the abundance of them are conspicuous. There are literally thousands of these objects of filamentous or spheroidal shapes in a few square centimeters of a sample of rock 30 microns in thickness. This gives some idea of the abundance and extent of biological activity at the time of initial deposition of the chert.

I might say a word about the age of the Gunflint. Professor Patrick M. Hurley and his colleagues at MIT devoted considerable time to this problem in connection with the general question of the age of the Animikie (Canada) Precambrian system (Hurley, et al, 1962). The dating of the Gunflint is, I think, probably as well established as any Precambrian sediment. The age is on the order of 2 billion years. Fortunately, interbedded within the Gun-

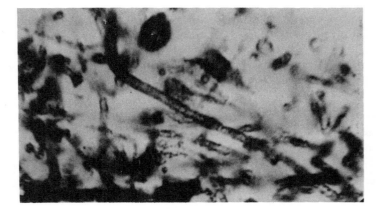

Figure 4. Algal filaments and spore-like bodies from the Gunflint chert. (Thin section photographed in transmitted light, x 1200)

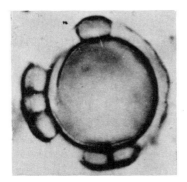

Figure 5. Complex microorganism (*Eosphaera tyleri*) from the Gunflint chert. (Thin section, x 1735)

flint and contiguous to the cherts themselves are authigenic clay minerals (originated at the site), and the dating is based on argon-potassium ratios in illite-montmorillonite mixed-layer clay minerals. Confirmation of the minimal age of the Gunflint is substantiated by strontium-rubidium dates on the underlying conglomerates, which experimentally give values of 500 million years old. So I think the Gunflint establishes pretty much of a reasonably acceptable benchmark as far as middle Precambrian age is concerned. We can appreciate the complexity of the organisms and their morphology, taken in conjunction with the organic geochemical data and the carbon isotopic ratios, and have a pretty coherent body of information that points to the existence and activity of a very complex biocoenose.

I will just run through a few of these peculiar forms. This thing (Fig. 5) has no living counterpart, to my knowledge. It is small, about 30 microns. It possesses a complex morphology. Between these two spheres, there are discernible small tuberclelike ovoid bodies that represent what one might be tempted to consider budding stages of reproduction.

There are other organisms of considerable complexity in Gunflint chert; a few representatives (Figs. 6 and 7) are quite comparable to living organisms. My interpretation is that they are *Oscillatoria*- like organisms. They are very comparable in size and morphology to members of the Oscillatoriaceae, modern blue-green algae.

This type of morphology is also found among certain of the iron bacteria, which are all obligate aerobes. Some of the sulfur bacteria, of which *Beggiatoa* is a well-known example, is another possible analogue. These sulfur bacteria also require free oxygen. Based on morphology alone, of the three possibilities for affinity of this Gunflint organism, I think it is more reasonable to interpret the one in Figure 6 as being a blue-green algae rather than an iron or a sulphur bacterium. There is nothing in the rock, itself, which would indicate any metabolic preference for the sulphur bacteria or, for that matter, the iron bacteria. This is part of the argument in which the carbon isotope ratios help, as we will see shortly.

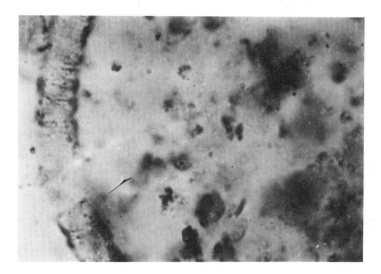

Figure 6. Filamentous blue-green alga-like organism (*Animikiea septata*) from the Gunflint chert. (Thin section, x 1760)

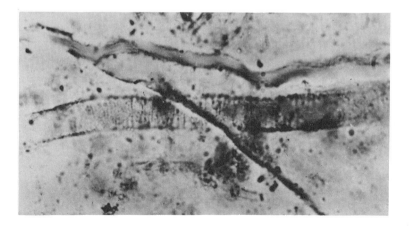

Figure 7. Structure comparable to that shown in Fig. 3. Note preserved transverse cell walls. (Gunflint chert thin section, x 1350)

With the next level of observation on these cherts Bill Schopf
and I had a great deal of trepidation, namely, the application of
electron microscopy (Schopf, et al, 1965). We started first with
the Gunflint chert. This (Fig. 8) is a carbon replica, a single replica
of the surface of a polished, etched block of chert. Chert is an extremely hard and competent rock and takes an extremely high
polish. Its surface can easily be etched with hydrofluoric acid so
the technical procedure is really quite simple, although tedious.
This is a micrograph of a shadowed single carbon replica. The organic remains are sharply outlined. They have the shape and axial
dimensions of modern bacilli. In fact, the clustering together of
cells like this is quite suggestive of bacterial colony growth.

Sagan: What is the scale?

Barghoorn: One micron—pretty small. You notice that there
are other peculiar things in here. These are probably remnants of
bacterial breakdown products, that is, cells which have undergone
lysis.

Rich: What do you think the crystalline inclusions are? They
look like microcrystals that have resisted———

Barghoorn: They do look a little angular, but I don't think they
are crystals. As a matter of fact, the mineral composition of the
matrix is quite extraordinary. If you subtract the carbon and organic matter, it is practically pure silica. Although there are small
amounts of pyrite, siderite, and calcite, I would be more inclined
to think these features are remnants of cell walls.

Eglinton: What about the "organisms" you had previously shown
(Figs. 4 and 5) as seen under the light microscope? Presumably
you can see those, too, under the electron microscope

Barghoorn: In random sampling of replicas of the Gunflint, you can find all sorts of remnants, filaments, and shreds. We never got an electron micrograph of any of those eospheres.

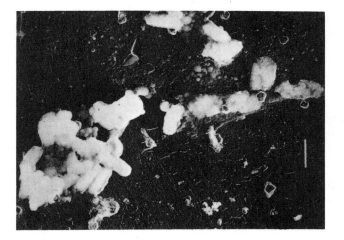

Figure 8. Electron micrograph of bacterial cells from the Gunflint chert Single carbon replica, 1 micron scale

Schopf: No, but many filaments and spheroidal bodies have been studied by electron microscopy. In general however, it is just much easier and less time consuming to study the microfossils in petrographic thin sections; unless, of course, the particular fossil is unusually small.

Eglinton: I am looking for a correlation between the light micro-scope evidence and the electron microscope evidence.

Barghoorn: I think they completely support each other.

Eglinton: I haven't seen the big spheres or filaments on the electron micrographs.

Barghoorn: I didn't bring slides showing these long filaments. Actually there are big shreds and large structures that fully conform in size to what you see in the light microscope.

Horowitz: Under the light microscope, do you see any microstructure in the big objects?

Barghoorn: The best structures that can be resolved under the white light microscope are the larger structures. They are clearly embedded in the chert. If you try to take these structures out they fall apart, and all these pictures that I am showing you, except the electron micrographs, are of thin sections of the rock itself. These aren't macerations. The organisms are sealed up in the chert, so to speak, and are three-dimensionally preserved.

Horowitz: These structures are no longer organic, are they?

Barghoorn: Oh, yes. I was very puzzled by this at first, so many years ago I took thin sections of the Gunflint and built a little well of petroleum jelly, filled it with hydrofluoric acid, sealed it with a plastic cover glass, and watched what was going on. The hydrofluoric acid dissolved the silica. This is risking your lenses, but you could see the objects coming out, flying around as the silica dissolved. Whole spores, pieces of filaments, and other parts all come out. In fact, if you dissolve the Gunflint rock in hydrofluoric acid and wash and centrifuge, you can recover the organic sludge in quantity.

Margulis: You should try germinating it!

Fox: Is the evidence for its being organic that it doesn't dissolve in hydrochloric acid?

Barghoorn: No, no, no. You can take that sludge and extract it with benzene methanol or normal heptane and you recover reasonable amounts of extractables.

Fox: Solvent extractables?

Barghoorn: Yes. It is not a spectacular amount, but it is appreciable—milligrams per 100 grams of original rock sample. It gives you something to work with.

Woese: Have you attempted any enzymatic digestion of this stuff?

Barghoorn: No, although there are various techniques that could be used. Someone has raised several points concerning our work, namely, the question as to whether these things are laboratory contaminants. I think irrefutable proof that they are not is the fact that organic, three-dimensionally recorded imprints of the microfossils are present in the rock.

Rich: Are the lines (Fig. 8) artifacts?

Barghoorn: These are scratches. When you etch, of course, you get a microscopic network of lines from the action of HF.

Schopf: This depends upon how much you etch the rock; that specimen was etched very slightly.

Barghoorn: Later when you look at the Fig Tree, you will see the distinct borders of the main boundary.

Now, I would like to say a few words about trying to interpret these Gunflint forms in terms of modern correlatives. In some of

the more peculiar fossils (I'm sorry I didn't bring the right slides
with me) you notice a radiating, almost octopus-like structure. Interpreting what these may be is of some interest. The slide I'm
showing you now is of *Metallogenium personatum,* Lyalikova's name.
These organisms are iron bacteria—iron and manganese—oxidizers—
described a few years ago by N. N. Lyalikova, a Russian microbio-
logist (Kuznetsov et al, 1963). Because of the very remarkable
similarity to the general forms found in Gunflint, I think these are
interesting possible homologues. However, here again, the modern
forms are aerobic organisms. They require free oxygen, and they
use it to oxidize ferrous iron.

Fremont-Smith: Are we looking at individual organisms or groups?

Barghoorn: That is a matter of opinion. It is like the question,
"What is an actinomycete?" (Actinomycetes: A large group of
true bacteria where cells naturally stay together forming a mycel-
ium that superficially resembles higher molds.) It is a group of
filaments that have a common attachment and proliferate. I would
say that they are multicellular organisms with complex morphology
in their colonial form.

The *Kakabekia* (Siegel et al, 1967) question came up this morning and I would like to spend a few minutes on that because I did not
realize there was that much interest in it. This (Fig. 9) is a
selection of structures in the Gunflint, particularly common as
microfossils in chert of the Gunflint formation near Kakabeka
Falls, in the Port Arthur area of Ontario. The cherts there are
dense, black, and are featured by the relatively common occurrence
of this organism. The fossil is also known from the other outcrops
of Gunflint one hundred some miles to the east, but it is uncommon
elsewhere.

I interpret this as a presumed ontogenetic sequence. The organism has a basal bulbar structure, a stalk, and an umbrella. This is
expressed in varying degrees in these different   stages of growth
and senescence. One reason these four (Figs. 9a, b, c, and g) look
particularly different is not because they differ much in morphology
but in the angle at which you are observing them. All of course are

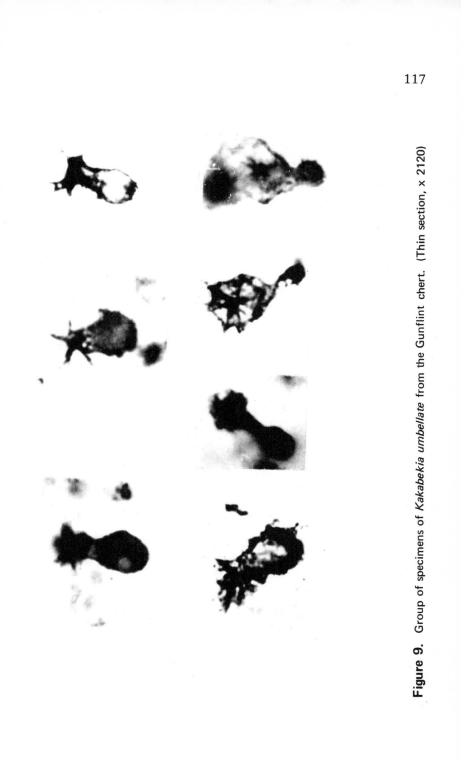

Figure 9. Group of specimens of *Kakabekia umbellate* from the Gunflint chert. (Thin section, x 2120)

three-dimensional structures but suspended at different angles within the hyaline matrix. So it is simply statistical circumstance how you encounter them with the eye. By selecting thousands of such specimens (literally, you can find thousands of specimens within one single section) one can choose a group which, I think, represents an ontogenetic series. There has apparently been little diagenic change structurally during dehydration of the chert itself. I think that what we are looking at is a true representation of the complex morphology of an organism that has a very distinct series of developmental stages. A description of a live organism which closely resembled this fossil from the Gunflint was published a couple of years ago (Siegel & Giumarro, 1966). Sanford Siegel, at that time working at Union Carbide Research Institute on simulated extraterrestrial environments, was amazed to see how closely *Kakabekia* compared, in his estimation, with an organism that he had cultured from soil slurries grown on agar plates in ammonia-rich atmospheres.

Compare the Gunflint *Kakabekia* (Fig. 9) and the morphologically comparable organism that Siegel had in soil cultures (Siegel & Giumarro, 1966). It is obvious that there are some differences, but they are remarkably similar in basic morphology and size.

Shelesnyak: Couldn't you account for the difference between the appearance of the old and the new just on the artifact of constriction? Couldn't the differences be explained by shrinkage in the old form, and lack of shrinkage in the new, when it was fixed?

Barghoorn: Absolutely.

Ponnamperuma: How meaningful is the similarity between those two?

Barghoorn: This is completely a matter of opinion.

Ponnamperuma: We are rather offhand about dismissing the organized elements in meteorites but when it comes to examples like this, we seem to put a lot of store in visual observation. I was wondering about the judgments. Where does the switch in criteria come in?

Barghoorn: The switch between what?

Ponnamperuma: The way we look at the organized elements of meteorites and of Precambrian sediments.

Barghoorn: I don't think we can interpret any of these organized microstructures out of context. Gunflint chert contains a wide assemblage of organisms. Finding one that looks peculiar in terms of modern organisms is no reason to suspect it is not an organism now extant. After all, many preserved forms are now well known.

Horowitz: Most of the organized elements in meteorites are simple spheres. If you'd come to objects with this complexity in carbonaceous chondrites, it would be exceedingly improbable that they could be contaminants—but the organized microstructures that occur in meteorites in millions per gram are simple things with very little morphology.

Fox: That is not always true. I have some pictures that will show otherwise.

Horowitz: For meteorites?

Fox: Yes (Fox, 1964).

Barghoorn: What I would like to try to present to you—and I am not asking you to accept all this without due skepticism—is that we are dealing here with a geological, sedimentological, organic geochemical situation that makes sense only in terms of a preserved microflora or microbiota. Of course, the Gunflint chert is only one unit of a geological formation that shows some 300 feet of black shale in which the organic matter is of biogenic origin, yet not preserved in structure. Cherts are unique rocks in a sense. They are formed by deposition of silica from solution, which, ultimately with time, converts to cryptocrystalline chalcedonic structure.

Morrison: Would you say they are an analog to the lithographic stones?

Barghoorn: No, they are really comparable to shales. What is the mineralogy of lithographic stone?

Siever: Pure calcium carbonate. Both cherts and lithographic stones preserve fossils well, but the lithographic limestones are mechanical; the primary particles are grains of carbonate, a few microns in diameter, that make up a soft lime mud on the sea floor. I think you have to see this formation of a chert as some kind of a setting-up process, almost like plaster of Paris. I don't think there is much contraction. We see no evidence of any cracks.

Barghoorn: A biologist might want to make the analogy that the preservation of these organisms in cherts is like embedding tissue in paraffin in the laboratory.

McElroy: How much is known about Siegel's *Kakabekia*-like organism? Is it an aerobe?

Barghoorn: No. A lot of work has been done on it, but unfortunately, I didn't bring a reprint of Siegel's (Siegel, et al, 1967) paper with me.

Fremont-Smith: Tell us a little about it.

Barghoorn: It is very sluggish in development. It looks brown and spoiling, which Siegel interprets as precursors. You can't see the organism in the soil samples under the microscope. A soil suspension is smeared on agar plates containing sucrose, asparagine, and silicate. The organism seems to like silicate. These plates are put in sealed jars; Siegel adjusts the partial pressure of the gas mixture above them by valves. He runs the gas in at normal ambient pressure. The gas mixtures that seem to be the most favorable for growth are about 30 percent ammonia, 5 to 10 percent oxygen, and the rest nitrogen. However, it will grow in the absence of oxygen. The incubation time to get good, visible colonies is no less than seven days and can be as much as three weeks. It is, so far as he can see, not motile and is extremely difficult to study because he has to use dry lenses; he can't use oil immersion lenses. You try to take the thing out and smear it on a slide and it goes to pieces, so it is a problem to examine this thing with real good optics.

Rich: Does it invade the agar?

Barghoorn: Apparently it grows entirely superficially. It apparently has neither chlorophyll nor a typical nucleus.

McElroy: Doesn't he have it on a defined medium yet?

Barghoorn: He has a whole series of media.

Rich: Is that stalk holding the umbrella up?

Barghoorn: It's hard to say; it looks like a floating organism.

Sagan: Does this bug require both ammonia and molecular oxygen?

Barghoorn: No, just ammonia. It doesn't require oxygen but will grow in atmospheres of low oxygen tension. To keep his cultures happy, Siegel just sprinkles some ammonia hydroxide into the jar.

Sagan: But it does all right in the absence of molecular oxygen? What is the molecular oxygen requirement? Is it an obligate aerobe?

Reynolds: I think, if I am not mistaken, it grows a little better in a small amount of oxygen.

Sagan: And what did you say about it liking silicates?

Barghoorn: It seems to thrive, or at least it appears in greater abundance, with silicate added to the medium.

Siever: I think there is something funny about the fact that there is no orientation of the *Kakabekia* in the Gunflint. You find it in every different orientation, and this looks like a remarkably sensitive hydrodynamic condition. One would expect settling or something like this to result in some preferred orientation.

Barghoorn: You mean the fossil organism *Kakabekia?*

Siever: Yes.

Barghoorn: I would be more inclined to think it was planktonic.

Siever: All planktonic organisms respond very nicely just to settling. This thing has a very peculiar drag.

Barghoorn: I see what you mean. You could argue that an *Oscillatoria* cushion is not planktonic, and yet you can break up the matted filaments and they could grow individually in suspension. It would be very interesting to culture this bug in an aqueous medium, to try to get a better expression of form. It apparently possesses a very soft external boundary membrane and no rigid cell wall.

Horowitz: Is its decomposition in air due to the 20 percent oxygen in the atmosphere?

Barghoorn: No. In scraping it off the agar, the organism is usually broken up.

Sagan: Does he know how it reproduces?

Barghoorn: Not really; it seems to grow out from some spore-like object.

McElroy: It looks like a nonphotosynthetic *Acetabularia* (a marine siphonaceous green alga with an umbrella-like head).

Barghoorn: Let me say this: If the fossil *Kakabekia* and this living organism are genetically related, so to speak, it is no more remarkable than the fact that extant *Oscillatoria* and *Oscillatoria*-like organisms in Gunflint are also related, nor that the *Metallogenium* and its oxidizers are very similar to microbes seen in the Gunflint chert. I don't see any insurmountable intellectual obstacle in accepting this as a remnant fossil.

Horowitz: Except that if *Kakabekia* were living at the same time as *Oscillatoria,* it has these very peculiar requirements for ammonia in the atmosphere and the *Oscillatoria* requires oxygen. There may be a conflict here.

Sagan: This may not be a real contradiction. We are again attempting to derive metabolic similarities from morphological ones—but the organisms may have remained quite similar morphologically while their entire biochemistry evolved, for all we know.

Margulis: But blue-greens (like *Oscillatoria*) also can tolerate very anaerobic conditions. They survive the whole range from the almost totally anaerobic all the way up to the aerobic. It shouldn't be surprising at all to find *Kakabekia* and *Oscillatoria* both extant in Gunflint times.

Barghoorn: The blue-green's tolerance for environmental change is incredible; for example, some survive a pH up to 13. The environmental requirement for ammonia is a difficult thing to unravel. Even today soils contain micro-niches in which ammonia is available. Throughout the course of geologic time there probably has been a continuity of these special ecological niches which, quantitatively, may be extremely minuscule. The soil environment, if not that found in the recent bottom sediments, is probably the most complex ecological situation that exists on the earth.

Sagan: Are the niches with high ammonia content biogenic?

Barghoorn: The original soil?

Sagan: No; today, in places where you find lots of ammonia locally, is the ammonia produced biologically?

Barghoorn: One of the *Pseudomonads* (genus of gram-negative rod shaped bacteria) can process ammonia. This has been measured; it uses one thousand times its body weight of urea per hour. It is a manure organism, a classic case. Ammonia production also can go on at a very rapid rate under limited but available environments. Decaying protoplasm of these organisms provides a good source of ammonia if you have anaerobic conditions.

Eglinton: I think you are going to move over to the Fig Tree, aren't you? Before we leave the Gunflint, we have over 2 billion years between us and it. Is there a nice sequence of samples for this sort of ecological niche that goes all the way up the geological column?

McElroy: Why don't you ask Phil (Abelson) to say a few words about one that exactly fits your question?

Eglinton: There is the Rhynie chert that contains all sorts of organisms, but I wonder whether there isn't some nice, simple chert somewhere that is much younger.

Barghoorn: Much younger than Gunflint?

Eglinton: And another one, say, at a half a billion years ago?

Barghoorn: That is what we have. We have a chert that is one billion years old, which is just what we need.

Eglinton: And another one, say, at half a billion?

Schopf: The Middle Devonian Rhynie chert of Scotland, for example, is about 350 million years old (Croft & George, 1959). The type of preservation and the general lithology of the Bitter Springs—one billion years old—the Gunflint—2 billion years old—and Rhynie—0.35 billion years old—cherts seem quite similar.

Eglinton: So there is a good correlation. Passage of time has not resulted in different morphologies (for what are apparently organisms in the same genera) to any serious extent.

Barghoorn: In fact, you have a sequence of cherts with the same lithology scattered throughout the geologic column. Looking at the Precambrian cherts' sequence gives possible answers to the total sequence of events. (That is, the formation of the cherts themselves implies a certain constancy in the local environment—the differences reflected by morphologies of the microfossils trapped in the silica most likely reflect genuine evolutionary changes.) I must admit that they are scattered in different places in the world and preservation is frequently exasperatingly poor, although organic remains are there. There are plenty of cherts throughout the world. I would say, wouldn't you agree, Ray (Siever), that cherts are more abundant relative to the total lithology in the Precambrian than in the post-Cambrian?

Siever: I don't know. I have that feeling but no good statistics. The Cretaceous and post-Cretaceous cherts are thick and abundant, and we can explain these on the basis of quite a different kind of event—the evolution of the diatoms.

Reynolds: Also before you leave the Gunflint, could you tell us the source of the term Gunflint?

Barghoorn: Gunflint cherts were used, believe it or not, as gunflints. The type locality is Gunflint Lake, Ontario. If you ever get up into that part of northeastern Minnesota, you will find it on the Canadian border, and as you go eastward you can find outcrops of Gunflint cherts, black cherts, green cherts, white cherts, brown cherts, and red cherts, all the way over to just beyond Schreiber, Ontario. There are 140 miles of outcrop. The Gunflint Basin is big and the exposed cherts are simply a remnant of a very wide range in deposition.

The Fig Tree Series

Barghoorn: Now I would like to say a few words about the Fig Tree. The Fig Tree Series of rocks has received a great deal of study (Barghoorn & Schopf, 1966) as is usually the case in the economic exploitation of auriferous (gold-containing) formations. The Fig Tree Series is part of the Swaziland system, and the Swaziland system has chronologic correlatives in several parts of the eastern Transvaal and the adjacent southern part of Rhodesia. It is of unusual interest because it is very old and contains thick units of black shales and also thick units of cherts that vary in color. Of these, the black cherts are, of course, the center of our interest.

The Fig Tree rocks are in a sense, as I think Phil (Abelson) said this morning, "just lying there and nothing has happened." This is about the size of it. The Fig Tree shales are almost unmetamorphosed. You can pick these shales up and break them in your hand. It is almost like Carboniferous shale. I have samples of the chert here if any of you would like to look at them. The organic matter in many typical samples appears to show no recognizable morphology. One sees a distinct bedding pattern, indicating the primary structure of the rock, with varying degrees of organic matter alternating with varying degrees of the percentage of the silica itself. The organic matter which, as I have mentioned, runs up to about one percent, is much more gravely altered here than in the case of Gunflint.

These are examples of the structures that we just published a note about (Schopf & Barghoorn, 1967)—ovoidal, spheroidal bodies, and in fair size. These are well in the size range of white-light microscopy—spheroidal objects of a size consistent with the range of many unicellular, single-celled, blue-green algae existing today. The size range, the general morphology, and the distribution within the sediment are all normal.

Schopf: The size distribution of twenty-eight of the spheroidal bodies in thin sections of the rock were measured. The typical normal curve implies a rather homogeneous population of spheroidal organisms as though all were of the same species.

Barghoorn: The grain boundaries of the chalcedony granules are important in settling the question about whether these bugs are in the rock or whether they fall into the preparation, and I think the case can be closed. The bugs must be *in* the rock because you couldn't conceivably get these organisms transected by the grain boundaries unless they were there when the boundaries were set up. You can also notice the low density or low frequency of these organisms in the Fig Tree as compared to those in the Gunflint. I think this is real, rather than just simply a gratuitous circumstance of sampling. I think that these organisms were not present in any great abundance at the time of deposition. We've found some material in these rocks that looks like polymeric remnants of organisms—organic matter that has been sort of smeared out. I think we raised the question in our paper (Barghoorn & Schopf, 1966) whether this might be abiologic organic matter.

Rich: Have you tried to get the polymeric material out into solution?

Barghoorn: You can't do analytical work on it. You can dissolve the rock in hydrofluoric acid and obtain a black sludge. Of course you can wash and pipette this out and look at it under the microscope, but it breaks up into small units physically.

Rich: What is needed is a better extraction method.

Barghoorn: This is intrinsically difficult.

Abelson: One often sees what looks like perfect preservation of organic material. For example, with clamshells there are instances in which the organic matter at the hinge will seem to have exactly the right form. If you didn't know that it was 20 million years old you could say,"My, that looks just like a clam hinge of today," but then when you examine the organic matter you find that (in spite of the morphological integrity) there have been drastic chemical changes.

Barghoorn: I think this is carrying on further what happens in what is normally called "coalification." You end up with less and less oxygen and less and less nitrogen, more and more carbon, and the molecules beginning to fall apart. It is intriguing and would be important to know for just how long some of these molecules hang together. The porphyrins, for example, are in fragments which, molecularly, are pretty well broken up.

Sagan: In the photomicrograph (Fig. 4) you showed us little things that were maybe 15 microns across. They had little facets or lumps on them. You said that this was similar to some unicellular forms and you deduced that it was unicellular. Could you go into the argument a little more in detail? How do you know, for example, that the facets or lumps aren't cells, and that you aren't looking at a metazoan?

Barghoorn: The size would preclude this.

Sagan: This assumes the constancy of protistan cellular size with time, and maybe that's not constant.

Barghoorn: You mean, could the individual reticulate patterns be the result of a multicellular, spherical, colonial organism?

Sagan: Yes. I am just asking

Barghoorn: I don't think it is reasonable for several reasons. One is the small size of the individual reticules of this reticulum; the other is the possibility that this reticulation resulted in alteration of the organic remnants, a pseudomorphological response due to contraction of the organic material. This type of effect can be seen with spores preserved in recent sediments. You may get minute structural patterns developed as the result of coalescense of individual fractions of the organic remnants. I don't think this answers the question completely, but it seems more reasonable to me that these are original structures.

Sagan: You say you have an alternative explanation for the lumps, and that the whole thing is the size of a contemporary cell?

Barghoorn: Yes.

Rich: Cells aren't all that constant in size. They vary over two orders of magnitude in length, say, which is a pretty good range.

Margulis: Why can't that cell be something like *Chromatium*, a large anaerobic photosynthesizer? This organism, by the way, never evolves oxygen but deposits sulfur. Do you think there is any evidence at all that these were oxygen-eliminating photosynthesizers?

Barghoorn: I don't think you can prove by circumstantial evidence that they are oxygen-eliminating, but I think they were photosynthetic. I don't think it could be due to heterotrophs.

Margulis: But you can't really distinguish between the two types of photosynthesis, can you?

Barghoorn: There are a number of arguments as to why the photosynthetic bacteria could not be the most primitive organisms, but as far as determining from the geochemical evidence,

I don't think you can really prove it.

Horowitz: What is your reason for thinking they are photosynthesizers?

Barghoorn: The argument is largely based on the carbon isotopic fractionation and the fact that there is so much carbon in these rocks. How can it be possible to produce all this reduced carbon? For every molecule of oxygen you "secrete" an atom of carbon. The amount of carbon in these rocks is so large in terms of sedimentary volume, it seems only reasonable that it is photosynthetically reduced. Photosynthesis, if I can quote Carl Sagan, is a sophisticated form of photodissociation. This seems to me a more reasonable assumption.

The Fig Tree is at the present moment the end of the road. We have just about run out of rocks to carry the study farther back in time. The Nonesuch shale of Michigan (about 1 billion years old) actually contains liquid petroleum and, as far as I know, is the only known case of liquid petroleum in the Precambrian (Barghoorn et al, 1965).

Miller: What is the present status of the Bulawayan limestone? (Precambrian sediments near Bulawaya, Rhodesia, dated approximately 2.7 billion years ago.) Are you confident that this was laid down by the blue-green algae there?

Barghoorn: I went there and I must admit it is a somewhat disappointing locality, but I don't see how you could get those *Collenia*-like structures except by biological processes, namely, algal growth. The Bulawayan limestones contain up to one percent carbon. The carbon is graphite; unfortunately it contains no preserved structures and the bulk of the matrix is carbonate: Magnesium and calcium carbonate.

Miller: I am told that this (Bulawayan biogenic limestone) looks very much like some of the limestones that are being laid down off the Bahamas at the present time.

Barghoorn: In fairly deep water.

Miller: Yes, and as I understand it, the mode of deposition off the Bahamas is under dispute. It is not clear whether this deposition is simply inorganic precipitation.

Barghoorn: Yes, that is true. It is a long-standing dispute.

Miller: Would it have been possible to have laid down the Bulawayan limestone nonbiologically?

Barghoorn: I think the inclusion of organic matter in an organized relationship to the matrix means that you have to have organisms growing. Whether the organisms were actually excreting limestone seems perpetually debatable. You can create two hypotheses: The deposition of the carbonate is caused by the metabolic activity of the organisms or the carbonate is precipitated because the solubility factor is changed by photosynthetic extraction of CO_2. As we know in the marine diurnal cycle, the pH may vary from 7.8 at night to 8.2 or 8.3 diurnally, and this will affect the solubility of carbonate to a considerable degree. Under tide pool conditions it may reach 9.6 or 9.8 in full sunlight. Of course, one argument about carbonate being biogenic is the fact that in the same environment some organisms will precipitate and others won't. [If it is purely a chemical and not a biological phenomenon, the amount of carbonate precipitation in a given environment will be constant.]

Schopf: With regard to the Bulawayan structures, Tom Hoering (1962) has measured the ratios of C^{12} to C^{13} in the reduced organic carbon present as graphitic laminations, and in the inorganic carbonate carbon. These measurements show a fractionation of presumed photosynthetic origin between the two types of carbon.

Miller: Isn't the possibility of the intrusion of these materials a problem that one has to worry about in a limestone? Why couldn't they have just been brought in by ground waters?

Limestones are subject to permeation by water and some organic material might have been carried into them.

Barghoorn: I don't have a slide of MacGregor's original exposure in 1941. The judgment of whether the structures are biogenic or not rests in the evidence: See MacGregor (1940).

Abelson: The point is that you have to worry about small molecules. The petroleum naturally migrates, but the graphite is not about to migrate in the same way.

Siever: Also, you can follow these kinds of structures back through the entire geologic column. I don't think there is really much question about the Bahamas and the affinities of a Bahaman algal mat carbonate. There is some question about some other Bahama carbonates but not these, I think.

Barghoorn: You mean the oolites? (Oolite: A limestone composed of many small grains of calcium carbonate cemented together like fish eggs in a layer of sedimentary rock.)

Siever: Yes, the question of the oolite and fine muds should concern us. But through all the geologic column we have hundreds of examples of these kinds of things that are undoubtedly algal in origin.

Bitter Springs Formation

Miller: While we are dealing with the question of Precambrian fossils, I thought I would ask Dr. Schopf to make a presentation of some of his work on the Bitter Springs Formation in Australia.

Schopf: First, let me say that the material I will here be summarizing on the Bitter Springs microflora is discussed in considerably more detail in a paper now in press (Schopf, 1968).
Black cherts of the Bitter Springs Formation of central Australia contain a biologically diverse and evolutionarily interesting

microfossil assemblage. This is yet another example of the "black chert facies" which we have been discussing this afternoon and which seems to be rather widespread throughout the geologic column. The Bitter Springs Formation occurs along the northern margin of the Amadeus Basin, an area of extensive sedimentation from about 1.8 billion years ago until well into the Ordovician (approximately 0.5 billion years ago) in the southern portion of Northern Territory, Australia. The formation is predominantly composed of cherty limestones and dolomites interbedded with minor shaly units. Algal stromatolites of the genus *Collenia* are abundant toward the middle of the formation and this, coupled with the occurrence of carbon-rich black cherts, suggested that microscopic algae might be preserved. Interestingly enough, deposits of gypsum (calcium sulfate), gypsiferous dolomites, and halite (salt) have been reported from the Bitter Springs, the oldest probable evaporates of which I am aware.

The Bitter Springs flora is approximately one billion years in age. The fossiliferous cherts lie beneath sediments which date at 820 million years, and they are younger than deposits dated at 1440 million years. Age determinations have not been made on the Bitter Springs sediments, but based on stratigraphy and the few dates available in the sedimentary sequence, an interpolated estimate of one billion years seems quite reasonable.

The Bitter Springs organisms, growing in biohermal algal communities in a marine, or at least saline, environment were entrapped and preserved by amorphous silica. Upon lithification this primary silica crystallized to chert, and this fine-grained, chemically precipitated matrix is primarily responsible for the unusual quality of organic preservation exhibited by the Bitter Springs microorganisms. Very little work has been done on the organic geochemistry of the Bitter Spring cherts. In general, the organic content varies from about 0.3 to 1.0 percent by dry weight, and of this only a small fraction (roughly 0.5 percent) is soluble in a benzene-methanol solvent solution. Infrared spectra of this soluble fraction indicate that methyl, methyl ene, carbonyl, and perhaps ester groups are present. These data are consistent with the petrologic evidence indicating that the organisms are preserved as geochemically altered but morphologically intact organic structures.

A wide variety of microscopic plants are preserved in the Bitter Springs cherts. The most common of these are filamentous blue-green algae, some of which are remarkably similar to particular living algal species, and spheroidal blue-green and green algae. In Figure 10 are shown three types of Oscillatoriacean filaments, each of which is comparable in general morphology to a particular living alga. The broadest of the filaments (Fig. 10b) is quite like *Lyngbya* in morphology and is enclosed by the remnants of an organic membrane or sheath. Note that several of the cells near the apex of the filament are subdivided by partial septations; in living *Lyngbya* these septa provide the normal means of cell division resulting in vegetative growth. Of the other algae shown, the capitate trichome or filament (Fig. 10c) seems morphologically quite comparable to members of the modern genus *Microcoleus,* whereas the filament with the "gumdrop-shaped" terminal cell (Fig. 10a) is similar to modern *Oscillatoria.* It should perhaps be emphasized that these fossils are *within* thin sections of the chert, and therefore their indigenous nature is well established.

A large number of spheroidal algae are also present in the Bitter Springs deposit. In Figure 11 is shown a colony of mucilage-embedded blue-green algae. In this case, the algal colony has been freed from the rock by hydroflouric acid maceration. Colonies of this type are locally quite abundant in the chert and the fact that their component cells adhere, even after being freed from the enclosing silica, indicates that their gelatinous matrix is well preserved.

In Figure 12 are shown several of the nucleated [eukaryotic] green algae of the assemblage. These are the oldest organisms now known in which the presence of a nucleus, as evidenced by the well-defined "nuclear residue," can be unequivocally established. Note that some of these "chlorococcoid" algae appear

134

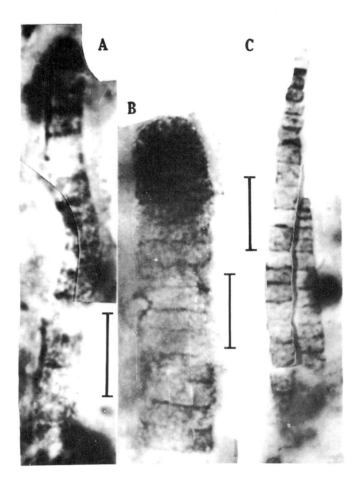

Figure 10. Filamentous blue-green algae about one-billion years old in thin sections of black chert from the Bitter Springs formation of central Australia, 1 micron scale. (a) Septate alga comparable in morphology to members of the extant genus *Oscillatoria.* (b) Broad filament composed of disc-shaped cells and enclosed by an organic sheath; similar in morphology to *Lyngbya.* (c) Capitate filaments comparable to the modern alga *Microcoleus vaginatus.*

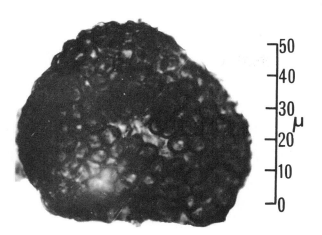

Figure 11. Colonial blue-green algae in a hydrofluoric acid-resistant residue of Bitter Springs chert. Component cells of such colonies adhere when freed from the encompassing silica, indicating an organic embedding matrix.

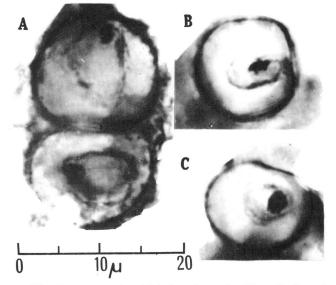

Figure 12. Nucleated spheroidal algae from the Bitter Springs chert, the oldest organisms now known in which the presence of a nucleus can be unequivocally demonstrated. (a) Two spheroidal cells freed from the chert by hydrofluoric acid maceration. (b) and (c) Plasmolyzed algae in thin sections of the chert.

plasmolyzed (cells broken up) with an apparent separation of the two wall layers.

Cells, each one apparently preserved in the process of mitotic division (typical cell division of nucleated higher organisms) are shown in Figure 13. That this represents stages of division rather than of fusion seems evidenced by the flat-sided "lima-bean shape" of the newly produced daughter cells. The organic spheroids near the center of the cells (n) are interpreted as representing partially degraded nuclei. These nucleated algae seem particularly significant because they represent a much more advanced level of cellular organization as compared with that exhibited by microorganisms from Early and Middle ecologically comparable Precambrian sediments. And it seems quite probable that the higher organisms of the Cambrian, such as those of the Late Precambrian Bitter Springs formation, had evolved from their asexual, prokaryotic ancestors.

Finally, it seems worth mentioning that the Bitter Springs formation is roughly contemporaneous with the Nonesuch Shale of northern Michigan, a sediment notable for the variety of biogenic compounds it contains. Pristane, phytane, and steranetype hydrocarbons have been identified in crude oil associated with this billion-year-old sediment, and the n-alkanes appear to show "odd-carbon preference" (Barghoorn, et al, 1965). Moreover, photosynthetic activity is evidenced by the C^{12}/C^{13} ratios measured in organic and inorganic carbon of the Nonesuch sediments, and by the presence of fossil porphyrins, structurally related to chlorophyll, which occur in the siltstone matrix. The organic geochemical data from the Nonesuch Shale and the microfossils from the Bitter Springs chert indicate that both prokaryotic and eukaryotic photosynthetic microorganisms were widespread in Late Precambrian time.

In other Bitter Springs samples one sees a series of unicells arranged in pseudofilamentous pattern with an obvious mucilaginous sheath surrounding the colony. There is a question about little black spots, one of which is found in each of the cells, inside of the cell wall. The interpretation is that they are pyrenoid-

137

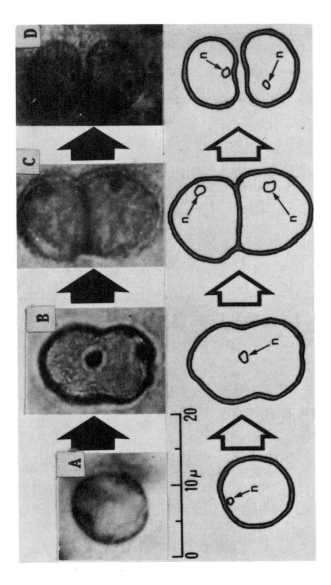

Figure 13. Nucleated algae in thin sections of the Bitter Springs chert representing a mitotic sequence with the nuclear material (a) apparently being equally distributed between the two resulting daughter cells. (The dark spot near the bottom of the invaginated cell (b) is the result of superimposed organic detritus and is not related to the microfossil.)

like, at least in morphology. I haven't done any chemistry on them. I hope to do some electron microscopy to see if they are, in fact, pyrenoids, *per se.*

Sagan: What are pyrenoids?

Schopf: Pyrenoids are starch-storage bodies, essentially, around a proteinaceous center—little starch platelets often found in algae.

Margulis: Are they found only in eukaryotic algae?

Schopf: Yes. They are found in the reds and greens and other higher algae, but not in the blue-greens.

Eglinton: Would electron microscopy help you in discussing the chemical composition of those bodies?

Schopf: I don't think electron microscopy will help too much in terms of chemistry but it will let us see structure. They are apparently a series of plates arranged in a little circle, which is what one would expect. If I can do some electron microscopy perhaps I can resolve the structure better.

Rich: Why can't you do positive staining in the electron microscope?

Schopf: Yes, right.

Rich: That is what you do in chemistry.

Eglinton: Do you mean stain specifically for lipids?

Rich: Yes, and for other cell components. For example, you can use uranyl acetate which is very good for nucleic acid.

Schopf: This is what we will try to do: Combine heavy metal staining with the electron microscopy to see a little bit of the chemistry and correlate this with the structure.

Shelesnyak: There is a very intriguing aspect. You talked about the preservation of the mucilagenous coat. Do you have any speculation about the medium or the situation that would preserve this? It strikes me, from our contemporary conditions, that this is something that has to be preserved rather quickly.

Schopf: I would agree. I should think that the fact that a few cells are "frozen" in the process of cellular division also points to rapid preservation, implying that their encasement in chert happened quite rapidly.

Barghoorn: I think the presence of the "coat" also could be interpreted as an optical effect of the chert; that is not actually the original organic matter but simply an effect on the microfossil.

Shelesnyak: But then you argued later that you have a clumping, which you believe was due to retaining of the adhesive quality of mucin.

Schopf: I think this is correct. Optically one can see a light brownish organic matrix which, although no doubt chemically degraded, has retained sufficient resilience to cause the cells to adhere and remain aggregated even after they are freed from the mineral matrix.

Shelesnyak: This type of phenomenon (preservation of mucilagenous coat) should give you certain criteria for a rate of the geological preservation process, which seems to be inconsistent if compared with contemporary laboratory techniques for doing precisely this.

Siever: I might point out that there are other places where you find preservation of the results of mucilagenous binding such as, for example, in most of the fecal pellets of various animals. Although they are held together temporarily—and if you take a modern sediment you can crush them very easily—they do preserve. There are both silicate and carbonate rocks, Paleozoic in age, in which we can distinguish pellets quite neatly. The mucilagenous material itself is now gone or altered, but it stayed there long enough to give structural integrity.

Miller: Several points in Dr. Schopf's talk are immediately raised, namely, the problem of the organic material and its identification as well as the question of oxygen. Does the presence of porphyrins imply that oxygen was present? Was there photosynthesis? I wonder if some of those who are interested in the Precambrian organic compounds of Precambrian rocks might have some comments.

Ponnamperuma: I want to ask a question before you get on to that. Is Bitter Springs the oldest shale in Australia?

Schopf: This is a chert. No, there are older rocks. Some sediments of the Hammersley Range are on the order of 2 billion years old.

Barghoorn: There are many much older rocks. Bitter Springs is remarkable in that there is a sequence of later Precambrian interbedded with a "well-dated" Cambrian sequence. The older rocks are largely in western Australia.

Ponnamperuma: In the identification of the porphyrin, do you know what metal you had there?

Schopf: The visible spectrum of the Nonesuch porphyrins is characteristic of a vanadyl-porphyrin complex.

Ponnamperuma: This immediately puts me in mind of the vanadyl-porphyrin in the Orgueil meteorite.

Schopf: Vanadyl-porphyrins have, of course, been found in many crude oils and are well known from many younger sediments. Those of the Nonesuch Shale are notable primarily because they appear to be the oldest porphyrins yet reported.

Ponnamperuma: Is vanadyl here by replacement or have the porphyrins themselves evolved through the ages?

Schopf: It is generally assumed that fossil porphyrins originally were magnesium porphyrins, probably derived from chlorophyll (all microbial and plant chlorophylls today are magnesium-chelated porphyrins), and that the magnesium was replaced by vanadyl during diagenesis.

Miller: Could it be that the porphyrins were the cytochrome iron porphyrins of anaerobic organisms?

Schopf: Sure, this is a possibility. The detailed chemistry of the Nonesuch porphyrins has not been studied.

Barghoorn: One thing that is important, in answer to Cyril's (Ponnamperuma) question is that the porphyrins in the Nonesuch are in the shale, not in the oil. For porphyrins to have been introduced preferentially into the shale and not have them carried by the oil would be an utter impossibility.

Sagan: Is vanadyl replacement of magnesium in fossil porphyrins really possible?

Abelson: It is not only possible, but Santa Maria crude oil has one percent and more vanadyl porphyrins.

Sagan: Is it clear that's how it was made?

Abelson: All the people who have looked at it have said that this was what had happened, that vanadyl has replaced the magnesium.

Sagan: But if we know nothing about it———

Miller: Carl, the magnesium comes out very easily.

Sagan: And the vanadyl stays?

Miller: I think the vanadyl is held very strongly in the porphyrin. It will also, I think, displace the iron from an iron porphyrin.

Sagan: And that more than compensates for the difference in abundance?

Miller: Yes. These are well known, for example, in the tunicates.

Shelesnyak: I would like to go back. In your presentation (Fig. 13) you showed an apparent cleavage of two cells. You used the word *mitotic*. Did you really mean mitotic division?

Schopf: I meant mitotic in the sense that there is a morphological unit undergoing division, and that during this process material interpreted as representing the remnants of the nucleus is being distributed to the daughter cells. There are no chromosomes visible, nor is there a "mitotic figure" (spindle, asters, or other manifestations of the achromatic apparatus of the typical eukaryotic mitotic division) preserved. It would be quite spectacular, of course, if this were the case, but it seems quite fortunate to have as much morphology preserved as we do. After all, this represents one of the few examples of preserved nuclei now known.

Shelesnyak: In other words, you could be seeing cleavage without any mitotic structural organization. In your comments, you were introducing what struck me as a very high level of biological cellular behavior.

Schopf: That is correct; the eukaryotic cell represents a high degree of biological organization.

Margulis: That is, if the microbial photosynthesizers described really belong to *Chlorococcus* (a genus of green algae) as you claim, this does imply a high level of biological organization.

Schopf: I think that by Bitter Springs' time the eukaryotic level of organization had evolved. Not only were prokaryotic, nonnucleated blue-green algae present, but by this time the nucleus, with its potentialities for mitosis, meiosis, and genetic exchange through sexuality, had appeared. This, then, set the stage for the diversification of eukaryotic forms, which led into the Cambrian (Sagan, 1967).

Shelesnyak: This would be a very critical landmark.

Fremont-Smith: Sort of premitotic? This is not quite full mitosis and it is not quite un-mitosis. We need a term in between. Is this your point, Shelly?

Shelesnyak: No, I was just asking whether the use of the term was really justified.

Fremont-Smith: This depends on how we define the term "mitotic." How far back does it go?

Shelesnyak: If you feel it is really mitotic, then what is being said is that at this time in geology, a very high level of cellular function had already been established.

Fremont-Smith: This could be a high level that you would not yet quite call mitotic.

Shelesnyak: That is right; that is for him (Schopf) to decide.

Fremont-Smith: An intermediate level is what I am trying to suggest. You may need a name for it; I don't know. I would like Schopf to comment.

Schopf: I should think that, for the figure shown (Fig. 13; Schopf, 1968) the reasonable interpretation would be that these organisms were mitotic—that this was mitosis in the sense that we know it in extant organisms.

Fremont-Smith: But we have to say what is to be included in the term "mitotic." We must indicate certain functional activities that we define as mitotic, and something earlier than this would not be quite that.

Morrison: Isn't this going backwards? You have identified the organism by a number of things—shapes, starch plates, and God knows what else, and then you say, "This looks consistent with that; this is the identification of mitosis." If you have that isolated plate you can't say, "That is mitosis."

Schopf: Based on an isolated photograph or a single specimen, no. But in the biological context provided by the rest of the micro-flora, and based on many examples, I think the identification is just-ified.

Margulis: But the fact is that you have evidence for a chloroplast. If you found a pyrenoid (and let's accept that it is a pyrenoid), then you have evidence for a chloroplast. Now, there are no organisms containing chloroplasts that are not eukaryotic, that is, that are not in the higher group of organisms. So the claim that these cells are eukaryotic is based on morphological analogy, but the heterocysts, nuclei, and the equatorial plates are also identified by morphological analogy. All the rest of it is by analogy, too, so he is on pretty good ground.

Horowitz: There were some remarks made here that I would like to comment on. The assumption seems to be that before the eukary-otes appeared there was no sexual recombination and, therefore, evolution was slow. After the eukaryotes appeared there was a great efflorescence of species, but of course sexual recombination is known in bacteria and even in viruses. The implication perhaps would then be that the prokaryotic type of sexual recombination either isn't very effective or doesn't take place often.

Barghoorn: We have talked about this at length in our group and one way you might think about it is that these prokaryotic organisms are superpolyploids. A polyploid organism contains more than two entire copies of its genome. You get favorable mutations but the genetic material is so diffuse that it is impossible to select them (mutations) out. Whereas in the eukaryotes you get a nucleus and all the complexities of a nuclear chromosomal combination; dele-tions; crossing over; and all that sort of thing. These (favorable mutations) are then perpetuated by sexual recombination.

Horowitz: But that is what happens in bacteria.

Barghoorn: But the rate of the proportional change, quantitatively, is much smaller, isn't it? You are in a better position to answer this than I am.

Horowitz: One's impression is that sexual recombination is rarer among bacteria than among higher organisms, which have to recombine sexually to maintain themselves, whereas bacteria do not. You may be right that it is very rare or inefficient, but this is a new argument that should be pursued.

Barghoorn: In a way it is, and Bitter Springs is important in this respect because it adds to a somewhat staggering conclusion that a lot of these blue-green algae have been hanging around for several billion years, and we haven't seen much change in their morphology. In other words, they haven't expressed any great mutational pressure. It seems reasonable to me that the mechanism and the explanation for this would be the diffusion of genetic material in these prokaryotic cells. You can't preclude mutations clearly, but it seems to me that the stability built into these blue-green algae and bacteria is extraordinary in terms of geologic persistence.

Rich: I think it is a matter of degree. We use the word *sex* to cover many things!

Margulis: Yes, but it only means one thing! It means offspring produced by two different individuals; no matter how you get it, that is all it ever means.

Rich: But the system is different in terms of the eukaryotic organism and the———

Horowitz: The mechanics are different but the result is the same.

Margulis: There are two big differences between the prokaryotic and eukaryotic sexual systems. One is the total amount of genetic material that can be distributed to the offspring is much higher in the eukaryotic mitotic system. The total amount of DNA is much higher and, more than that, meiotic systems insure that recombination accompanies reproduction—often every generation. That is what goes on with people—genetic recombination and reproduction are completely correlated. In these lower forms, by no means is recombination and reproduction the same thing. In fact, reproduction in most prokaryotic organisms doesn't involve genetic recombination at all.

McElroy: Unless you say the mutation rate is different, it doesn't make any difference how polyploid you are. You are going to accumulate mutants that can segregate out in the long run. Thus differential ratio of evolution must be based on some other factor, unless you are willing to admit differences in the mutation rate. Otherwise, it makes no difference whether it is sexual or asexual. They will come out and segregate.

Barghoorn: One would suspect that external forces, such as radiation effects, involved in producing the mutations must have been much greater in the Precambrian.

Margulis: No. You can have as much radiation as you want and produce as many mutations as you want. If two favorable mutations, each in different organisms, don't get together—if, for example, they don't get together because there is no sexual recombination—then you can't produce the advantageous offspring. That is what recombination is all about.

Sagan: Essentially, in asexual reproduction, mutations have to wait in line for a favorable combination; whereas on recombination you have a shuffling of genetic possibilities and some combinations will be much more efficient than others.

McElroy: That is what I was saying.

Horowitz: But the point is that you do get recombination in the lowest living organisms.

Rich: It is a matter of amount. How much recombination do you get, and is sexual recombination obligatory?

Horowitz: That could be the answer. All I am saying is we don't have any evidence from nature that tells us how much sexual recombination is going on in bacteria.

Orgel: In ecological situations, one just doesn't know how much recombination there is for viruses or bacteria.

Margulis: You can be sure it is less for bacilli than for snails.

Horowitz: Less recombination per generation or less per unit of time?

Sagan: On the question of mutation rate, certainly at the time of, say, Bitter Springs, there is no reason to think that the natural radiation environment of the earth was significantly different from what it is today.

Barghoorn: But you have a long gap from Fig Tree time to Bitter Springs time, some 2 billion years.

Sagan: But if you look at the radiation environment, there are a few things that might have been very different in primitive times and a lot of things that are unlikely to have been different. We have already mentioned the possibility of ultraviolet windows in the atmosphere. It is conceivable that the UV flux at the surface of the earth may have been much larger, although you can imagine places subsurface or beneath the waters where the UV flux was tolerable. Solar protons of the usual energies are unlikely to penetrate in any atmosphere, whether or not we had a magnetic field. The same is true of X and gamma rays. I don't know what sort of long-term variations in cosmic-ray flux are plausible. Maybe Phil Morrison would have a word to say on that.

Siever: Long-term variations in cosmic-ray flux would depend on the magnetic field, however.

Sagan: Yes. It also depends on what energy cosmic rays we are talking about.

Shelesnyak: But isn't all this on the basis of the assumption we are making—that the organisms at that time had the same types of sensitivities.

Sagan: That is the next point I was going to make. Organisms today regulate their own mutation rate in a number of ways. We know that today there are particular adaptations to undo mutational damage—for example, thymine dimerization.

Shelesnyak: We don't know anything about the sensitivity of the pre-organism to the types of radiations or environmental factors we are talking about now, those to which contemporary organisms are sensitive. In other words, we are not matching systems.

Sagan: Isn't it more likely to be the other way around? Today there are some very elaborate mechanisms to control and, particularly, to reduce the mutation rate, whereas in primitive times these mechanisms were unlikely to have evolved.

Shelesnyak: Is there any evidence for this?

Sagan: There is evidence for sophisticated mechanisms for undoing radiation damage to contemporary biological systems.

Kramer: I raised an eye, too, at Dr. Barghoorn's statement because the implication seemed to be that sexual mechanisms and recombinations are independent of an environmental selective factor, one that is responsible for the large evolutionary, morphological changes that we find in organisms. I just wondered whether Dr. Barghoorn meant that once you had gotten to the level of sexual reproduction independent of a selective factor, this would result in a tremendous evolutionary development.

Barghoorn: When you have chromosomes and chromosomal mechanisms to redistribute genetic mutational effects, the situation is far more efficient in allowing variations to survive. There is a greater possibility. I am not trying to explain evolution, but this certainly makes sense from what we know of sexual recombination.

Kramer: Let me put it another way. Is your implication, then, that prior to the advent of sexual mechanisms, the environment was relatively uniform compared to the environmental changes that took place after the advent of sexual mechanisms?

Barghoorn: No. I think this is a double-barreled question. I think that, for one thing, these primitive plants have an ecological tolerance or amplitude that is far greater than for highly specialized organisms. They have a built-in buffer against adversity—let me put it that way—whereas the more highly evolved an organism is morphologically and physiologically, the smaller the niche (with respect to both biological and physical factors) the organism can occupy. Thus, with the evolution of increasingly complex physiological systems (and their correlated morphological expression) you have an increasingly small bore in the funnel of diversity, which sexual reproduction allows to be accelerated beyond the rate of simple prokaryotic organisms. I am not arguing; I think Horowitz is perfectly correct that we still have to face the facts of the geological record. These bugs just didn't change morphologically. We still have them around.

Reynolds: They were really radiation-resistant, too.

Sagan: In fact, adaptive radiation is usually attributed not to fantastic increase in mutation rates but to an increase in selection pressure. Certainly there were huge changes in the environment of the earth to which organisms had to adapt. Just to take one example, there was an absolutely crucial change from a reducing to an oxidizing environment. That must have been an extremely powerful selection factor.

Margulis: Yes. Especially in the prokaryotes. There is no evidence that adaptations to change in oxygen tolerance and utilization were operating in the evolution of the higher eukaryotic cells at all.

Burlingame: With relation to changes in the environment, I don't know whether any of you have read this business by Uffen, the geologist———

Sagan: Yes, but that argument is silly. The argument of Uffen is that the earth has gradually been forming an iron core; that it started out without such a core (many geologists will go this far); that when there was no core, there was no magnetic field; and that if there were no magnetic field, charged particles from the sun reached the surface of the earth with impunity, causing fantastic increases in mutation rates.

A variant of this argument is that even in contemporary times, when the magnetic field flips its axis, it may go through zero-field strength for a few thousand years and at that time there is a huge flux of charged particles coming in. Uffen is mostly talking about solar wind particles, but the solar wind particles are stopped by the atmosphere at an altitude of about 105 kilometers even in the absence of any magnetic field.

Morrison: This (Uffen's theory) is designed to explain the remarkable fauna found at the earth's magnetic poles.

Simulated Precambrian Microfossils

Miller: I would now be very pleased to call on Dr. Fox to discuss some of his work on carbonaceous chondrites.

Fox: I am not going to discuss "our" work on carbonaceous chondrites. I propose to show some comparisons. These are slides that bear on experiments in synthetic micromorphology (experiments to synthesize microscopic-sized objects analogous to objects found in sediments or chondrites). Many of these comparisons result from experiments performed for other objectives. Some of the results might also be referred to as "carbonaceous snowflakes," to use Dr. Morrison's (1962) term.

Figure 14 is reproduced from a paper by Claus, Nagy, and Europa (1963). This is one of the "organized elements" of the *Ivuna* or *Orgueil* meteorite; it is not purely spherical as Dr. Horowitz implied. Most of what I have to say may bear more heavily on these bodies being aspherical rather than on the micropaleontological, but this is an "organized element," and the authors describe tubular protuberances on the exterior. The photograph on the right (Fig. 14b) comes from an experiment not done for this purpose but is the result of reviewing photomicrographs which we had accumulated in the course of studying the morphology of units formed by adding water to the thermal polymers of amino acids (high molecular-weight compounds made by heating amino acids). This sequence is a ridiculously simple pair of operations. Under the optical microscope, we see hollow protuberances in the synthetic particle also. These are all in the range of size of about 10 to 20 microns in diameter.

Figure 15a is also from a carbonaceous chondrite. One can see the inner structure and the outer structure. Figure 15b is a synthetic microparticle with inner and outer structures, again comparable in size.

Figure 16 is also a comparison, taken from the paper by Claus and Nagy (1961). This does bear more closely on some of the comments with respect to the micropaleontological arguments. The authors in this case referred to an "organized element" caught in the act of "cell-division" and pointed out a plane of constriction and two daughter halves. On the right (Fig. 16b) is a synthetic particle that can be compared. The two simple steps I mentioned earlier have been followed in this experiment; the thermal polymerization of amino acids—in fact, all eighteen that are common to protein—and the addition of water. This treatment can be carried out with cold water, but it usually works best by simply adding hot water and letting the clear solution cool. Then the particles are deposited; this entire experiment takes but a few minutes. Vast numbers of various kinds of these microparticles are deposited (on glass microscope slides). A third

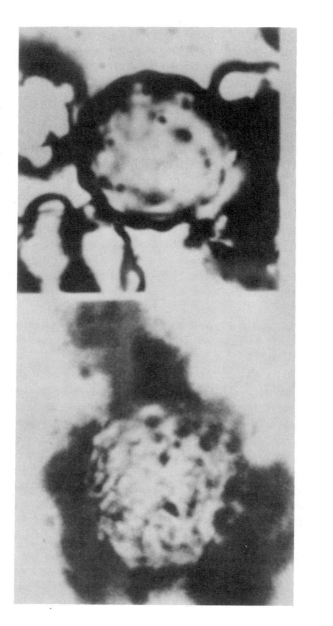

Figure 14. (a) "Organized element" from *Orgueil* meteorite; (b) proteinoid microparticle produced in the lab. Each shows hollow protuberances on the surface.

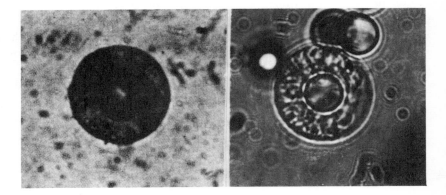

(a)   (b)

Figure 15. (a) "Organized element" from meteorite; (b) synthetic proteinoid microparticle. Each shows a sphere within a sphere and additional structure in the annular space.

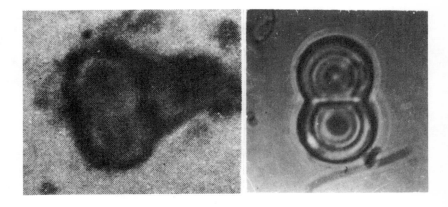

(a)   (b)

Figure 16. (a) "Organized element" from meteorite undergoing "cell division"; (b) synthetic proteinoid microparticle dividing due to increase in pH.

step has been introduced here. The pH has been raised by adding a bit of McIllwain's buffer, raising the pH one or two units and allowing that buffer to diffuse in under the cover glass. Then after some minutes there is obtained a simulation, as you see, of cell division.

Sagan: You didn't press down on the cover glass, did you?

Fox: No. That gives another kind of figure (Fig. 17). Other studies (Fox & Yuyama, 1964) by time-lapse have shown gradual development of what you see.

Miller: What kind of buffer is this?

Fox: This is a phosphate-citrate buffer.

Horowitz: But it is also a simulation of cell fusion, isn't it?

Fox: Without knowledge of the studies (cited above) one would have to consider them either cell fusion or cell division. The time-lapse studies show that under these conditions what is being looked at is, indeed, simulation of early steps in division of the microparticle.

Burlingame: These are taken in aqueous solution?

Fox: Yes.

Burlingame: What happens if you dehydrate (remove water from the specimen by drying out or successive immersions in organic solvents)? Can you preserve the structure?

Fox: Yes, as usually made, they are quite stable to dehydration. Or do you mean dehydrate them at this stage?

Burlingame: Yes, does the structure stay preserved?

Fox: I remember one experiment in which we got some twinning; in that case I can't say whether that was fusion or fission, but the microspheres were slowly dried and then heated

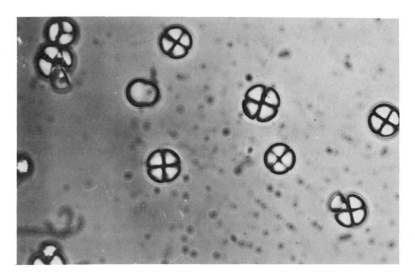

Figure 17. Proteinoid microparticles that have cleaved due to pressure on coverglass.

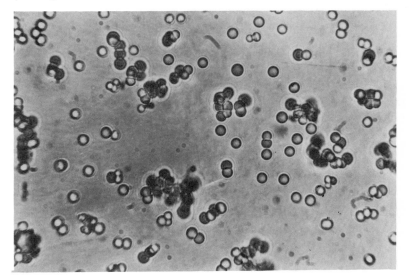

Figure 18. Microsphere from thermal proteinoid. Individual and associated microspheres can be seen as well as one that has "budded."

in an oven at 100°C. When water was added to them, they recovered their original morphology. They are quite stable. Smith and Bellware (1966) reported on the stability of proteinoid microspheres, and there have been reports from other laboratories (Young, 1965) on this property.

Kramer: Do these structures actually go on to separate?

Fox: Yes, but with some dissolution of the polymer.

Rich: What is the concentration of amino acid in the mix before you start heating?

Fox: There can be various ratios in the mix but "concentration" is not a relevant concept in the absence of solvent, other than pyroglutamic acid.

Rich: What is the most dilute solution you can use? Or, to put it another way, if you simply add other miscellaneous things, say silicates, at what stage does the microparticle not form?

Fox: We have not found ratios at which they don't form, but we have added various phosphates in various ratios to the amino acids and Mr. Bruce Gordon (Gordon, B., C.R. Windsor, & S.W. Fox, unpublished experiments) added silicon dioxide or sand in a high ratio of sand to amino acids. In fact, in the presence of sand one gets polymers that form more cleanly. I think they are cleansed by leaching and passage through the sand, which is a sort of purification technique. In a terrestrial type of reaction such as this one, with no solvent present, the total reactants are at infinite concentration regardless of the size of the mass or micromass of reactants. The reaction is, therefore, understandably not disturbed by materials, including nonsolid byproducts, which are not in the reactant phase with the amino acids. Among the materials that have been added in various proportions up to ninefold are phenol, citric acid, starch, succinic acid, ferrous phosphate, calcium phosphate, salts of cerium, titanium, lanthanum, magnesium, zinc, and others. In most cases the polymers and their yields are unaffected, except that yields of acid polymers are increased by the presence of phosphates or of organic acids. Carrying out the polymerization on lava does not affect it adversely (Fox, 1964b).

McElroy : Did you follow the surface tension changes when you did this, which is obviously what must be happening?

Fox : No, we didn't. Dr. Kleinschmidt at NYU is beginning to look at that, relative to the binding of basic proteinoids with polynucleotide.

In Figure 18 are some of the simple microparticles. Dr. Morrison asked how uniform they are. You can see that these are quite uniform. In fact, the diameter is about 1.9 ± 0.1 microns in this case. There are some associations. The stability covers a wide range, and this range overlaps the range of stability of contemporary bacterial cells. These units respond to hypertonic solution of salt by shrinking, or to hypotonic solution by swelling. They have a kind of osmotic property.

Miller: Do you think the osmotic property is due to a membrane, or to swelling of a charged polymer, for example, like Dowex 50.

Fox: I believe, essentially, it is due to a kind of membrane; some further pictures to be projected suggest that.

Figure 19 shows a 10-micron scale. This is again a light micrograph of some of the larger particles that have been made, revealing some of the possible internal structure and also a kind of double ring around the outside, seen in other experiments.

A second population of these microparticles, quite uniform in size, makes up the filaments. They string together so that filamentous forms are seen. We haven't investigated the small microspheres further, but they are seen also in many of the micrographs of "organized elements" formed from chondrite sections. Under the conditions that pertain for meteorites, we infer that nature performs the kind of experiment we carry out. We use compar-

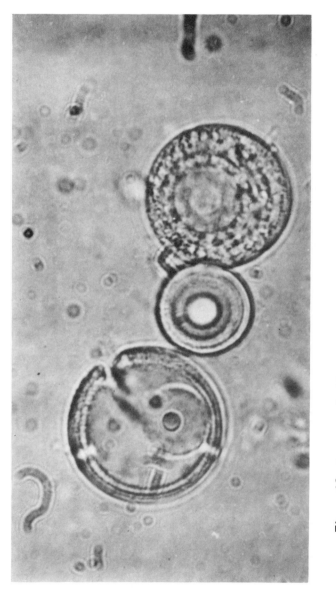

Figure 19. Large proteinoid microspheres. Also present are filamentous associations of small microspheres.

able conditions in the lab.

Eglinton: None of these are sections, are they? Have you embedded any and then sliced them?

Fox: No, none of these are sections, but I will show you sections shortly. In Figure 20 is a preparation we made under the cover glass. Sometimes when they are made this way by heating the microslide with a microburner and allowing it to cool, they will form these configurations. I showed these (Fox & Yuyama, 1963) without comment, to Dr. Chester Nielsen, a systemic algologist (that is, phycologist: Student of algal taxonomy) and asked him what they were. He said, "Where did you get them, from fresh or salt water?" Actually, it was salt water because we used one percent sodium chloride solution.

In Figure 21 are two electron micrographs of sections of proteinoid microspheres. (We have some other electron micrographs which I didn't feel were quite relevant to the topic we are discussing this afternoon, but which I would like to show later on when we get to models of the origin of membranes.) These have been made as indicated earlier, by raising the pH. You can see under these conditions a double layer—double walls—that had been observed many times under the light microscope.

Horowitz: How thick are these membranes?

Fox: The annular spaces run typically between 50 Å and 200 Å, and the individual layers seem to be about 150 Å to 500 Å, although they arise in quite a variety of specifications. These show also the process of fission.

Horowitz: You said you were going to show us some *Kakabekia*-like organisms from chondrites.

Fox: No, I didn't say that.

Fremont-Smith: You said you were going to show us something.

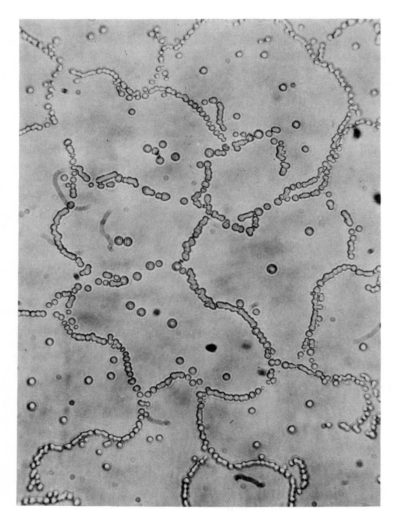

Figure 20. Association of proteinoid microspheres

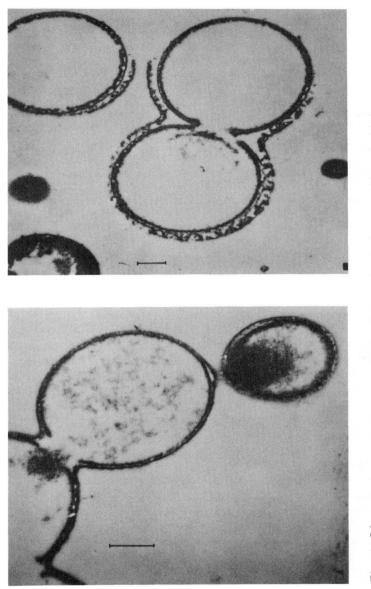

Figure 21. Sections of proteinoid microspheres stained with osmium tetroxide, embedded, sectioned, and electron micrographed.

Fox: I have shown you some units that are not simply spherical.

Horowitz: There is a question whether the numerous inclusions in chondrites are spherical or complex in morphology.

Fox: Dr. Barghoorn's kind of figure (Fig. 5) has been published for the chondrites, and again we have seen this kind of thing inadvertently in our own experiments. What size is it?

Barghoorn: Twenty-eight microns or so.

Fox: That is about as large as the largest ones we have seen.

Sagan: The structure of this one (Gunflint specimen, Fig. 5) I understood you to say was two concentric spheres with little spheres in between them.

Barghoorn: We have 150 specimens of them, and they all show this indentation when well preserved. This is a basic feature of them.

Fox: Indentations are seen in some of the proteinoid microparticles, for instance, Figure 19. McCauley (Fox, McCauley, & Wood, 1967) has seen many kinds of indentation, some due to pressure, some not.

Schopf: What conclusion would you draw from your studies, Dr. Fox, based on the morphologies you have observed?

Fox: I believe that morphological specifications, of themselves, are not adequate for establishing that a fossil is a fossil of a once-living organism. One conclusion I would draw is that one can't yet draw any firm conclusion for some of the fossils or some of the "organized elements." That is really what I mean by saying I think that the probability of the occurrence of units of this sort, or of mineral substitution products thereof, when one looks at the whole picture is great enough to add another alternative explanation to what is seen in chondrites, and I think also to what is seen in the micropaleontological objects.

Horowitz: Sidney, what is the alternative explanation, when you say there is an alternative explanation?   Do you mean that the fossils described today in cherts are really protein microspheres;   is that it?

Fox: Yes, that they are proteinoid pre-organisms, or mineral replacements thereof, instead of organisms;   and it seems to me that if this proved to be the correct explanation, in some ways it would be more significant than if they were organisms.   Another view is simply that the laboratory experiments   accurately describe natural experiments in meteorite or in geological formations.   The conditions of the laboratory, the meteorites, and the chert overlap, if one allows for mobility in the geological realm.

Margulis: How much isotope (C^{12}/C^{13}) fractionation do you get in your proteinoids?

Fox: I don't think that would be relevant.

Horowitz: Don't you make these out of amino acids put together under optimum conditions?   Don't you take purified chemicals from bottles off the shelf and mix them together?

Fox: In some cases.   In other cases, we mix them together with other materials, including materials from the crust of the earth, as Dr. Rich inquired about.

Miller: What happens when you mix the amino acids with something like sodium chloride?

Fox: I don't remember the exact proportions, but that experiment has been done for another purpose, and the amino acids polymerized.

Miller: You don't recall the yield and you don't recall the ratio of sodium chloride to the amino acids?

Fox: When potassium chloride and molybdenum oxide were present as one gram to 3 grams of amino acids, the yield was increased. I can tell you from experiments that have been done that the polymerization is very rugged. It is very hard to displace it, to make it go awry.

Horowitz: But still, the amino acids have to collide with one another and they have to combine in some way, and if you have enough stuff in there it will slow down this process of collision. Furthermore, you will have chain-stopping substances in a natural environment that will terminate the growth of the polymers.

Fox: You might have in some cases, but if you have amino acids formed in the atmosphere—for example falling into a hot pool or on hot lava and the water evaporates promptly so you have, essentially, dry amino acid in the pool or on the lava—you have the conditions for condensation. The lava would have been washed by the rains (Fox, 1964b).

Horowitz: What about all the salts that were in the pool?

Fox: We haven't tried all the salts. Many of the salts do not interfere in any serious way, or they catalyze, as I have already indicated, but the question can be asked endlessly.

Horowitz: How about the sugars, aldehydes, or cyanide derivatives?

Woese: What is the point you are trying to make?

Horowitz: The point I am trying to make is that microspheres are prepared under laboratory conditions in which chemically pure substances are mixed together and heated.

Fox: That is not always true, as we have already stated here, and already published earlier.

Horowitz: I am trying to get at this question: In a natural environment, a plausibly natural environment where you try to produce these, what would you get? If you added amino acids to mud from the bottom of the sea and carried out the same thermal process, would you expect to produce microspheres?

Woese: I think we showed this morning, though, that we can't define these environments well enough to rule out what Dr. Fox would consider a reasonable environment.

Horowitz: To me, it seems exceedingly unlikely that you will get amino acids in the concentration that I think is required to produce a structure.

Morrison: What are the necessary concentrations?

Woese: I think that is being a little too dogmatic at this point.

Morrison: What is a typical concentration?

Fox: Of what?

Morrison: A typical global amino acid concentration.

Fox: That cannot be answered for the primitive earth. For the contemporary laboratory, these amino acids, either with or without contaminants of the kind that Norman (Horowitz) has been talking about, are dry. Or, if one starts with an aqueous solution, one evaporates the water, adds heat, and the amino acids begin immediately to condense.

Morrison: But in the aqueous solution in the beginning, how much is amino acid, how much is water, and how much is gook?

Fox: That is going to vary with the particular geochemical solution.

Morrison: I am not talking about———

Fox: It varies also with the experiment.

Morrison: Of course. Any case varies. Give me an idea.

Fox: In some experiments we use one part of ferrous phosphate to the amino acids. In other experiments, we have used nine parts of sand to one part of amino acids of all the kinds that make up the mixture.

Morrison: In what volume of water?

Fox: The volume, you see, is the volume represented by nine parts of sand and one part amino acids dry.

Orgel: And the water is all evaporated off?

Fox: If we start with water, the volume can be the volume that is ascribable to the amount of water that we started with.

Morrison: Can it?

Fox: Yes, indeed.

Morrison: It is not obvious to me that if you have a sandy layer underneath a great pool of water (containing organic matter) and if you evaporate it all away, that you might not find just individual little spots of stuff.

Fox: First, you may find little spots of stuff, but when the water is all evaporated, it (the remainder) is all in a single mass. But little spots of stuff are, anyhow, conceptually sufficient by physicochemical principle and the fact that any microquantity could be the start of life. The limitation is mainly the amount of amino acid.

Siever: I think you can approach it from another point of view—what the natural environment must have been like. I think anybody who has seen the Gunflint and is familiar with these kinds of (geological) sections would probably rule out any high temperature environment. I will listen to what Elso (Barghoorn) has to say on that, but it looks very much as if the Gunflint was a normal temperature aqueous environment with many of the ions commonly present in modern natural waters.

Barghoorn: Yes. There are no evaporates present.

Siever: There are no evaporates at all, no chlorides.

Barghoorn: I would just like to ask a few questions. First, I don't see the relevance of this proteinoid microstructure work to the problem we are dealing with, the environment which produced the Gunflint microfossils. Secondly, in the work that Adolph Smith (Department of Physics, Sir George Williams University, personal communication) has been doing in Montreal (I think this answers Morrison's question)—he uses one percent nucleic acids, and he evaporates these down on a slide and then regenerates them by adding water, using 1 percent, 5 percent, using pure water or citrate. He can get all sorts of combinations, but I don't think it has any relevance to our problem here.

Morrison: Don't be too harsh. It has relevance, but it certainly seems to me that if there is a different kind of a system— A. Smith's system—with difference concentrations, that does the same thing as Fox's system. It isn't clear to me that just because there are no evaporates in the Gunflint, there isn't another unknown system—unknown to us—which makes morphological forms similar to those in Gunflint chert. We couldn't say that for sure. I am not trying to say it is a geological———

Barghoorn: Preservation of microfossils takes place in geological environments.

Morrison: But what actually occurred in that geological environment you don't know. Therefore, if he (Fox) says amino acids make proteins and I take some other chemical that I don't know (I am neither a geochemist nor geologist), it might under different circumstances do it, too. The only thing I am worried about is given the overall concentration, what are the probabilities of getting an elaborate joining of those molecules?

Fox: We can say, qualitatively, that having tested a number of these—although naturally not having tested all possible combinations—it is obvious that the polymerization condensation is a very rugged reaction. I think the relevance is that with a very rugged reaction under conditions which not only existed, as we can infer, on the primitive earth but which exist on the contemporary earth, we can understand how morphologies of this sort might easily arise, assuming that the amino acids were available. Contributions of pressure are also easy to visualize.

Barghoorn: How would you get the filaments closely resembling those of extant multicellular organisms?

Fox: In some of the ways that were shown. For example, by slight pressure. In the geological environment, this might be due to a film of colloid, such as is associated with bodies of water like lakes and lagoons.

Barghoorn: And this gives you things that look like *Nostoc* (contemporary blue-green filamentous alga, for example, Fig. 10)?

Fox: Yes.

Barghoorn: But if you examine yours carefully, it doesn't have the morphology of a filamentous blue-green.

Morrison: The whole septate quality was missing. However, this is the baby-and-the-bathwater problem. Just because most morphologies in proteinaceous microspheres are not directly related to extant organisms does not mean the work in general is not relevant. I think it was very clear in the chondrite work that there are many simple objects and few complex objects. The first tendency is to lump them all together and say, "Since there were many objects, there could have been contamination; since they were complex, they had to be organic." It turned out that there was another parameter. Some were complex and some were many, and they were not the same. So just because there is a filamentous form that looks like an *Oscillatoria* (I thought very strongly like it), the thing with the little disc with five little discs around it might not be *Oscillatoria*. It might turn out to be something quite different. That doesn't destroy either work, but it shows that the situation is complex.

Horowitz: In the fossils, you have complexity in high populations.

Morrison: Then you are in better shape.

Horowitz: That is what Barghoorn has—complexity and dense populations.

Barghoorn: Morphologically, multivariables might be coordinate, as expressed by a variety of organisms. When I said irrelevant, I should have clarified that. The total environmental situation in which these deposits formed are not salt pans and evaporates, as in Fox's simulations. These are sedimentary deposits. It is the total geologic context that I think makes this (Fox) work irrelevant at least to the Gunflint and Fig Tree.

Rich: I think the argument, Phil, is that the fossils show a spectrum of organisms of varying complexity. The more complex ones clearly appear biological, as judged by a large number of analogies. I think just extrapolating that down to the simpler ones it is likely, but certainly not certain, that they, too, are biological. The laboratory-produced forms are pretty simple, in general, although they do mimic some of the simpler microfossils. In the absence of data showing the kind of detailed morphological comparison, we don't have to assume that the simpler forms in the geological specimens are artifacts.

Morrison: I would say even more. I would say that the whole complex, the continuity through geologic time and the whole picture presented by Professor Barghoorn, convinces me that the simplest explanation is the ecological context of the algae. It had none of this great big macrostructure, bio-organs—there is very little doubt of this. But that is a different story from saying that a morphological distinction all by itself will demonstrate this. It is quite relevant, I think, to show morphological patterns, but don't do it with the implication that when you have a thing like this, then you surround it with all these remarkable results we have heard about today. I, for one, am convinced to a plausible degree of conviction that it is extremely likely that Schopf and Barghoorn have shown *bona fide* fossils ot ancient microbes, but that is very different from seeing sort of a single slide culled out of many thousands and have people say, "This is something really grand," because it isn't.

I think we have been through that lesson with the meteorites; that is what I am thinking about (Sullivan, 1964). These chondrites microparticles, et cetera are not particularly relevant to the microfossil work that has such a wealth of different kinds of data. It seems to me the geological stuff takes on a different quality from carbonaceous chondrites or some future thing we might possibly find.

Margulis: Dr. Fox, are you arguing that the Fig Tree material can be explained on the basis of proteinaceous microspheres?

Fox: No, not the Fig Tree material.

Margulis: But you won't buy just morphological evidence by itself?

Fox: That is what I believe at this point. As criteria of life I also wouldn't buy any single kind of evidence, even though I would pay more attention to the morphological than to some other single types.

Fremont-Smith: Let me ask this question, and I am showing my ignorance and sticking my neck out. As I see it, it has been shown that by putting together certain combinations, chemically and physically, one can get these spheres that behave in ways that are in some respects analogous to what we see in some living forms. It is, it seems to me, entirely possible that these mechanisms, these physical mechanisms, can be made use of by biological material, and they do not necessarily operate as biological material. For example, we know perfectly well that amoebae use surface tension and that surface tension is a physical property. Therefore, one would expect all physical properties to be available to biological material, and it might very well be that what has been demonstrated has been some ways in which something else, which we call biological, can make use of physical properties and function.

This may be a very foolish way of saying it, but it seems to me it is not an either/or but it might be a combination of both. Does that make any sense to you?

Fox: Yes, it certainly does. I think it helps us in focusing our attention on those physical processes that are germane to the biological state. One either regards life as possessing a vital quality of its own, or of being a complex of physical and chemical structures and processes. On the basis of the latter premise, we can define an objective of identifying the necessary and sufficient physical and chemical structures and functions—necessary and sufficient in simultaneous association.

Kramer: We certainly accept the fact that living organisms make use of chemical materials and yet nobody claims chemical materials are living organisms. I don't see why we can't go along with the same thing—with physical properties that Dr. Fox has indicated.

Fremont-Smith: They are influenced by radiation, which is a physical property, or by temperature.

Reynolds: I would even go farther than that. I would say it would be very surprising if primitive organisms did not exhibit the same kinds of properties that would be exhibited by still simpler systems.

Horowitz: That the laws of physics and chemistry apply to living systems is a fact we all agree on.

Morrison: What is the free energy per unit volume? Yours (Fox) are rather large. Free energy makes information.

Woese: I think one other thing should be pointed out. These very old "fossils" may exhibit fairly complex forms but this doesn't necessarily mean that these are organisms in the modern sense—that is, they have well-developed genetic systems, with thousands of genes, the capacity to translate accurately, et cetera. There is no proof that a "modern" cell existed at that time.

Margulis: Are you talking about Fig Tree times?

Woese: Yes.

Margulis: You may be correct about the Fig Tree, but the Gunflint and Bitter Springs organisms must have had developed genetic systems.

Woese: I'm talking about the single fossils that Dr. Fox can simulate. There is no reason for us to assume they have a fully evolved genetic system, et cetera.

Sagan: That is a whole question that we are supposed to talk about tomorrow, whether in the absence of genetic systems, in the absence of replication, is it reasonable to talk about evolution?

Morrison: What is the time span, what time has elapsed from the earliest to the latest Fig Tree samples you have searched?

Barghoorn: Relatively small. Ramsay (1967) estimates probably more than 10,000 feet of sediment and, by radiogenic dates, the times all bracket from within about 3.1 billion years ago to 3.0.

Morrison: That's not my question. I want to know what is the amount of time, T_1-T_2—not for 10,000 feet of the formation but for the samples you have looked at. In other words, are you looking at samples spread over 10,000 feet or over 1 foot or what?

Barghoorn: It is very difficult to answer that question because the Fig Tree rocks are intensely folded and we find cherts interbedded. There is no way of readily correlating strata.

Morrison: You can give a statistical answer.

Barghoorn: I would say a matter of decades or centuries, not anything of any major magnitude. Very short. You can't really quantitate this precisely.

Fremont-Smith: A geological millisecond.

Siever: A minimum of 10° and a maximum of 10^4 years.

Morrison: That is interesting. The first generation time of these beasts isn't probably only one generation time, so it is a kind of stability represented by the absence of a wide spread of different morphological types.

Horowitz: I don't think we have to stop discussion but I think we ought to leave the room.

The morning session ended and the meeting was adjourned.

PREBIOTIC ORGANIC SYNTHESES

PREBIOTIC ORGANIC SYNTHESES

May 23, 1967

Horowitz: This morning we want to talk about laboratory experiments dealing with the prebiotic syntheses of the molecular components of biological systems. We will begin with the work on the biologically important monomers and go on to the polymers. This afternoon we can discuss the more speculative questions. So let's, without further ado, get started on the monomers. I know that Leslie Orgel has some new things to talk about in this area. Leslie, would you care to start the dialogue?

Synthesis of Biologically Important Monomers

Orgel: If cyanoacetylene (HC=C—C=N) is treated with sodium cyanate (NaCN) or ammonium cyanate (NH_4CN) at 25°C, a yield from 5 to 20 percent of ureidoacrylonitrile can be isolated from the solution. Between pH 7 to 12, this substance cyclizes to cytosine (one of the nitrogenous pyrimidine bases of the DNA and RNA polymers; these nucleotide polymers are involved in the genetics in all known contemporary organisms). Cytosine is formed in better than 70 percent yield over a wide temperature range. This reaction

175

does not lead to uracil (an RNA base) directly, but uracil can be obtained by the hydrolysis of cytosine. Recently we have studied the kinetics of the hydrolysis of this reaction, and it is quite clear that a period of 100 years, under any reasonable conditions, is adequate for its completion.

Horowitz: I didn't hear the temperature.

Orgel: Temperatures anywhere between 30° and 100°C, probably lower, but we have not tried.

Ponnamperuma: What is the yield at the lowest temperature?

Orgel: The lowest temperature we have tried is about 10°C, but then I cannot guarantee the yields for that. The careful experiments were done at room temperature. I do not think there is any reason to believe the yield would change much at somewhat lower temperature.

Ponnamperuma: Your yield of 70 percent would be valid for 30°C?

Orgel: That is a minimum yield, between 30°C and 100°C, and between pH 7 and pH 10. It is roughly the same over the whole range. The 70 percent yield of cytosine was from the ureido compound; the yield starting from the cyanate was only 5 to 20 percent.

We did experiments in which we passed an electric discharge through a mixture of nitrogen and methane. We obtained hydrogen cyanide (HCN) as a major nitrogen-containing component and got up to 50 percent yield based on carbon. The second nitrogen-containing component, cyanoacetylene, was present in up to 7 percent yield based on total carbon. Thus we feel we have a reasonable prebiotic source of cyanoacetylene.

Let me make it clear that in matters of where intermediates come from, we are pantheists. We do not belong to any of the "churches." We note in the literature that cyanoacetylene is produced by the action of nitrogen on acetylene (HC≡CH) and,

therefore, can be made by ultraviolet irradiation, although we
have not done this. It is also obtained on passing hydrogen cyanide
through a heated tube at 800°C, so it could be made that way. We
are not concerned with where it comes from, only that it is very easy
to make.

Where does the cyanate come from? We believe it comes from
the hydrolysis of cyanogen. We have confirmed that cyanate can
be replaced by cyanogen in these experiments.

The next topic I should like to talk about is the concentration
range in which the reaction occurs and whether it could be prebiotic. The yield of 5 to 20 percent applies within the range of
cyanoacetylene concentration from $0.01M$ to $0.10M$. When you
get below $0.01M$, the cytosine yield falls off. We have been able
to detect cytosine using $2 \times 10^{-3} M$ cyanoacetylene plus $4 \times 10^{-3} M$
of cyanate; under these conditions we obtained 2 percent rather
than 5 percent of cytosine. When we reduced the concentration
by a further factor of 5, we could detect no cytosine.

The final question, then is, "Is it rational to assume such high
concentrations?" Although they are much lower than many "prebiotic" experiments have employed in the past I, myself, still do
not see any easy way of achieving them. I think there is a very
real puzzle there. Eutectic freezing does not help in this particular
reaction because the cyanoacetylene is frozen out from the solution.
It is not very soluble in water, so you cannot concentrate it by
eutectic freezing. The only success we have had was by introducing
cyanoacetylene and cyanogen above an ice surface. Under those
conditions we found a trace of cytosine, but we really pushed to
detect it.

Horowitz: Are these (cyanoacetylene and cyanate) unstable in
water?

Orgel: They are unstable in water. That is why you cannot
build the concentrations up.

Horowitz: Does anyone else have something to offer on the pyrimidine synthesis?

Orgel: You were concerned about the origin of acetylene and HCN (hydrogen cyanide). I think if you look at the astronomical data we have, you will find that these two molecules, or the respective radicals C_2 and CN, are some of the most abundant organic compounds observed in cosmic bodies. They are also some of the most stable chemical species.

Ponnamperuma: A question arises here. Dayhoff's recent equilibrium calculations (Dayhoff et al, 1967) have suggested that if aromatics (ring compounds) are formed, it is very hard to make any of the heterocyclic bases (ring compounds containing both carbon and non-carbon atoms in the ring: e. g., uracil and cytosine are pyrimidine heterocycles containing nitrogen in the ring).

Orgel: But high localized temperatures, discharges, or an ultraviolet source are postulated—all of which are incompatible with thermodynamic equilibrium.

Ponnamperuma: But the assumption that I think Dayhoff makes in her calculations is that what would happen in a non-equilibrium reaction in a short time is what eventually would take place under complete equilibration.

Sagan: I think that Dayhoff, Lippincott, and Eck (1967) are very aware of the differences between thermodynamic equilibrium and disequilibrium reactions. I certainly do not think they would say that if you cannot make, let us say, purines with thermodynamic equilibrium that, therefore, purines were not made.

Ponnamperuma: The suggestion was that if the aromatics are formed, there would be a difficulty in making purines and pyrimidines.

Sagan: Such calculations are useful if it turns out that at equilibrium you produce certain molecules in high yields. Then there is some reason to believe, I think, that those certain molecules were around.

Orgel: May I suggest that there is an overwhelming reason for believing that these things can be made, namely, that you can do it in the lab. If the calculations show that they can't be made, then there is something wrong with the calculations!

Horowitz: Even if we could not make them in the lab, there would be an overwhelming reason to believe they were. Cyanoactylene is a product of the spark discharge.

Orgel: Or heating.

Horowitz: What about the cyanate?

Orgel: That comes from cyanogen.

Horowitz: The reaction with water?

Orgel: Dr. James Ferris and Dr. Robert Sanchez of the Salk Institute have shown that if you take pure hydrogen cyanide and pass it through a heated tube, you obtain a mixture that contains acetylene, diacetylene, and cyanoacetylene. These are essentially the only components. This finding is clearly explained by the stability of the triple bonds; the products you get out contain CH bonds and CC triple bonds and CN triple bonds. You may also get aromatics. Both cyanogen and cyanoacetylene are produced by thermal methods as well as by discharge methods.

[This discussion was followed by a brief summary of the paper by Sanchez et al, 1968.]

Orgel: As to the problem of concentration, what we have suggested—and I do not know whether it is right or not—is that concentration by freezing may be the most appropriate method for cyanide; normally you can concentrate by evaporation, but cyanide is much too volatile. It is more volatile than water and if you warm it up, the cyanide just escapes. We suggest that you freeze out the ice. For a typical experiment you take $0.001M$ of cyanide which, as I explained, will give virtually no tetramer (diaminomaleonitrile, Fig. 22), because it is too dilute. You stand the control solution around at $-10°C$ in the presence of either sufficient methanol or magnesium chloride to

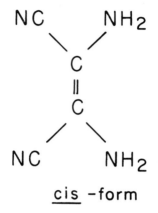

cis -form

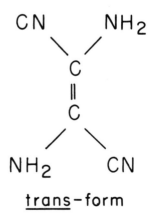

trans-form

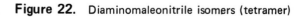

Figure 22. Diaminomaleonitrile isomers (tetramer)

prevent freezing. The experimental solution you freeze to -10°C. What you find is that in the solution that remains liquid, you get no tetramer, while in the solution that freezes you get tetramer. If you are patient and wait about nine months, you can get up to 10 or 15 percent of tetramer.

Siever: Could you do this freezing out in an ocean that is high in electrolyte content?

Orgel: You could do it, but you would have to go to lower temperatures in order to achieve a corresponding liquid volume. The depression of the freezing point of water depends on the total number of molecules and ions in solution.

Siever: So, a greater temperature (lowering) would be needed?

Orgel: Yes, if you use magnesium chloride (to freeze the solution at lower temperature) down to about -60°C (before the water freezes) for example, and I think there are some eutectics that go down even lower.

Morrison: I recognize that there is a lot of implied background I do not understand, but I cannot see that a particular percentage yield is awfully relevant. If you just make a little bit of the relevant organic compounds that is all I care for. Your reactions follow later.

Orgel: Your approach is very hard to justify except in the vaguest of fashions. I would say the following. It is much more difficult to generate an organized structure from a complicated mixture containing interfering substances than it is from a mixture containing the relevant substances in much larger amounts. We have generally adopted the approach that if you can make high concentrations of relevant substances under plausible conditions, this is better than making smaller amounts.

However, as we have said before, there may be many ways of producing life on earth and some of them may well have worked with yields very much less than we are able to get in the lab. It does seem to me a point, which is almost self-evident, that if you are looking for something, the more you can get of it the better.

Morrison: If you know what you are looking for.

Orgel: We believe we know what we are looking for because we believe that it is sensible to look for molecules that are biologically important now.

Morrison: That seems to be peculiarly wrong-minded, but that is another story.

Orgel: Let me say again, if you do not believe that, it seems to me sensible to suggest looking for something else. It does not seem reasonable to say that it is no good proceeding as you are but without saying what else you should be looking for. If you will tell me what else I should be looking for, I will be very happy to look for it, if I think it reasonable.

There are so many organic chemicals that it would be pointless just to look at the whole lot, and one of the clues we have is that we believe life now has continuity with the way it began. Therefore, it seems to me that in the absence of other theories, there is no other rational approach. It is not that life may not have begun in a completely different way; but if it did, how do we know what to look for?

Morrison: I am no biochemist but I am prepared to say: Look for the intermediates. I do not care about the final product. The intermediates are just as good.

Orgel: We are talking about intermediates.

Morrison: You keep talking about whether it had a yield of cytosine of one percent. I do not see why you do not look for, say, cytosine precursors. Perhaps the precursor is even better. I think your task is to find out what you cannot easily make. As far as I know, you can make anything.

Orgel: I suggest you have a try.

Morrison: I would not think of it.

Rich: Leslie (Orgel), have you or have other people tried what I have called syntheses in the whole: That is to say, you have a spark discharge, a handful of sand, and lots of miscellaneous debris, and then you look for the production of cytosine, uracil, and so on.

Orgel: This is the opposite of what we are trying to do. We believe you should learn the kinetics of each step and when you think you understand it adequately, then try to put the thing together. We have not really gone to this later stage yet. We can get as far as purines quite easily. Sooner or later someone should do a giant experiment to try to do all the syntheses simultaneously, but I think it would be foolish to start that way.

Ponnamperuma: We have some information on that with regard to the amino acids, about which I will say a word later.

Horowitz: Let us do the purines and pyrimidines first, Cyril (Ponnamperuma).

Miller: I would like to say something about yields. If you take the example of ATP, the yields are very important. The reason you want ATP is because it contains the so-called high-energy bond. This is high free energy, not high energy or enthalpy.

If the ratio of ATP to ADP is too low, it is no longer a high energy bond, so that the yield in this case is very clearly an important matter.

Morrison: I regard that as extraordinarily cogent. It seems to me that as long as you talk about needing a reasonable concentration of free energy that makes good sense. Do not worry about a given structural feature because there may have been alternative structural features.

Miller: If you say just a very small amount of cytosine will do the trick but you do not know how it was done, I think you are evading an essential issue. The problem of how to form a self-duplicating polynucleotide under dilute or even relatively concentrated conditions seems overwhelming. It is a mistake, in my opinion, to sweep these problems under the rug by saying, "Well, we do not, will not worry about yields; a little bit will do."

Morrison: I was simply saying, look for something or a wide range of compounds occurring in large yields and storing up large energy. I do not really understand fully why you think one should go back through the present molecules and stop only at something very close to what the present materials are.

Miller: Here you have a somewhat different point. Why do we look for just the molecules that occur in present living organisms? I would say the simplest hypothesis is that they were basically the same. This may not be correct, but that is the way the physicist would make a very simple hypothesis.

Morrison: The physicist would never make an hypothesis about biology, because biology is characteristically the system in which there is not just one way of doing something, but there are all kinds of ways. External criteria select the ways in which it has been done.

Miller: We know of one system that works.

Morrison: You also know something else: The present system is one which is peculiarly subject to change and to improvement.

Miller: Right, but it is the simplest hypothesis to say that the first molecular system was similar. The justification of this shaky hypothesis is that when you do one of these primitive-earth laboratory-model experiments cleverly enough, you get just about the compounds that do occur in living organisms, and you get these in the principal yield.

Morrison: Oh, you do? That would be my criterion: Get the things that come out the most abundantly.

Miller: In fact, in the case of a simple electric discharge experiment, the most abundant compounds, with the exception of formate, are the amino acids. You might say, "Well, that is not relevant." I could write a detailed argument to show that the amino acids were among the most abundant compounds in the oceans of the primitive earth.

Sagan: Stan, is that really right? I recall that in your original experiments there was something like 85 percent of them unidentified.

Ponnamperuma: He implied the most abundant of the *identified* compounds.

Miller: Formate by hydrolysis to cyanide presumably was the most abundant.

Ponnamperuma: I would say hydrogen cyanide.

Miller: The second most abundant compounds were glycine (H_4CNH_2COOH) and glycolic acid ($H_2COHCOOH$). The yield for each was about two percent. The precursors would be cyanide and formaldehyde ($H_2C=O$) which were very abundant. I would say I do not believe there is any single compound that was present in more than one percent. If it were, I would have found it.

Rich: Phil (Morrison), there is another kind of argument along the following lines: It may have been that the first information-containing polymer is gone and that it did not use purines and pyrimidines. But we do not know what it is. We might invent it at some later stage but we are just beginning and doing the obvious things first. Once we know how to do this, we may indeed go back and do something less obvious. But now our rationale is: Look, it is probable that we had to make the simple organic precursors to extant polymers in an abiogenic manner. This is the first place to start. If it is enough, the whole story will fall out as a consequence and save us the search for an alternative information-containing polymer.

Fox: There is another argument that can be applied to this question, and that comes from the lessons of comparative biochemistry in the last three decades. You can find the court record of this in the Florkin-Mason (1960-1964) treatise, seven volumes on comparative biochemistry.

What those volumes reveal is that when one looks at all organisms in terms of content of organic compounds, the similarity is overwhelming as compared to the differences. If you line these up in almost any conceivable way, from contemporary to primitive or primitive to contemporary, and extrapolate to zero time, using zero time as the origin of life, you come out with largely the same set of compounds. Of course there are some exotic differences here in contemporary organisms but the first place to look for investigational clues, I think, is at what constitutes (those compounds ubiquitously distributed in) contemporary organisms. I must say, too, that I have listened to much confused discussion because some people have attempted to force models of the primitive to conform exactly to the contemporary—biologically, geologically, or biochemically.

I would like to make one other comment. I agree with the notion that large yields are satisfying in many ways, but I do not think that is a justification for dismissing out-of-hand compounds or processes that give small yields, since some of these—for other reasons than just the criterion of yield—may have been more crucial in the primitive situation. Perhaps this is the point that Dr. Morrison was aiming at in his question.

Third, I would like to ask Dr. Orgel a question with respect to his data. Do your data support a Strecker mechanism for the synthesis of amino acids?

Orgel: No, I think they are pretty conclusively against the Strecker mechanism. Shall I talk to this?

Abelson: Let me talk to it. When we look at the contemporary structure of the atmosphere, we find that the ambient temperature at the ground is on the average about 15°C; on ascending in the atmosphere, temperature drops rather rapidly down to about 214° absolute (°K) at about 15 to 20 kilometers, and then, on our present earth, temperature rises again because there is an ozone layer. But above the ozone layer the temperature drops down to about 180°K at about 80 kilometers before rising to some 1400°K at about 150 kilometers. The temperature at the top of the atmosphere is high because of impact from solar winds, from very short X rays, and so on.

In any kind of atmosphere that did not have the free oxygen, the drop to the lower temperature would occur at much lower heights. Even today in our own atmosphere, this low temperature at about 15 kilometers acts to insure that the upper atmosphere is relatively dry. The percentage of water at the top of the atmosphere is much lower than it is at sea level.

In our laboratory we have considered what would happen to an atmosphere formed from outgassing with its mixture of carbon dioxide, carbon monoxide, nitrogen, and hydrogen. We have made experiments using an electric discharge in a vessel with a cold trap, so that water is removed corresponding to the realistic situation at the top atmosphere.

We have done it with and without cold trap, and Tom Hoering examined the products of this irradiation in the mass spectrometer. This meant that we could look for things like hydrogen cyanide and formaldehyde. Those numbers (Table 2) are relative amounts, peaks on the mass spectrometer. In the mass spectrometer one

Table 2

Relative Composition of Gases after Irradiation

Starting Substance	Time (days)	Trap	HCN	CO + N₂	CO₂
$4CO_2\text{-}6N_2\text{-}2H_2$	1	warm	0.09	100	30
$4CO_2\text{-}4N_2\text{-}4H$	1	warm	0.48	100	26
$4CO_2\text{-}4N_2\text{-}8H$	1	warm	1.5	100	13
$4CO\text{-}4N_2\text{-}4H_2$	2	warm	1.5	100	9
$4CO\text{-}4N_2\text{-}4H_2$	2	cold	26	100	2.6
$4CO\text{-}2N_2\text{-}6H$	1	cold	60	100	4.0
$4CO\text{-}2N_2\text{-}24H_2$	1	cold	80	100	2

Table 3

Products from UV Irradiation of 0.02 M HCN
(yields in micromols/millimol HCN)

	0°C	20°C	25°C
Glycine	11	16	35
Serine	2	2.5	10.3
Alanine	1	0.9	1.6
β-Alanine	—	0.15	0.2
Asparagine	—	0.9	1.1
Glutamic acid	—	0.1	0.15

can scan all the mass numbers and see if there is any formaldehyde, any acetic acid, or any of many hydrocarbons; if an unknown were there, it would show up in the mass spectrometer, corresponding to its mass.

So the product from the discharge, and particularly when conducted in the cold, is hydrogen cyanide. Formaldehyde, if present, is less than one thousandth that of HCN. Suppose we made some formaldehyde up topside? This would be exposed to ultraviolet radiation. Formaldehyde is degraded photochemically at wavelengths shorter than 3700 Å.

Horowitz: Would not the photolysis be producing energy?

Abelson: One of the wonderful things about HCN is that it is so tough. It loves high temperatures. That is another thing against formaldehyde. Formaldehyde decomposes fairly rapidly at 500°C. If we do cut out the Strecker synthesis and say that there was not formaldehyde, then there is a nice question to ask organic chemists: "How do you make carbon-carbon bonds at 25°C or 20°C or 0°C in dilute solutions?" How do you make the carbon-carbon bond? The answer is hydrogen cyanide.

I have conducted a few experiments with HCN, and Table 3 shows the results of one of them. We found that, yes, if you have HCN alone at 0.01M it will not polymerize in water. However, in the presence of ultraviolet light, the polymerization of HCN and formation of ultraviolet-absorbing components occur. Here is the result of an experiment. I point out to you that in terms of glycine alone, 38 $\mu M/mM$ constitutes a yield of 7.6 percent of the HCN carbon returning as glycine, and over 3 percent of the HCN carbon appearing as serine.

Sagan: What sort of ultraviolet light did you use?

Abelson: This was the standard mercury source.

Sagan: 2537 Å? (The wavelength of emission of standard germicide in lamps.) That is the photon acceptor? What is absorbing the light?

Orgel: The tetramer (Fig. 22).

Abelson: There is one other area where I disagree slightly. As I said, I conducted an experiment in which I made some of this highly colored stuff. You get brown stuff—the tetramer polymerizes and you get a long chain or something that is highly absorbent—and then to a small amount of this tetramer I added 0.001M of HCN, shined the ultraviolet light on it and made amino acids.

Orgel: I don't disagree with that.

Abelson: The point is, in that case you do not have this dimer-going-together to make a tetramer. There is somehow an existing structure to which additional HCN can add.

Orgel: The experiments that I described were done in the absence of ultraviolet and those that Dr. Abelson described were done in the presence of ultraviolet, so there is no possibility of disagreement in that sense. However, I would make the point that tetramer is an extremely efficient initiator of polymerization. We have worked on this in considerable detail and it turns out that the *trans* form of the tetramer is more effective; the normal form of tetramer is *cis*. You can take clean cyanide under conditions in which it would not polymerize at all and add to it a trace of tetramer. Polymer soon comes out. If you pre-irradiate the tetramer to make the *trans* isomer, it goes even faster.

Ponnamperuma: Where you have cyanide, you will have a little of the polymer.

Orgel: No, no, we get very clean cyanide containing less than 10^{-5} M tetramer by preparing it in acid solution. It is optically clean (spectroscopic analysis shows absorption characteristic of cyanide alone) at 300 mμ, which establishes the concentration of tetramer as substantially below 10^{-5} M. You might distinguish a laboratory situation where there is no difficulty in getting clean cyanide from what may have happened on the primitive earth. Can I tell you some more about the formation of the amino acids, because there are two different ways in which amino acids are formed in cyanide. Glycine is made by a unique route: The hydrolysis of tetramer. If you hydrolyze a 10^{-3} M solution of tetramer at pH 9, you obtain a better than 70 percent yield of glycine and no other amino acids. If, on the other hand, you take a 10^{-1} M solution of tetramer and hydrolyze it, the yield of glycine falls about 35 percent. On hydrolysis, instead of remaining clean the solution will first go brown and then deposit brown polymers. If you hydrolyze the brown polymer, you get other amino acids. Glycine is produced by the hydrolysis of tetramer; the other amino acids are produced by a second route: Hydrolysis of polymer produced by the tetramer-initiated polymerization of hydrogen cyanide.

Horowitz: Is the polymer a polypeptide?

Orgel: The tetramer is diaminomaleonitrile, which initiates the formation of an extremely complex material of unknown structure.

Horowitz: But the complex material, have you reason to think it is a polymer?

Orgel: I do not know anything about its structure.

Eglinton: You mean you have no information about its elemental composition?

Orgel: It contains carbon, nitrogen, and hydrogen in the right proportions.

Rich: Is it a linear or cross-linked polymer?

Orgel: I know nothing about it.

Rich: Is it soluble in a nonaqueous solvent?

Orgel: Somewhat soluble, but it is a heterogeneous material, part of which will dissolve. If you extract with ethyl acetate, a fraction of the unknown polymer comes out. If you extract with solvent with a higher boiling point, a little more comes out. It is a very difficult material about which I know nothing.

Horowitz: Phil (Abelson), were you finished speaking?

Abelson: I am prepared to yield the floor to Dr. Orgel. He obviously knows a lot more about it than I do.

Ponnamperuma: I want to say something that has a bearing on what both Dr. Orgel and Dr. Abelson have said, but first I want to ask Dr. Abelson a couple of things about the formaldehyde. I am extremely concerned about this. Is it possible formaldehyde is formed but it gets polymerized and never reaches the stage where you detect it? That is one question. Secondly, if there are traces of ammonia, could hexamethylene $(CH_2)_6$ be formed, and so you do not see the formaldehyde in the analysis by mass spectrometric determination—besides, formaldehyde would not reach the upper regions for photolysis? Is this a valid idea?

Burlingame: The formaldehyde polymer is very volatile under high vacuum conditions, but at higher masses you would see it if it were there as a polymer. It also thermally degrades very readily.

Ponnamperuma: Stanley Miller claims he identified formaldehyde in the electric discharge experiment earlier. Palm and Calvin (1962) said the same thing.

Abelson: Look, these are different experimental conditions, among other things.

Miller: By the way, the formaldehyde forms a very stable compound with cyanide: Glyconitrile. Did you find any of this at mass 57 in the mass spectrometer?

Horowitz: What is the compound?

Miller: Glyconitrile. This presumes that ultraviolet light, rather than electric discharges at the top of the atmosphere, caused the decomposition of ammonia. If you are going to argue the validity of models, I would question whether this is the right model.

Abelson: Okay, if you are going to argue against my using electric discharge, then I will argue that the high concentration of water vapor in your methane ammonia mixture is quite unrealistic.

Miller: This is presumably a model for electric discharges that do, I think, occur near the surface of the earth rather than "way up above."

Sagan: Could we have some further elaboration on that? It seemed to me that you were saying that ultraviolet absorption was occurring above the mesopause. Certainly most of the UV light is being absorbed below the mesopause.

Abelson: Yes. In fact, most of the ultraviolet energy is absorbed at the surface of the earth. Except for UV absorption by ammonia, the atmosphere is transparent.

Sagan: Isn't that just what we are arguing about? If there are aldehydes or ketones in the atmosphere, then they are going to absorb ultraviolet light.

Abelson: They are going to be destroyed.

Sagan: But they are also going to absorb. There is the question of what is their steady state concentration.

Abelson: They are going to be destroyed, period.

Sagan: That certainly is not right. The materials are being produced at a certain rate and they are being destroyed at a certain rate. There is going to be a certain steady state concentration. The question is, "Is that steady state concentration opaque to ultraviolet at a given wavelength?"

Abelson: It does not have to be opaque. If you have a cross section for a chemical that is 10^{-20} and you have 10^{23} quanta per square centimeter per year capable of destroying this molecule, then this says———

McElroy: The quantum yield then would be less than one in 1000.

Abelson: The quantum yield is one.

Eglinton: Did you find any acetylene or cyanoacetylene?

Abelson: We had a slight amount of methane and a very, very small amount of acetylene.

Orgel: I am surprised there was so little acetylene. We have done similar experiments and usually found a fair amount of acetylene.

Ponnamperuma: We get a lot of acetylene.

Miller: To come back to the formaldehyde matter, carbon monoxide seems to be one of the compounds thought to be important in the primitive atmosphere. There were experiments done between 1920 and 1930 (Taylor and Marshall, 1925; Taylor, 1926; Marshall, 1926; Caress and Rideal, 1928) which show that when CO is activated by either hydrogen atoms or ultraviolet, formaldehyde is formed in very large yield: Approximately 10 formaldehydes per hydrogen atom.

Abelson: It is nice work to get a hydrogen atom.

Miller: You can get them quite nicely. It is hard by ultraviolet but you can get them in electric discharges. It does seem to me that even in a very dry atmosphere, the CO and hydrogen would give formaldehyde. You have argued for the presence of CO from geochemical considerations. As for the protection of formaldehyde, all that has to be done is to transport it to the ocean fairly rapidly; it is protected in the ocean.

Abelson: It is not protected in the ocean.

Miller: It is protected from ultraviolet.

Abelson: Not in alkaline pH.

Miller: It is protected from ultraviolet.

Abelson: That may be, but it is not protected against internal oxidation–reduction to go to methanol plus formic acid (Cannizzaro reaction: Formaldehyde + base = methanol + formate:

$$2CH_2O + OH^- \rightarrow CH_3OH + HCOO^-).$$

Miller: That is another reaction, but only one part in 10^4 of dissolved formaldehyde is unhydrated. When it is hydrated, it does not absorb ultraviolet. An aqueous solution of formaldehyde has no ultraviolet absorption. From the standpoint of ultraviolet it is indeed protected once it gets into the ocean.

Orgel: Let us just talk about the Cannizzaro reaction.

Miller: There are many reactions that formaldehyde can undergo. One of the fastest, of course, is reaction with cyanide and ammonia. To make a flat statement that you can not have the formaldehyde around or make amino acid by the Strecker synthesis is not giving sufficient consideration to what some people would call side reactions, but others might call the principal reaction.

Orgel: When I said that these experiments argue against the Strecker synthesis, I was not talking about Dr. Miller's experiment; I was not expressing a view on the wider issues of what happened on the primitive earth. There is no evidence whatsoever for the Strecker synthesis in the polymerizations of cyanide.

Miller: The major issue is whether aldehydes are formed in the gas phase and react as such, or not. It is perfectly true that if you make acetylenes in the gas phase, they will undergo hydrolysis to aldehydes; but I think this would give a somewhat different overall picture.

Horowitz: Let us not get into the gory details of the organic mechanisms. There are a number of other important things.

Sagan: I do not guarantee that this is important, but I'm still puzzled by Dr. Abelson's remarks about the absorption. It is certainly true that formaldehyde absorption occurs at such long wavelengths that the Planck distribution of solar radiation is going to destroy it rapidly; but surely there are other ultraviolet absorbers (for example, acetaldehyde) that should be reduced in lower yields but which will absorb at much shorter wavelengths. There the argument about the exceedingly rapid destruction rate does not seem to hold.

Also, this question of the diffusion time in the stratosphere. I do not understand that, because if there is a small amount of formaldehyde, as you say, then the ultraviolet light is stopped not high up but far down and, in that case, it is occurring in the troposphere and not above the mesopause. Have I misunderstood you?

Abelson: I am saying that formaldehyde can be destroyed by a quanta of wavelength less than about 3500 Å, radiation today penetrates down to the surface. Wherever formaldehyde is, from here to the top of the atmosphere, it will be shot at by quanta at a very great rate such that when formed, its life will be short.

Sagan: That is formaldehyde at the surface of the earth. It may very well enter into interesting reactions before———

Abelson: You see, you are talking about hypothetical reactions without giving any flesh to the hypothesis; for example, coming up with a nice, efficient method for making formaldehyde with wavelengths comparable to 3500 Å. For instance, if you have a mechanism that requires, say, 2500 Å radiation to do this task, then there are going to be so many more quanta in the energy range of 3500 Å to 2500 Å that these will act to reduce very, very materially the effective yield of———

Sagan: This is perfectly plausible. But do you agree that these reactions are occurring in the troposphere and not the mesosphere where the cold trap and circulation arguments are most controlling?

Abelson: I think probably on the primitive earth there was only one   temperature minimum, and that the big reactions occurred above it.

Sagan: Why do you think that? It is certainly a question of the optical depth of the gaseous constituents.

Abelson: It depends on which wavelength you are talking about. But the energetic radiation really capable, for instance, of breaking N_2 into N, and so on—that radiation is going to be stopped by the———

Sagan: Okay. Then you are talking about much shorter wavelengths than we have been talking about up to now.

Abelson: Because ammonia is so easily destroyed, your nitrogenous component is mainly in the form of nitrogen, and you have to find some way of activating that nitrogen to do business.

Miller: How do you propose to activate this nitrogen?

Abelson: I propose to do it with 800 Å radiation, or 600 Å radiation—very short ultraviolet at the top of the atmosphere.

Miller: You have not done this sort of experiment, I gather.

Abelson: There are a few little technical difficulties, as you well know, about doing this type of experiment. That is why I did the other one, which is easy.

Sagan: When you talk about the ammonia not being there because of photodissociation, is not the photodissociation itself a kind of useful reaction?

Abelson: It may be useful on a one-shot deal, but after the first 30,000 years the amount of ammonia that would be around would be minimal.

Sagan: That is certainly a function of the outgassing rate.

Abelson: Yes, but there are sufficient number of quanta, so that even if ammonia were outgassed from the interior of the earth, there is a difficult problem maintaining it in the atmosphere.
There would be a distribution of ammonia between ocean and atmosphere and, insofar as it were in the atmosphere, it would break down. There is quite a problem in maintaining enough ammonia to meet Stan's (Miller) criteria about ammonia concentration in the ocean.

Siever: Isn't that a question of matching time scales? If you (Sagan) talk about outgassing providing enough ammonia and he (Abelson) is talking about the destruction of ammonia, I think you are in quite different time scales. He (Abelson) is going to destroy the ammonia much faster than you (Sagan) can provide it, even with a rapid outgassing.

Abelson: Are you sure there was outgassing going on over three billion years.

Siever: I do not think you have to worry about that, but even with a more rapid outgassing at the very beginning, we are still talking about the time scales probably of the order of millions of years.

Horowitz: Is that true even on the "Big Burp" hypothesis (that the secondary atmosphere was outgassed all at once due to ancient volcanism)?

Siever: At worst or at best, however you prefer to look at it, an initial large outgassing will take place probably over many millions of years, whereas the destruction will take place on the order of 10^4 years, or something like that.

Fox: But if a little ammonia gets caught in a reaction chain and is converted to something that is no longer ammonia but is in the direction of organisms———

Siever: All right. Then you are constricting the time scale to make the whole process go on within 10^3 or 10^4 years.

Sagan: Certainly volcanic outgassing is not the only source of the ammonia. Stan (Miller), did I understand what you said?

Abelson: The other source is an agile mind.

Sagan: We are all, I hope, using agile minds. If I understand what Miller said yesterday, he has ammonia and ammonium hydroxide in the oceans. There is a certain equilibrium abundance of ammonia above it. If you destroy the atmosphere, ammonia will leave the ocean and enter the atmosphere. Isn't that right?

Miller: The equilibration of the atmosphere is a fast reaction, but there is also the problem of resynthesis of the ammonia in the atmosphere. You can easily make ammonia from electric discharge of nitrogen and hydrogen. Ammonia might also be made by the 800 Å ultraviolet light. Nitrogen atoms can be made from 800 Å light. This might form ammonia in the presence of hydrogen. Cyanide would also be made.

Abelson: We looked at that, of course, with the mass spectrometer, and while there was a small amount of ammonia, the big component was HCN.

Horowitz: Cyril (Ponnamperuma), you wanted to say something a minute ago.

Synthesis of Amino Acids

Ponnamperuma: I wanted to say something in connection with HCN and present some of our recent results. I thought I would put the first slide (Fig. 23) on for the sake of those who may not have seen that picture before, and for some of the others it might be nostalgic. This is a modification of the apparatus used earlier by Miller and Urey (1959). The brown material in the upper flask consists of aromatic hydrocarbons. It is a very efficient process. We find at the end of 24 hours of this discharge, over 95 percent of the methane is converted into organics. A lot of it is gunk, by organic chemists' definition. In the flask below is a water solution, and in that you have about 18 percent of cyanide. This result has some bearing on what was said before. We don't see any of the purines or pyrimidines. We have looked very hard. If there were any adenine, guanidine, cytosine, or uracil formed—anything more than 0.001 percent—we would have seen it, but we do not. However, when we come to amino acids, we see them very clearly.

We were very concerned when we first analyzed the data. For six months we could not confirm Miller's results and we could not confirm Abelson's work. We got a number of spots on a paper chromatogram, perhaps a trace of glycine, but none of the other amino acids that had been claimed to be formed.

Figure 23. Apparatus for an electrical discharge through methane, ammonia, and water.

However, it finally dawned on us to look at some of the material at the origin (that is, insoluble material that does not migrate up the paper chromatogram), so we hydrolyzed the stuff and ran it on the analyzer, and lo and behold, we had ten amino acids.

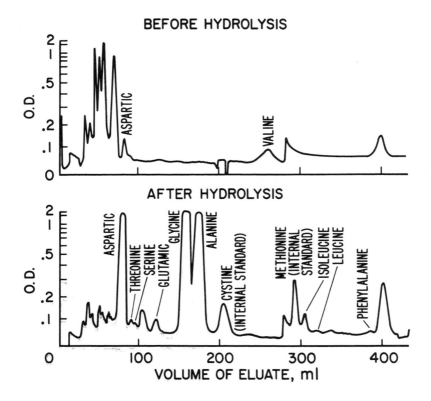

Figure 24. Paper chromatographic separation of end products of an electrical discharge through methane, ammonia, and water before hydrolysis.

Orgel: Can you tell us what those other spots are?

Ponnamperuma: Figure 24 is a picture we got on the analyzer before hydrolysis. We had some dross at the beginning—acidic material—which disappeared under hydrolysis. The next picture shows the results after hydrolysis. Nine amino acids were formed on the neutral and basic column, and we confirmed these results by preparing the NTFA derivatives of the amino acids for gas chromatography. We feel confident that there were ten amino acids synthesized.

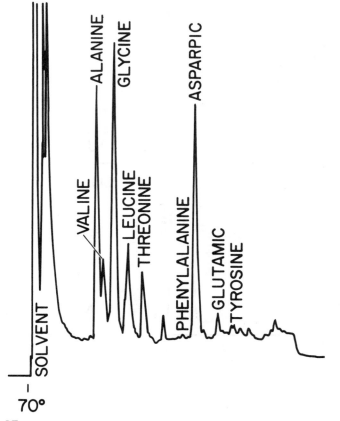

Figure 25. Amino acids from an electric discharge through methane, ammonia, and water after hydrolysis.

Are these amino acids hooked up together? That is the immediate conclusion one comes to. Is this a function of the cyanide? We do not know this. One suggestion made was that perhaps we were going through a more refined synthesis, where we were getting a backbone of nitriles which, on hydrolysis, give the amino acids. So, the next thing we did was an experiment with unlabeled methane, adding to it radioactive glycine, and did an electrophoretic separation. Several bands were found; we examined the four most prominent of these bands. Presumably, the glycine is incorporated whole into the system. Clycine, alanine, and aspartic were found in the first; glycine, alanine, aspartic, glutamic in the second; glycine, alanine, aspartic, glutamic, and serine in the third.

We have no sequence analysis in this, we just know the distribution. We have not been able to establish the presence of peptide bonds by infrared analysis, because the amount of material is so small. We are trying now to do that. The suggestion I am making is that possibly the amino acids are formed first, and in the soup there is some kind of polymerization taking place.

Orgel: Are you familiar with the work of Markham (Lowe, et al, 1963)?

Ponnamperuma: Yes, I know that work.

Orgel: He has very similar results. He found one thing you have not reported, namely, a large amount of urea (NH_2CONH_2) in the polymer in addition to the amino acids. The general conclusion was that while these polymers might contain some peptide bonds, they certainly were not polypeptides.

Markham did exactly the experiment that Oró did—heating ammonium cyanide with glycine. He also obtained fractions with vaguely polypeptide-like properties.

Fox: As I remember, they did not rule out deketopiperazines.

Orgel: There were many things they did not rule out. They only said they did not establish them.

Ponnamperuma: The ten amino acids give the mass spectra of standard NTFA derivatives. The yield of phenylalanine was too small for derivative preparation.

Abelson: I have never seen any phenylalanine in comparable experiments.

Miller: Has the leucine also been done in the mass spectrometer?

Ponnamperuma: The NTFA derivatives have been examined. We prepare the NTFA derivatives in the whole mess and then take the peaks as they come out and get a fragmentation band.

Horowitz: Cyril, how do your conditions differ from those of Orgel and Miller?

Ponnamperuma: We are building up a lot of cyanide in this. We use concentrations of half an atmosphere of methane and half ammonia. My explanation for the fact that Miller did not find some of the amino acids in his paper chromatograph is that his system of separation went through some hydrolysis. He probably had some initial peptides which, by his system of elution, were broken down.

Horowitz: But, still, he (Miller) does not find phenylalanine or half a dozen of your other amino acids.

Orgel: That is very important, because we tried very hard. We made polymers straight from cyanide and hydrolyzed under a variety of conditions and used the standard amino acid analyzer techniques. We found glycine, alanine, and aspartic acid. We did not find serine because we were using alkaline hydrolysis, which would destroy it. We found nothing else in sufficient quantity to be identified; but I imagine with a mass spectrometer one could make much more sense out of the results on the mixtures.

Ponnamperuma: Or with gas chromatography.

Burlingame: Why didn't you just make the ethyl esters and run those?

Ponnamperuma: We prepared the esters, the NTFA derivatives, for the gas chromatograph (GC). It is simple enough to trap those.

Burlingame: Aren't they very temperature-sensitive, though?

Ponnamperuma: We run them in the GC at temperatures of 180° C or so.

Horowitz: I do not want to belabor this point but I am trying to find out how Cyril's (Ponnamperuma) experimental conditions differ from everyone else's. You did not require the mass spectrometer to see these. You saw them on the amino acid analyzer. It does not require high sensitivity.

Ponnamperuma: Maybe the proportions are different—half an atmosphere of each of the gases. Maybe we are building up a lot of cyanide and the amino acids are coming by way of the polymer. We start with half molar methane, half molar ammonia, and 100 milliliters of water. Juan, (Oró) didn't you find phenylalanine in your heat experiments?

Oró: The synthesis of phenylalanine and other amino acids by the action of ultraviolet light on simple mixtures was reported by Russian investigators (Pavloskaya & Pasynski, 1959). Similar results have also been obtained in other laboratories (Fox, 1965c; Oró, 1965).

Horowitz: What was the gas mixture?

Oró: They were aqueous solutions containing essentially formaldehyde and ammonium salts. The detection of amino acids was made by paper chromatography. Under certain conditions, hydrogen cyanide is formed in these irradiated solutions. I would like to add that using basic hydrogen cyanide mixtures directly, several investigators have isolated or detected not only amino acids but also amino acid polymers, purines, and other biochemical compounds (Oró, 1963; Lowe et al, 1963; Fox 1965; Oró, 1965; Sanchez et al, 1966; Ponnamperuma et al, 1967). (The detection of pteridines has also been reported by Ruske, 1968.)

Morrison: How does this help the general problem of what rough fraction yield is identifiable in these familiar compounds, and what is not?

Margulis: Please tell us naive people how much of the yield is so-called "unnatural" amino acids—not those twenty or so found in living organisms?

Rich: What happens, Cyril (Ponnamperuma), if you treat your stuff with, say, pronase? Do you liberate any amino acids?

Ponnamperuma: We tried to hydrolyze the artificial polymers with proteolytic enzymes, and we came up against a stumbling block with our standard ones. We were working with micro-quantities. All the literature references said pronase would give 35 percent breakdown of triglycine (dipeptide composed of three glycine residues). When we tried to do this on a micro-level we could not get glycine released. We are still working on the technique.

Rich: If you try this sort of experiment with radioactive labeling of your stuff, you can add large amounts of carrier oligopeptides.

Ponnamperuma: I suppose up to a point we could; we are trying this. We are trying to work out a satisfactory method.

Rich: If your mixture contains amino acids linked by peptide bonds, you should liberate up to about a quarter of them.

Horowitz: But what if some of them are D amino acids—would pronase act to break down the polymer?

Rich: No, it won't. Assuming the polymer is random, that is, it contains both natural levorotary and dextrorotary amino acids, you should get———

Abelson: I will bet Cyril (Ponnamperuma) a case of beer that what he has is the polymer with nitrile. The hydrolysis is simply bringing out the amino acids present in this complex structure.

Ponnamperuma: How did the glycine get off the polymer? This is my question.

Abelson: You know, when you have all those double bonds and that highly reactive polymer, what comes naturally is for the amino acid to get in and react with the polymer. Your hydrolysis then takes the glycine off.

Fox: I would like, along these lines, to ask Dr. Oró, Dr. Orgel, and Dr. Ponnamperuma, in turn, what they can say about the molecular weight of these polymers. Then I would like to ask any of them to comment on the relationship to Matthews' (Matthews & Moser, 1966) contribution.

Oró: I think it is obvious from the literature that the polymers obtained by these procedures do not have the molecular weight of the polymers obtained by your procedure.

Fox: That is not why I asked.

Oró: Right. It is obvious, starting with a chemical procedure that builds the molecules step by step, that the first polymers you may obtain are not going to be very large. So perhaps it adds a little more realism to this type of synthesis. I am not saying that we should not strive toward making high molecular-weight polymers. I think we should. The point I am trying to make is that if you take the active polypeptides, enzymatic or or otherwise, you will find that perhaps you do not need a very high molecular weight in order to have activity. So it is quite possible (and this is strictly a working hypothesis) that in the chemical evolutionary process, one of the steps was the synthesis of small polymers—perhaps six to ten amino acids residues—which had some catalytic or other activities. In summary, it is my feeling that it is not an absolute biological necessity to make big polymers, although eventually it ended up this way. As an example, take the active centers of enzymes—the small portion of the protein molecule which actually binds the substrates and effects the chemical reaction between them—they have about four or five amino acids.

Fox: But they (the active centers) are not generally active by themselves.

Oró: But they do have a percentage of the enzymatic activity and this, I think, is a point we should not overlook.

Fox: In which case, the histidine?

Oró: You know this well, because you are doing experiments with histidine.

Fox: I cannot think of any other.

Oró: Histidine, serine, cysteine.

Fox: Yes, cysteine; that is right. I do not disagree with you, qualitatively speaking, but I would like to have the answer to the first question. Do you know the molecular weights of your polymers?

Oró: No, I do not.

Ponnamperuma: I can answer what the molecular weights of the polymers are right now. We tried to separate this on a Sephadex column but the extrusion limits were molecular weights of 200 and 2000, so we know the polymer is within that range; maybe we have five amino acids in one, and two in the other.

In answer to a point that Dr. Abelson made, we have made a determined effort to do a micro-infrared analysis but have not yet been able to demonstrate the presence of a peptide bond. Up to this point I would say it is because our technique is imperfect. We want to improve it before we definitely say that a polypeptide is not present.

Morrison: Is the fine brown stuff you get vapor or is it condensed?

Ponnamperuma: That is condensed. It is a carbon-hydrogen-nitrogen compound, not free hydrocarbons. Nitrogen is incorporated into that. May I finish? I have a couple of slides which fit into what I have been saying.

In previous experiments, we used methane and ammonia in water. In this one (Fig. 26) we removed the water and started getting the dark polymer. The interesting point here is that all

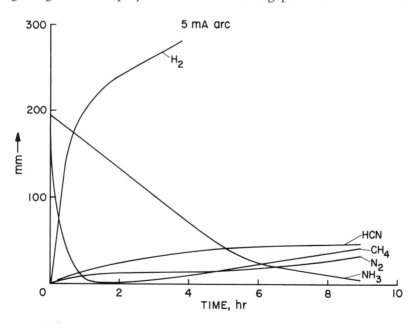

Figure 26. Electric discharge through methane and ammonia.

of this is full of material that can be dissolved in methanol. Presumably we are making nitriles. We have examined the end products of this reaction, first what is in the gas phase, and then what we could pump out at about -70°C. The reason for using methane and ammonia in the absence of water was to get some idea of the mechanisms that may have been involved in our previous synthesis. As a second reason, maybe we are simulating the upper regions of the Jovian atmosphere. We have examined the gas phase at room temperature, and we find that most of it is cyanide. We cannot get away from that: Whatever we do with methane and ammonia, we come up with cyanide. Not in the solid phase, however. In the gas phase we have a lot of free cyanide. We can pump out a lot of ammonium cyanide. When we looked at the volatiles pumped out at -70°C we came out with some residue of ammonium cyanide that we could not remove; we get some of the nitriles. Perhaps an interesting point is that you get the glycinonitrile, the C-methyl derivative, the N-methyl, and if you hydrolyze these you get the amino acids. Here is a pathway for the amino acids and the difference between this and the Strecker synthesis is only, as Stan (Miller) pointed out, a semantic one; but nitriles are formed and hydrolyzed into amino acid.

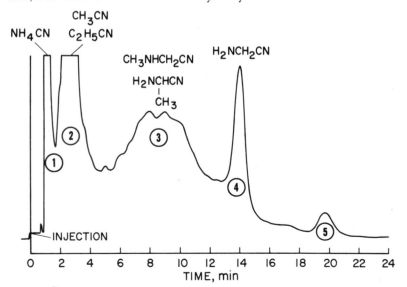

Figure 27. α-aminonitriles produced by an electric discharge through methane and ammonia.

If you turn to the polymer, so far what we have got we know is polymeric. The whole thing is soluble in methanol; this is in contrast to what happened in the previous experiment where there was a large amount of gunk formed, untreatable by the kind of extraction procedures we are working with. When we make an attempt to separate this on a Sephadex column, we get a number of different bands. None of these gives us the nitrile absorption. We are probably getting a C=N polymer-type material.

Another interesting point is that we can prepare the same thing by making ammonium cyanide and allowing it to sit around. On examining that further, we found that there, again, we did not get a nitrile absorption, but we found a lot of free ammonia. So if we start with free HCN and a trace of ammonia, we get the same thing. This seemed to be some kind of complex formed by hydrogen cyanide in the presence of ammonia.

To answer Sid's (Fox) question about Matthews and Moser's work, I think the red material we are getting in the anhydrous reaction is probably very similar to their polymeric stuff. We have not done the hydrolysis and analysis of that.

Horowitz: Does anyone have any more identification of the red gunk or the yellow gunk that Phil Morrison was interested in and thinks may be the stuff of life?

Rich: Can it be used by microorganisms as food?

Ponnamperuma: Not the stuff from the methane-ammonia mixture alone, but that from the methane-ammonia-water mixture has been used. People in the (NASA) life detection group have grown a few microorganisms on it after pumping out any free cyanide.

Rich: So, if it is not the stuff of life, it may be the food of life.

Horowitz: Is it used by any microorganisms or by specialized ones?

Ponnamperuma: I don't know.

Horowitz: As a carbon source, nitrogen source, or both?

Ponnamperuma: I wouldn't be able to give the details.

Siever: How easily degradable is it, thermally or any other way?

Orgel: It is a very heterogeneous material. If you take cyanide and hydrolyze it, it first goes yellow, and then light polymer deposits. If you leave it longer, the stuff gets dense and flocculant and finally comes out as a solid black material. This material is very hard to hydrolyze. Even if you boil it in normal alkali for, let's say, three months, there is still a substantial residue.

Siever: The question is whether some of this stuff, if it becomes that resistant, is wet.

Orgel: Yes, that is why we tried it out for enzymatic properties, but it doesn't have any of these obvious qualities.

Rich: It is probably a crossover polymer, wouldn't you think?

Orgel: I think so.

Oró: It is a highly cross-linked polymer where the repeating units are carbon-nitrogen heterocycles (Volker, 1960). If it is used by DuPont (Corporation), it might mean that it is degraded by microorganisms. I would like to say that we have grown microorganisms in the residual product of an HCN polymerization.

Margulis: When it is used by microorganisms you have to get rid of the HCN, is that what you are saying?

Oró: It was an observation of accidental microbial growth in one of the products from HCN reaction mixtures.

Margulis: In your mixture, do you get any growth without removing the HCN?

Oró: I really cannot tell. However, since unreacted HCN hydrolyzes rapidly to formate, it is likely that the mixture was mainly HCN polymer and ammonium formate.

Margulis: Were they anaerobic bugs?

Oró: No, these were aerobic.

Horowitz: Are the organisms that use it just random common organisms; or hydrocarbon———

Oró: It had some of the growth features of a mold.

McElroy: Is that right?

Oró: Work by Schneour (1966) shows that graphite is attacked by non-sterilized soil. If graphite is decomposed by soil microorganisms, it is not difficult to accept that polymeric HCN could also be attacked by microorganisms.

Orgel: I am a bit dubious about that, because it was not done by actually isolating the organisms but merely by identifying an increase in CO_2.

Ponnamperuma: Schneour took graphite and made it radioactive and looked for organisms using it.

Barghoorn: Is this graphite or coronine (a 7-ring aromatic compound that contains hydrogen)?

Oró: The experiments were done with what the authors called graphite.

Siever: It was probably a carbon black.

Morrison: Is diamond a very good substrate?

Synthesis of Nucleic Acid Derivatives

Horowitz: Stanley, you have some pyrimidine synthesis remarks.

Miller: I have also been thinking about pyrimidine synthesis and have used a somewhat different approach. One was to see whether or not one can mimic, in a sense, the biological pathways of pyrimidine biosynthesis or degradation. Pyrimidines in biological systems are usually degraded by reduction of uracil to dihydrouracil. The ring is opened to ureidopropionic acid, and the urea is hydrolyzed off to give β-alanine. One possibility is to attempt to synthesize uracil by reversing the β-alanine reaction.

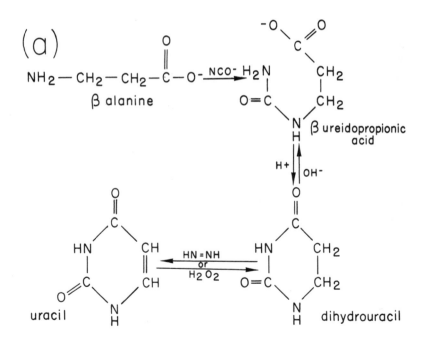

Figure 28a. Possible modes of pyrimidine synthesis. (a) Uracil

In all of these prebiological experiments, at least starting from methane, there are substantial yields of β-alanine. The question is, can this be used for pyrimidine synthesis? β-alanine and cyanate react to form β-ureidopropionic acid; this can also be obtained from β-alanine, nitrile plus cyanate. I won't enter into the question of how plausible the cyanate is. The β-ureidopropionic acid is in equilibrium with dihydrouracil, and the problem is to oxidize the dihydrouracil. This can be done in two more or less convincing ways. The first is to oxidize it with hydrogen peroxide. Hydrogen peroxide can be made by the action of electric discharges on water vapor. The second method of oxidizing the dihydrouracil is from hydrazine, either in the presence of oxygen or in the presence of peroxide. The oxidizing agent is diimide (HN=NH). Ordinarily diimide is a reducing agent, especially for aliphatic double bonds.

Diimide can also act as an oxidizing agent, and it oxidizes the dihydrouracil to uracil. It will also reduce the uracil to dihydrouracil. The normal biosynthetic pathway of pyrimidines in all organisms is from aspartic acid to ureidosuccinic acid, dihydroorotic acid, followed by oxidation to orotic acid and decarboxylation to uridine after nucleoside formation. On the primitive earth, glycine would be the most abundant amino acid, and cyanate would react with the glycine to form hyantoic acid. This in turn is in equilibrium with hydantoin, which can react with glyoxylic acid. There are a number of ways of synthesizing glyoxylic acid under primitive earth conditions (Fig. 28).

The dehydration of hydantoin-5-glycolic acid to carboxymethylidene hydantoin is a simple step. The rearrangement of carboxymethylidene hydantoin to orotic acid, which occurs by opening the hydantoin ring and closing to a six-membered ring, is a known reaction and is usually carried out in $0.1M$ KOH. This reaction also occurs at pH 8 or 9 although more slowly. I have not yet found a good method of decarboxylating orotic acid. It is a difficult reaction, apparently, but we are trying a number of methods to decarboxylate it.

These are possible alternatives for the synthesis of pyrimidines under primitive earth conditions. The real justification of this in terms of concentration and other conditions is hard to make at this time, but we are looking at it more carefully.

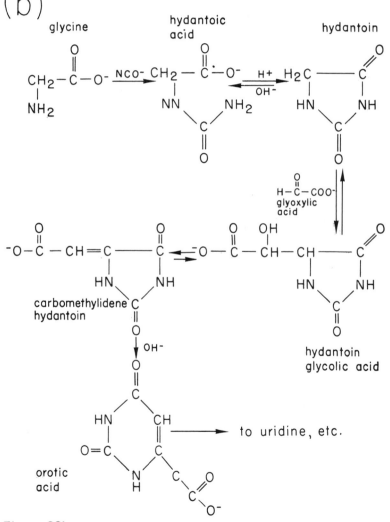

Figure 28b. Possible modes of pyrimidine synthesis. (b) Uridine

Polymerization Mechanisms

Horowitz: Thanks, Stan (Miller). I really think we should get on now to the next step in molecular evolution. It is obvious from what has gone on up to this point that although there is still much to be done, in principle at least we can synthesize amino acids, purines, and pyrimidines under more or less plausible primitive conditions. Having produced these, we are then in the position of having essentially an acid hydrolysate of tissue—small organic components resulting from acid breakdown of organisms. We still have to construct the organisms, starting with this acid hydrolysate. The big hump we have to get over—the big hurdle—is the condensation of the monomers into polymers. In an aqueous environment, the condensation is going to be very difficult. The free energies are in the wrong direction. The products, after they are formed, are all unstable and will hydrolyze spontaneously, so we have here a major problem in going from the monomers, which are apparently readily produced, to the polymers.

I know that several people in this room have been working on the difficult problem of producing polymerization. At the moment I think we have some promising leads, and I would like Leslie (Orgel) to start off a discussion of the possible mechanisms for polymerizing amino acids, purines, pyrimidines, phosphates, sugars.

Ponnamperuma: Let me ask a question here which seems relevant. We have considered various forms of energy—electrical discharges, ultraviolet, heat, ionizing radiation—that are available for synthesis of micromolecules. Presumably, one of the ways to approach polymerization would also be to use some of these forms of energy. One would tend to go to the milder ones, not blasts of electrical dicharges but perhaps heat, or gentle ultraviolet light at the longer wavelengths. To my way of thinking, this appears to be a starting point for discussion. I would like to get some reactions to this from people who have thought about it.

Abelson: The California contingent should be called upon.

Orgel: We have surveyed a series of potential condensing agents that might work in aqueous solution. We have come up with a general conclusion that may not be true but, I think, provides an interesting working hypothesis. We believe that many agents are equally efficient in one very precise sense. Under favorable conditions they all react with phosphate almost completely, so that these condensing agents—cyanamid, cyanogen, cyanoguanadine, ethylisonitrile, phenylisonitrile—are converted more or less quantitatively to reactive phosphate intermediates in the presence of molar phosphate. Whichever condensing agent you put in, you always get a reactive intermediate phosphate in better than 50 percent yield.

The next step in phosphate condensation is to put the phosphate onto something biochemically useful, and it is here that you run into trouble. Water looks like alcohol so that no matter what condensing agent you use, you find that most of the reactive intermediate phosphate is hydrolyzed by the water. Therefore, we conclude that there is really a major difficulty here. Whatever you do in aqueous solution along the lines we are trying—of course, there may be quite some different methods of doing it—you are either going to waste most of your condensing agent or you have to bring the concentration of the alcohol to an unreasonably high value. This forces us to the conclusion that homogeneous aqueous solution is not the correct place to do these things. They must be done either by absorption on solids or possibly by some completely different method, for example, by heating.

The other thing I would like to say is that we have a reagent we think is very promising, namely, cyanogen. It has only been mentioned once, I think, by Stanley (Miller). He mentioned it just once, but we have now done a good deal of work with cyanogen and we can, for example, produce 15 percent yields of uridine monophosphate from uridine, and inorganic phosphate with cyanogen and nothing else. Cyanogen differs from cyanamid in some ways. It doesn't seem to attack carboxylic acid,

so we have not succeeded in making peptides from amino acids
with cyanogen. This may be a disadvantage if you want to
make peptides, but it could be an advantage if you want to
have nucleotide-dependent peptide formation.

Fox: I would like to ask a question of Dr. Rich. I think,
inevitably, we must get all our clues on prebiotic chemistry
from the biotic situation, until someone devises another approach. We have to test the results and developments of those
results step by step against the biotic situation. I believe that
a question that might seem dimly related at first, but which to
me seems to be very pertinent is, "What do we know about
how ribosomes synthesize protein? Do they do this in a homogeneous aqueous solution, or what kind of situation is it? What
can be said about it?"

Margulis: Alex (Rich), you have about two weeks to answer
that!

Rich: No, no, this is easy to answer. We don't know the
mechanism, but we do know several things about it. It is not
a dilute aqueous solution; it is fairly concentrated. But it is
an aqueous solution.

Fox: Can you say anything about what proportion———

Rich: No, we really know nothing about the interior of the
ribosome, except that it is structured. It has large holes in it,
and it is a well-defined machine.

Let me make a comment, though, about this whole business
of polymerization tacking onto what Leslie (Orgel) said at the
end. I have a highly prejudiced view about the relevance of
polymerization reactions. My feeling is that the relevant and
important polymerization reactions are nucleotide polymerizations. I think Leslie agrees with this. My feeling is that mechanisms dealing with the polymerization of amino acids are
largely irrelevant. They may have made a series of molecules
around in the primitive earth or provided some kind of a nonspecific matrix. I don't believe amino-acid polymerizations were

important in terms of making what I would call meaningful molecules that had catalytic or other kinds of activity. Therefore, mechanisms of amino acid polymerization are irrelevant. Amino acids have to be around; they may even be in the form of polymers, but it doesn't matter whether they were polypeptides or any other kind of polymers. The important thing about amino acids is that they were around. The crucial step, to my view, is the coupling between a polynucleotide and a polypeptide synthesis. This will not be carried out by any mechanism for amino acid polymerization that is not polynucleotide-dependent.

McElroy: Could I interrupt there? To take a slightly opposite viewpoint, some of the evidence seems to indicate that maybe we don't need all of this protein for catalysis. You need protein for stereochemical reasons but very short peptides—ten amino acids residues or fewer could be very important in catalysis. In fact, we are getting evidence that even one enzyme could be converted now into a number of different catalytic activities.

Rich: I don't argue with that viewpoint. I would just say that without polynucleotides I don't see a ready mechanism for making appreciable numbers of molecules (even small ones such as oliogopeptides) that contain a defined sequence of amino acid residues. I may be quite wrong; there may be some mechanism that will give a high yield of small peptides of fixed sequence. I think it is unlikely.

McElroy: But on the first go-around, polymerization of amino acids may have been a chance phenomenon of which there was selective advantage.

Rich: I can believe in the chance formation of these improbable molecules, but what you must do is compound this with another level of improbability in order to get the thing going, and I don't think that is the way it works.

Fox: What do you mean by getting the thing going?

Rich: What I mean is to convert polynucleotide information, randomly polymerized polynucleotides———

Fox: But you are assuming "randomly polymerized." Amino acids are not polymerized in a random manner (Fox & Nakashima, 1967). Why should nucleotides react randomly?

Rich: Oh, my view—and it may be a minority opinion, although I hold it firmly—is that the critical step in the evolution of life has been the development of a process whereby one gets a reading out of this random polynucleotide information into defined polypeptide information. At that stage when out of this random polynucleotide array—when you get the formation of a catalytically active polypeptide because the peptide and nucleotide syntheses are coupled—you have a mechanism for repeating it. Then the thing starts to go. I even have a view as to which class of molecules were the most important, namely, the activating enzymes. Essentially these define the readout mechanism (Fig. 29). Once that is fixed, then the stage is ready for the whole system to go.

Pattee: Isn't that going in circles? You just said the most vital thing is the readout.

Rich: No, I am not going in a circle. What I am saying is that the first process involved a readout in the absence of an activating enzyme.

Pattee: By what?

Rich: This is the problem. This is what we have to find out.

Pattee: We agree it is the central problem.

Rich: I don't think it is an insoluble one.

Pattee: Neither do I. But since this is the central problem— the coding or readout problem—I don't see why you are so

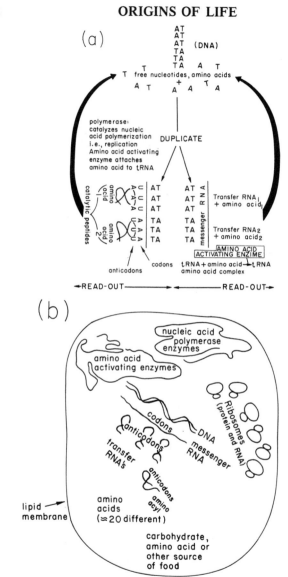

Figure 29. Replication and read-out. (a) Simplified diagram of DNA, RNA, and protein synthesis system in extant organisms. (b) Simplified diagram of extant minimal self-replicating system, characteristic of all living cells.

firmly convinced that the polymerization of nucleotides is the crucial step.

Rich: What I am saying is that polymerization of amino acids is largely irrelevant.

Pattee: You are entitled to this position, but I still don't see the reasons you say that.

McElroy: Present biochemical knowledge.

Fox: Before you get too far into this, I would just like to footnote that at some stage, when I am allowed to show some slides, I think we can examine an alternative point of view based on experiments. This is not to derogate the point of view that you are expressing, particularly for contemporary systems. The initial limitation of information could have been internal in the protein (Fox & Nakashima, 1967). I fail to see how at this stage we can rule out the primacy of polynucleotides (Schwartz & Fox, 1967) or polyamino acids (Fox & Nakashima, 1967), either or both (Fox, Waehneldt, et al, 1967).

Pattee: The way it is done in cells definitely requires enzymes.

Orgel: We must ask even in simple polymer systems: How did information get from one generation of molecules to the next?

Pattee: You have to show nonenzymatic replication.

Rich: That we can do. That is easy.

Pattee: That isn't quite all. The information must also be decoded.

McElroy: I thought Alex was going to say what I would have said, that I thought the coding begins in the protein, namely, the synthetase. To answer your (Fox) question with regard to the aqueous environment, it is quite clear that water is not inside the ribosomes where the acyl adenylates are located; if it were they would be immediately hydrolyzed.

Rich: I have done some experiments (they failed, but I think the idea is right) in which you take, say, a polynucleotide and make a complex of the type that Tod Myles and others have studied—namely, in which the monomers dissociate with the polymer—and have tried to polymerize them. Many people have tried. In our own experiments we in fact decided not to use an aqueous solvent for obvious reasons, but rather to try various kinds of anhydrous thermal polymerizations. They didn't work, but I am convinced that the mechanism, in general, can work.

I am just emphasizing what Leslie (Orgel) says. The point is that the polynucleotides have the capacity of self-replication. In 1955 at NIH—National Institutes of Health—we were working with polyadenylic acid and polyuridylic acid and found that they wrapped around each other to make a DNA-like double helix. I told this to Hermann Kalckar, Harvard Medical School, Boston, Mass. He said, "What, you mean without an enzyme?" I said, "Yes, without an enzyme. They just went." And he said, "My gosh, that's most surprising."

But it wasn't surprising to me because the molecules had this as a physical property. What he was expressing is what was then a reasonable biochemical point of view, namely, that enzymes were very important for all of these reactions. I think what we have found in terms of polynucleotide chemistry is that enzymes may not be so important. Molecules have programmed within themselves many of the properties which in fact are elaborated and used in very fine detail by enzymes. The point is that the molecules themselves have the properties.

McElroy: Isn't this true of polypeptides, too?

Fox: But nonrandomly synthesized polyamino acids contain information, perhaps adequate for the needs of the primitive system (Fox & Nakashima, 1967; Fox, McCauley, & Wood, 1967).

Rich: I will talk later about why nucleic acids are used. They have intrinsic pairing properties. They have a kind of complementarity upon which I will elaborate later. In fact, they have the ability to form stable double helices. They have this peculiar and very interesting metastable configuration. If you look at DNA, it is a bond between cohesive forces and disruptive forces. Just by varying the ionic strength—concentration of salt ions in the solution—you can tear the molecule apart or bring it together again. The molecule, in fact, has a number of physical properties that pull it together and some physical properties that tear it apart. This is, of course, just what one needs for a molecule whose function is to go through cycles of coming together and tearing apart.

McElroy: Like an antigen and antibody reaction?

Rich: Not quite.

McElroy: I am picking a ridiculous extreme, but I think polypeptides to a certain extent will do the same thing, and they have a sort of specificity there. Admittedly this specificity is not as great as we now see it in our evolved systems. What I want to say, though, is that it seems to me as though one could have gotten the polypeptides first, which were important in leading up to the polynucleotides.

Rich: I don't think so.

McElroy: I take the anticodon approach and you are taking the codon approach (see Fig. 28).

Rich: Yes. I took this—polynucleotides-codon first—point of view several years ago. It was then a heterodoxy that I think will shortly become orthodoxy in terms of mechanism.

Horowitz: I think this is all very interesting, but it is really the next topic. I think everyone agrees we have to have polymers of some kind if we are going to create life.

Rich: I will make a wager—a bottle of wine—that within

a small number of years, maybe three—let's say two—we will have lots of mechanisms for polymerizing nucleotides. The reason I say this is the following: If you look at the geometry of a complex with a polynucleotide and mononucleotides attached to it, the phosphate group is right next to the hydroxyl, so that this dehydration is just triggered to go, and all we need to do is find the right conditions—and I don't think it is a profound problem.

McElroy: I can do that with amino acid acyl adenylates.

Rich: There is another step I am thinking about now, and I don't have enough insight to solve, and that is the question of how do you couple the nucleotide polymerization (which I think is trivial) to the question of tacking amino acids onto the nucleotides and co-polymerizing the amino acids? That is the key problem. I have guesses but no real feel for it.

Abelson: Everyone is talking about these fine phosphates around—nucleotides are purine or pyrimidine bases attached to sugar phosphate—but in nature there isn't any one molar phosphate. At pH 9, it is going to be about 10^{-9} M phosphate.

Siever: There is also a redox potential that has to be taken into account for phosphate to be present. If you are talking about a primitive reducing atmosphere, you have to specify what the potential is.

Miller: Phosphate is quite stable to reduction.

Abelson: I mention this because in getting around the problem of mobilizing phosphate, one may get some key information.

Horowitz: We seem to be polarized as to which polymer is important, but I think everyone agrees that some kind of polymer is important. The thing I would like to thrash out before lunch is what we know and don't know about the mechanisms of polymerization; then later on we can worry about what polymers we want to make. Stanley (Miller), tell us about your cyanates.

Miller: There are certain boundary conditions on phosphate: That calcium concentration in the ocean at the present time is 0.01 $\overline{M}$; the pH is 8; and the hydroxyl apatite $(Ca_{10}(PO_4)6(OH)_2)$ is essentially saturated in the ocean. The concentration of phosphate is 3×10^{-6} M. At higher pH's the situation is much worse: The phosphate concentration is proportional to the square of the hydrogen ion concentration. In more acid solutions the phosphate becomes more soluble.

In nature, if you examine phosphate minerals, 80 to 90 percent of all phosphate is in the form of hydroxyl apatite, and this is true in sedimentary, igneous, and metamorphic rocks. The great stability of hydroxyl apatite at pH's greater than 7, and the wide occurrence of this mineral is an important boundary condition in considering phosphate chemistry on the primitive earth. If the ocean were more acid, brushite $(CaHPO_4 \cdot 2H_2O)$ and monetite $(CaHPO_4)$ would be stable minerals. They are relatively rare minerals on the earth at the present time. Not a single dihydrogen phosphate mineral is known in nature.

The experiment to use hydroxyl apatite as a reagent is to simply take the solid hydroxyl apatite, make an aqueous suspension of it, and add 1×10^{-13} M cyanate. A substantial yield of pyrophosphate is obtained as calcium pyrophosphate. The yield is a function of the pH and peaks around pH 6.5 or 7. The maxium yield is approximately 27 percent based on the cyanate used.

To a solid suspension of hydroxyl apatite is added potassium cyanate, appropriate buffer, and the mixture is shaken. The reaction is carried out for a long time to make it go to completion. The pyrophosphate is separated by column chromatography. This apatite reaction was tried with cyanogen. Sometimes pyrophosphate was synthesized in good yield, and sometimes no pyrophosphate was obtained. I think Dr. Orgel knows some more about why this reaction is erratic.

Neither thiocyanate nor cyanide give any pyrophosphate. Cyanate and cyanogen are the two compounds that work. Cyanate seems to be a plausible compound on the primitive earth. It could come from the decomposition of urea as well as other sources.

Ponnamperuma: Stanley (Miller), this hydroxyl apatite is in suspension. What about the situation where you get some of these out under relatively anhydrous conditions? Think of a pool that has dried up, if you want to get back to really primitive earth conditions.

Miller: I haven't tried the dried-up pool. I should mention that the cyanate reaction to give pyrophosphate won't take place if you use soluble phosphate.

Ponnamperuma: I am thinking of direct phosphorylation.

Miller: You have done apparently a different thing. Again I say that I don't see how you are going to get large concentrations of soluble phosphate. If it turns out, as Dr. Abelson says, that the pH was 9 or 9.5, the situation is much worse. You are always going to have a greater abundance of calcium, except in highly peculiar conditions. I don't know any place on the earth that high concentrations of phosphate occur in the absence of calcium.

Fox: You don't know it for the present time.

Miller: You are always going to have a higher concentration of calcium than you are of phosphate, and it is something that ought to be taken into account.

Ponnamperuma: A phosphorylation reaction will probably take place in situations away from dilute solutions where material has been deposited.

Orgel: On surface, yes.

Miller: If stoichiometric quantities of phosphate are needed on the primitive earth, the best way to do it is on a concentrated amount of phosphate, namely, hydroxyl apatite.

Sagan: The question of what form the phosphorus was in under primitive conditions doesn't seem to be an easy one.

Miller: If you set the pH, you set what the phosphate compounds are———

Sagan: Suppose there is no calcium in the sea water yet; the rivers haven't run down to the sea yet?

Abelson: The phosphorus in the volcanic lava is in the form of apatite, which is quite insoluble.

Miller: The hydroxyl apatites and the other apatites are unique in geology. The same mineral occurs in the three types of rock—igneous, metamorphic, and sedimentary. I don't think there is another example of this.

Siever: There is no place else for the phosphate to go.

McElroy: In the volcano you don't get temperatures high enough to get pyrophosphate from the apatite.

Miller: That's another issue. It has frequently been proposed that high-energy phosphates can be synthesized by simply heating phosphates to give metaphosphate polymers, pyrophosphate, and so on. If you try to write the stoichiometry, it is not possible to make metaphosphates or pyrophosphate with hydroxyl apatite. The stoichiometry is such that when you take the monohydrogen phosphates, water is eliminated to give pyrophosphates. When this is heated, the cyclic polymers and long-chain polymers are indeed obtained. However, at the present time there is not a single known dihydrogen phosphate in nature. Therefore this heating process, at least from the standpoint of making long-chain phosphate polymers, will not work in nature.

McElroy: Pyrophosphate will be enough; I don't care about going any longer.

Miller: Brushite and monetite are relatively rare minerals. Magnesium ammonium phosphate can be considered a monohydrogen phosphate. It doesn't occur very much in nature, but it does occur frequently in canned salmon.

Sagan: It is by no means obvious that because phosphorus is present as apatite in contemporary oceans and in contemporary volcanic lavas, apatite as such was the form of phosphorus on the primitive earth. Let me just ask a simple chemical question. Suppose you start out with methane (CH_4), ammonia (NH_3), water (H_2O), hydrogen (H_2), and phosphine (PH_3)— what happens?

Miller: This experiment was done by Calvin (Palm & Calvin, 1962), but I don't know what happened to the phosphorus in his experiment.

Sagan: That's what I'm asking: What happened to the phosphorus?

Miller: It would tend to get oxidized over long periods, the phosphine (PH_3) going to phosphate (PO_4). Phosphine is quite unstable.

Ponnamperuma: You had a difficulty in calculating the abundance of phosphine in the early atmosphere, didn't you?

Miller: A mixture of phosphine and water thermodynamically is very clear-cut. The equilibrium constant to form phosphate is 10^{40}. In the presence of one atmosphere of hydrogen, you simply cannot reduce, thermodynamically, your phosphate to phosphine. The same is true for all the other intermediate oxidation states of phosphorous.

Sagan: How about phosphoric acid (H_3PO_4)?

Miller: Phosphoric acid is the same as phosphate except it is acid. If you take the oceans at pH 8 or 9.5, the phosphate is precipitated as apatite.

Fox: Do you limit yourself to the ocean at pH 8? Isn't that the contemporary ocean and, also, isn't that an ocean rather than other parts of the hydrosphere?

Miller: I would be very interested in knowing where there is any phosphoric acid under natural conditions.

Fox: My question was about pH.

Siever: The pH of many natural isolated water systems, such as lakes or pools outside of the ocean, tends to be more alkaline than the ocean. There are some acid volcanic pools or hot springs, but I would not expect them to be quantitatively dominant.

Fox: We may have to deal with special conditions. I think volcanic pools, Dr. Siever, are more relevant than they might appear to be at first glance because, as Dr. Ponnamperuma suggests, in zones where heat is available, there are kinds of locales in which polymerization—formation of macromolecules without concurrent extensive destruction of the same macromolecules—can be more easily visualized.

Miller: What is the pH of volcanic pools?

Fox: I looked at one two weeks ago, the Soufriers at St. Lucia in the West Indies, and the pH of the water was 2.7, as removed from the pool and allowed to cool.

Siever: The Yellowstone pools vary anywhere from pH of 2 up to 7 or 8.

Miller: You may have a pH of 2, but the important thing is the concentration of phosphate.

Siever: These are sulfuric acid pools.

Abelson: The trouble with Sidney's (Fox) suggestion that life originated in hot drying pools is this: He can have a pH of one up to eight—no problem, even less than one if he wants it—but you have to remember that at any given time, only one part in a million (or less) of the earth's surface is involved; and the second thing is that volcanoes come and go, so you have a very short time span in which to create your miracle. Until one can see that we can't achieve these things in the ocean with 10^6 times as much area, some of us are going to feel that we ought to pursue the main chance in terms of area and time.

Fox: I agree; I think you should pursue it; but I don't think you should prejudge the situation. [See Appendix]

Morrison: That is a very nice point, but in a connected system there is always a small fraction of these hot pools. Connected volcanic pools have durations that must be extraordinarily small compared to a thousand years.

Abelson: Maybe not compared to a thousand years, but small compared to a million years.

Morrison: It is clearly small in comparison with a million years. We don't even have single volcanic regions that last that long.

Siever: The volcanic regions might last, but these pools come and go.

Fox: These, incidentally, aren't volcanoes; they are fumarole and hot spring regions, and I can show you maps which may convince you that they are far more extensive on the contemporary earth than might be imagined here.

Horowitz: What percentage of the surface of the earth is geothermal?

Fox: I don't think that is a question that should be asked or answered in terms of percentage of the surface of the contemporary earth in our context.

Miller: Why not?

Morrison: Ask how many square kilometers.

Fox: I think the time when you ought to ask that question is when you are in a position to answer the question, "How often did life begin?"

Miller: I think it is a very straightforward geochemical question.

Morrison: I agree.

Fox: Okay. For the contemporary geochemical question for 1185 hotspring localities in the United States alone I'll give you the data and you can calculate their percentage of the surface of the earth. For the past, during which life first came into existence, you can look at the introduction in Rittmann's (1962) book on volcanoes. He refers to the studies of the American geochemist F. W. Clarke (1924). Clarke found that over 95 percent of the accessible portions of the earth's crust had been through an igneous stage of molten rock and pyroclastics. The geologist Bullard (1962) presents similar analyses. Professor George Mueller [see Appendix] cites the geological evidence from hydrothermal veins.

Miller: It may be true that most rock is volcanic or igneous. The question is, "At a given time how much is heated or is tide pools?" For over 4.5 billion years this volcanic rock has accumulated.

Fox: Again, Rittmann (1962) indicates global conditions of thermal vaporization alternating with condensation of water. The critical temperature of water is only 374° C.

Abelson: I have visited many of the hot springs of North America and they represent less than one square kilometer.

Horowitz: When you have a geothermal area, you make a national park out of it; it is not the usual sort of thing. I don't think anyone would contest the possibility that the origin of life was an unrepeatable accident—that it was an event that had a probability of 10^{-25}, or something like that. It is conceivable, but on the other hand until we have excluded the possibility that it occurred through a natural and predictable sequence of reactions———

Morrison: I don't think that is quite fair. One square kilometer is quite plenty provided, as Phil Abelson pointed out, you can do things mighty fast, because there always is one square kilometer—but you have to act fast because the duration of that physical system is very small, so whatever happens has to happen quickly.

Fox: I would like to enter into the record that what I have been talking about, *contemporaneously,* are not, for the most part, national parks. Just in North America—and it is not the most geothermal area on the face of the earth—there are 1185 hot springs localities.

Siever: May I suggest another environment which seems to put together a good many things desired for these syntheses. These are the alkaline or mildly alkaline lakes that do have a certain continuity over a much longer time scale than volcanic pools. They may last up to a million years, or perhaps longer, which starts giving us the kind of time we want. They are present over a good deal of the western United States, in any place that has interior drainage.

Miller: Mono Lake, California, would be an example.

Siever: Yes, Mono Lake. There is a whole complex of these lakes. They have some rather interesting characteristics aside from the fact that they tend to have pH values that range anywhere from 8.5 up to 11 in some cases. There are places where you may expect apatite or a variety of phosphates.

They also, characteristically, have silicate minerals of quite a different variety than we are normally used to; there are a great many zeolites, extensive ion exchanges, and the kinds of labile silicates that one might wish to have to help any such process as the polymerizations we were talking about.

Morrison: The issue somehow, I think (and this is only vague) is that there is a problem of concentration and a problem of time. What we want is to maximize this product in some broad way; I am sure that is an important criterion. The ocean has this marvelous physical continuity with time which makes up for low concentrations. The small environments of this sort have a remarkable splendor in concentration, but are killed off by short time. An optimization along these lines is what, somehow, we are looking for.

McElroy: I would like to get back and ask someone to tell me more about the amino acid polymerization versus the polynucleotide polymerization, because it would help me in deciding whether it was polyphenylalanine that really allowed U (uridine) to line up to make a poly U (polyuridylic acid). If that happened it would be of advantage to some systems; it would replicate and be more competitive, so to speak. In other words, which one did come first?

I admit what is here now—that is, a polynucleotide system that determines the order in a polypeptide system—and there is no difficulty on the chemistry of it. It is just a question of what came first. It seems to me that this comes down to trying to realize what are the most likely things to polymerize, namely, the amino acids or the polynucleotides.

Rich: As I see that problem, my view is the following: There had to be a primitive nonenzymatic activating system involving a coupling between an amino acid and a nucleotide. My guess is that if one looks at ways of making anhydride linkages between these nucleotides and amino acids, one may find low orders of specificity. Let's go back. I even think at the beginning we may have had a singlet code—that is, one ordered nucleotide determines the order of one amino acid residue in a protein—instead of triplet code (see Fig. 28), but that is a different question, not relevant here.

Imagine that we are working with a singlet code and we ask, "What is the yield of an anhydride involving, say, UMP (uridine monophosphate), with aspartic acid versus any other nucleotide with a specific amino acid?" Let us say that we find that under a certain set of conditions, a particular yield of a given nucleotide-amino acid anhydride is higher than others for some small steric reason.

Then, I would imagine, if one had a mechanism for polymerizing nucleotides, using their intrinsic complementarity and some polymerizing mechanism yet to be uncovered, we would, in effect, have a lining-up of nucleotides with attached amino acids which would be statistical in nature. That is, when you have UMP, the probability of having an aspartate is a little greater than having other amino acid residues with the UMP. By some unknown mechanism this polynucleotide chain, containing all its side chains of amino acids, somehow would act as a catalyst for making the slightly informational polypeptide chain. I don't know the mechanism.

Sulston: I think we have had some results on this.

Rich: Okay. Then, when this occurs, we will have what I would call a statistical readout; not a rigorous readout but statistical in the sense that U tends to favor aspartate, for example. The system is not well defined. However, when you get a collection of polynucleotide sequences that happens to read out—produced by chance—a polypeptide molecule that enhances this initial biased probability, so that you get a more rigorous readout, the system is beginning to go critical in the sense that it begins to translate definitely.

The next step in this process would involve another polynucleotide with this. Now you have a system for making a definitive molecule based on this series of hypothetical events.

McElroy: That, I would buy completely. The thing I am saying is that, initially, it may very well have been that the template, in order to get a polynucleotide, could very well have been an amino acid sequence. But it has to turn out to have certain unique catalytic properties.

Rich: I have no objection to using random polypeptides, but I would say that you don't need polypeptides. You can have anything. I am prepared to use rocks or polymers or the funny yellow stuff. You don't need polypeptides. You do need a catalyst. The thing I find most attractive (which nobody has looked at very much) is Bernal's suggestion about using the lattices of rocks (Bernal, 1967). If that gives you a biased concentration between a given nucleotide and an amino acid, fine.

McElroy: I am prepared to accept your early argument of the polynucleotide. The only thing I am saying is that if you come up with a polypeptide as having unique advantages, then you can just as well go ahead and zip up with your polynucleotide, which has now the coding properties you want.

Rich: But it has to be there randomly, and that is the whole difficulty, you see.

Fox: I think the facts show that polypeptides don't have to be there randomly, and I think also it may be well to determine whether or not we are using the same concepts when we use the word *random*. Different uses of this word often pose a semantic problem.

Morrison: You don't really mean random; you mean unselected.

Rich: Unselected, yes.

Morrison: Nonrandomness has thermodynamic implications.

Rich: Yes, of course. The point is that many things are around that could have been catalytically active and, to my mind, a polymer of amino acids involving peptide bonds doesn't offer any great advantage, bearing in mind that it may be rather hard to make. The polymers that collect may not be polypeptides, and there are lots of other surfaces that could have this catalytic activity. It doesn't have to be a very high order of catalytic activity at best.

Horowitz: Of course, if you make polypeptides at random with catalytic activity, you are just as likely to make catalysts that break down the products you are interested in. There is no reason to think that every polypeptide is going to do what you want it to do.

Rich: The difficulty is, you have no way of reproducing your system, and that is the basic problem.

Horowitz: There is another mechanism of concentrating reagents to carry out polymerizations, and that is the eutectic freezing method. Sulston, you have something on that.

Sulston: I have been looking at very simple models of the type that Dr. Rich has been mentioning, really taking the protein biosynthetic system (see Fig. 28) and reducing it to bare essentials. I have taken the $2'(3')$-O-glycyl derivatives of adenosine, uridine, and UMP, to see whether on their own, first of all, they can produce any kind of peptide.

Horowitz: Will you state the reagents again? I missed them.

Sulston: The mixed $2'(3')$ isomers of O-gylcyl nucleosides and nucleotides.

One particular experiment I have done is to take $2'(3')$-O-glycyl UMP in aqueous solution. Around $0.3\ M$ concentration you get about 20 percent diglycine, 10 percent diketopiperazine, and the result gets hydrolyzed to glycine.

Horowitz: This is in the absence of any catalyst?

Sulston: Yes. It has been known for a long time that, in general, amino acyl esters do self-condense. Even in 1900 it was known that methyl glycine itself forms a reasonable amount of a horny product which is, in fact, polyglycine. Of course these experiments used high concentrations. Our experiments were designed to see if amino acids are more likely to form peptides when introduced into the reaction mixtures as derivatives of nucleic acid components than by themselves. First of all with the eutectic method, if you take $0.01\ M$ solution of this same glycine UMP, put it at $-10°$ C, let it freeze, sit for a month, and then look at the product, you find

exactly the same things: Diglycine; diketopiperazine; and glycine. Thus, using the eutectic method is quite comparable to
beginning with a more concentrated solution. I should also say
that the control solution at 0.01 M is just left around (at room
temperature), and you can get plain glycine.

McElroy: At what pH are you running these?

Sulston: pH 9.

McElroy: Can you keep the acyl compound around at pH 9?

Sulston: Yes, at $-10°$ C. At room temperature in
solution it will hydrolyze quite quickly. These experiments
are only of interest because they demonstrate the reactivity of
these acyl compounds; we really want to try to get some sort
of template system going. In two preliminary experiments I
have tried, the first was with glycyluridine and poly A and the
second glycyladenosine with poly U. I got nothing. In fact
the preliminary result seems to even be a sort of "anti-catalysis."
It looks as though the glycine residues are in fact held apart.
With the glycyladenosine and poly U, I'm pretty sure that some
of the helix is formed—I do see a viscous gel forming. This is like
the results of H. T. Miles (Howard, et al, 1966) showing the
helix is formed under comparable conditions.

Rich: I can add an interesting negative result, too. We have
prodded a poly U system in various ways, too, to see if we
could form dimers or trimers of polyphenylalanine; we failed.
Our search was not exhaustive; I'm still not convinced that it
won't work. People are just beginning to look at this class of
problems. I think we will eventually be able to get the appropriate polymers.

Ponnamperuma: May I get back to geology for a moment?
There is often a reference, especially in the Russian literature,
to a lot of polyphosphates lying around on the Kola Peninsula.
I wonder if one of the geologists would comment on the possibility or likelihood of such a thing.

McElroy: There is lots of it in the soil right around here.

Fox: You mean microbial polyphosphate?

McElroy: Some of it is microbial. For the most part, it is presumed to be mostly microbial, but nobody really knows.

Siever: I will stand by Miller's argument. All the phosphate you see in rocks of nonbiological origin is a form of fluoro-hydroxy apatite—calcium phosphate in apatite form. As a matter of fact, most of the organisms that produce phosphate in a hard form—shell, bone, and the like—also produce the same thing. Under most of the conditions of nature, phosphate has no place to go in chemistry other than to calcium phosphate. All these other phosphorous compounds are very labile.

Miller: If there had been a good identification of polyphosphate mineral in nature, it would appear in the mineralogy books, and there is none.

Siever: There are a lot of strange phosphates in pegmatites of one sort or another but, quantitatively, they do not amount to very much at all. These are curiosities more than anything else.

There is another point about phosphate which is a little bit disturbing: The amount of phosphate present in Precambrian rocks is very much lower than that in all post-Cambrian rocks. There seems to be some question of availability here, but I don't think this is a real stumbling block. In later times I believe we are just seeing the wholesale addition of biological phosphate added to the geologic column, and that the "background" is what we really see in Precambrian rocks, the natural nonbiogenic, essentially high-temperature apatite.

I have just looked at the maps of the thermal springs given me by Dr. Fox and in making a rapid estimate count, based on the Idaho map, I get 10^3 thermal springs in the eastern United States; the average diameter—I agree with Phil Abelson, having tramped around a good many of them—is about 10^{-2}

square kilometers. We end up with 10 square kilometers, in the whole western United States, of thermal springs.

Fox: Of course, the subsurface would have to be larger, and in earlier times could have been— — —

Abelson: Were you there, Charlie?

Fox: I wasn't there but the geologists were there, in a sense, when they inferred an outpouring of molten rock from what they believe cooled to the present time. I refer to the inference drawn with respect to the Great Northwest Plateau, just as one example, or those of Rittmann (1962) or Clarke (1924).

Sagan: The absence of other sorts of phosphates and phosphoric acid hinges on the pH of the ocean or whatever body of water we are talking about. I wonder what is the supposed rate of HCl in a primitive environment. There is now evidence for HCl on Venus, which is not a highly reducing environment. If there were a lot of HCl present at the time of the origin of the earth in gas phase at reducing conditions, what does that say about the pH of the ocean? And, parenthetically, where did the HCl go, before there was very much particulate matter washed out of the ocean?

Miller: In the first case let us consider that HCl is evolved in the volcanoes. The question is, does it evolve faster than the buffering system (in the oceans) can bring the pH back to its standard value of 8? The second point is that it is always said that HCl is being evolved from volcanoes. Harold Urey feels it is not a question of volatility, because the hydrogen fluoride, which also should come out as a volatile, is not concentrated at the crust of the earth. He believes that the solubles rather than the volatiles are being taken out via the volcanoes. The solubles rather than volatiles are concentrated at the surface of the earth.

Sagan: I don't care how it comes out. I want to know what happens to it (the HCl).

Miller: It comes out as sodium chloride.

Sagan: In the case of Venus, we see a part per million (wgt HCl/wgt other atmospheric gases) or something like that.

Miller: But Venus is a very different situation.

Sagan: Yes, but it is still a place where there apparently is not a lot of oxygen around.   If something like HCl is on Venus, I would expect it was on earth, too, when the conditions here were not very oxygen-rich.

Abelson: If we discount about 30 to 99 percent of the chloride as coming out as sodium chloride, and say that the remainder came out as HCl (which would be about a fair estimate), and take into account the fact that the HCl came out gradually and that the amount of alkalinity of weathered rocks was chemically equivalent to 10^3 times the amount of HCl, then the lifetime of any HCl, as such, is short.

Sulston: There is also the question of ammonia.

Siever: In fact, there is a good argument currently being made that a great deal of HCl is coming out in the ocean bottom, and that any HCl or chloride usually linked with some hydrogen, always has been coming out of the ocean.   It is quickly neutralized as it hits the floor of the ocean on the way up, and we never really see it in the atmosphere.   So, the question which we have discussed before is whether or not the atmospheric HCl is in equilibrium with the ocean.

Sagan: On Venus, I might just point out, there wouldn't be any oceans.

Miller: Yes, that changes it.

Sagan: One last aspect, Stanley (Miller): What is the buffering system you talked about?

Miller: The short-term buffering is the bicarbonate-carbon dioxide system, but a longer-term one is the ion exchange of the various cations on the clay minerals. There are still further buffering systems involving the formation of limestones and the degradation of various silicate minerals—the whole weathering process.

Sagan: So, even if one were to argue that because conditions were reducing, one of these materials wasn't around, that still wouldn't be a good objection; you would still have other buffers. Certainly, the silicates would be buffering. Your time scale is short, comparatively speaking.

Miller: This is what seems to be the case. I can think of several mechanisms to get the ocean more acid. This could be done by tying up the calcium. One way of tying it up is oxalate, and it is possible to make oxalic acid under primitive earth conditions.

Siever: This is worse; you get magnesium taking the place of calcium.

Miller: Magnesium won't take care of the phosphate. Calcium oxalate is very insoluble. Another point is that when you currently pull the gases out, the ocean goes basic because you are removing the carbon dioxide. If you have ammonia there and you pull it off, it tends to go acidic because you are pulling off a base.

Abelson: Even your oxalate mechanism won't wash if you convert all the carbon in the crust of the earth today, whether carbonate or reduced carbon. You still have more calcium left over than you would require to use up all the oxalate.

Miller: In a local area, you might do it. I don't find this very convincing, but there might be some tricks we haven't considered.

Sagan: The situation seems to be this: It's very hard to make the ocean acidic. And as a result, the phosphorus—I gather everyone agrees it is most likely to be in the form of apatite—is not going to be sitting in solution but mostly is in a solid phase somewhere. Therefore, it is interface reactions that are going to be important for phosphorous chemistry. It is a very interesting set of arguments.

Ponnamperuma: Unless we switch to micro-environments, you know.

Oró: If you were able to make the oceans acidic, that would not help the cause of abiotic syntheses. It may help in solubilizing phosphate, but then we would have hydrolytic conditions and everything would tend to remain hydrolyzed.

Miller: Acid conditions would be very difficult for the purines on the DNA.

Oró: By the way, HCN condensation reactions can be carried out under basic or acidic conditions. If you use acid conditions, what you get instead of amino acids and purines are triazines. These compounds are not now known to be involved in any important vital processes.

Ponnamperuma: It is curious that azines, together with adenine and guanine, were identified in a meteorite.

Oró: I have some reluctance to accept these data, as I do for some other work that has been reported on meteorites, even though the preliminary results you are referring to were published (Hayatsu, 1964).

Rich: Phil Abelson, you must construe that as a compliment.

Sagan: One last point. The idea that phosphorus is occurring on solid interfaces has one other appealing aspect to it, and that concerns abundances. The nucleic acids are made of five atoms: Hydrogen, carbon, nitrogen, oxygen, and phosphorus. The first four of these are the four cosmically most abundant atoms that are chemically reactive at all. Phosphorus, however, is far down in the abundance tables, yet we obviously need it for nucleic acid functioning.   If it turns out that there are some reactions which occur only on phosphorous minerals, or in local micro-environments with high phosphorus abundance, then there is a certain additional plausibility to the idea of primordial chemistry.

Ponnamperuma: I would like to point out the work done by Newman and Newman, who used apatite. In the process they were able to phosphorylate nucleosides on their thin-layer plate.

Horowitz: On this Panglossian note, I suggest we adjourn for lunch.

[The morning session adjourned at noon.]

Horowitz: I have put on the blackboard a list of unsolved problems—even unsolved in principle—which I would like to focus the discussion on this afternoon.

ORIGIN OF BIOLOGICALLY IMPORTANT MONOMERS—
AMINO ACIDS; PURINES; PYRIMIDINES; SUGARS

ORIGIN OF BIOPOLYMERS—SPECIFICALLY PROTEINS AND
NUCLEIC ACIDS

ORIGIN OF SELF-DUPLICATING [GENETIC] SYSTEMS

EVOLUTION OF THE RIBOSOMAL SYSTEM OF PROTEIN
SYNTHESIS

EVOLUTION OF THE AMINO ACID SET [THE 20 OR SO
AMINO ACIDS IN PROTEINS] AND THE GENETIC CODE

ORIGIN OF OPTICAL ACTIVITY

ORIGIN OF MEMBRANES, SUBCELLULAR PARTICLES, AND
CELLS

EVOLUTION OF METABOLIC PATHWAYS

I don't mean this list to be inclusive or exclusive of anything else that is relevant to the general problem of the origin of life. Other material will be welcome.

Pattee: What is the difference between your third and fifth items?

Rich: The fifth is the contemporary genetic code and the third is the code that preceded it.

Pattee: But I associate a code with any genetic system. Oh, I understand. The fifth is the precursor of the present code.

Morrison: Is the order of your topics significant?

Horowitz: The order is significant only in that I think one can't have a living system until one has a genetic system.

Fox: You might have cells.

Morrison: One could have a living system before one has an optically active system.

Horowitz: I don't think you would get optically active systems until you have a living system.

Margulis: And you don't have cells until you have a genetic system. I disagree with Dr. Fox.

Horowitz: Dr. Fox had some things he was going to start off with, so why don't you begin the discussion, Sidney?

Thermal Origin Of Amino Acid Polymers

Fox: Before beginning, I cite a few references to an extensive literature suggesting the origin of optical activity prebiotically (Havinga, 1954; Fox et al, 1956; Wald, 1957; Harada, 1965). Other references are in the bibliographies of these papers. I wish to state also that what I mean by cells is that of highly heterotrophic organized structures which contain their own information without containing contemporary genetic systems (Fox, McCauley, & Wood, 1967). I believe that primitive uncoded information could have been the evolutionary precursor of contemporary genetic systems (Fox & Nakashima, 1967).

What I present now is mostly new material, but it starts with some introductory slides for those who may be unfamiliar with what we have been doing. The equations of Figure 30 treat this problem of the energetics of the formation of the peptide bond in an elementary way and refer to the fact that Huffman (1942) tabulated the free-energy requirements for the formation per mole of peptide bond. He found for the few peptides which he measured from heat capacity and heats of combustion, that the requirement was in the range of 2000 to 4000 calories. The equilibrium constant that can be calculated from this value turns out to be very unfavorable, as was pointed out this morning.

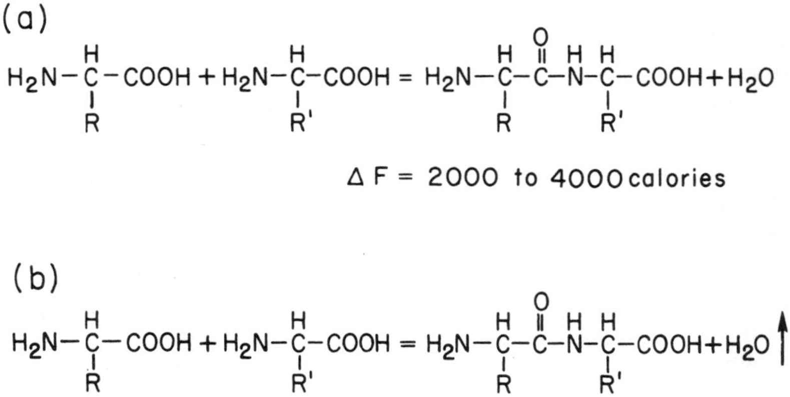

(a)

$$H_2N-\underset{\underset{R}{|}}{\overset{\overset{H}{|}}{C}}-COOH + H_2N-\underset{\underset{R'}{|}}{\overset{\overset{H}{|}}{C}}-COOH = H_2N-\underset{\underset{R}{|}}{\overset{\overset{H}{|}}{C}}-\overset{\overset{O}{\|}}{C}-\underset{}{\overset{H}{N}}-\underset{\underset{R'}{|}}{\overset{\overset{H}{|}}{C}}-COOH+H_2O$$

$$\Delta F = 2000 \text{ to } 4000 \text{ calories}$$

(b)

$$H_2N-\underset{\underset{R}{|}}{\overset{\overset{H}{|}}{C}}-COOH + H_2N-\underset{\underset{R'}{|}}{\overset{\overset{H}{|}}{C}}-COOH = H_2N-\underset{\underset{R}{|}}{\overset{\overset{H}{|}}{C}}-\overset{\overset{O}{\|}}{C}-\underset{}{\overset{H}{N}}-\underset{\underset{R'}{|}}{\overset{\overset{H}{|}}{C}}-COOH+H_2O\uparrow$$

Figure 30. Formation of the peptide bond. (a) The reaction forming peptide bond between two amino acids (R, R'). [Energetic data from Huffman (1942)] (b) The reaction can be driven to the right by removal of water as by exceeding the boiling point (Havinga, 1954).

One of the best treatments of this, incidentally, is in the last five pages of Dixon and Webb's (1958) book. The authors point out that the amount of one molar amino acid required to be in equilibrium with one molecule of protein of molecular weight 12,000 would occupy a volume 10^{50} times that of the earth. They also state that "the problem of the origin of life itself is largely that of the origin of enzymes." On the basis of thermodynamic reasoning, all we can expect in dilute aqueous solution is small yields of small peptides, unless the reaction is somehow coupled to another yielding energy.

The way we first visualized a way of overcoming this barrier (and there is more than one conceptual possibility, indeed) was to heat the dry amino acids above the boiling point of water. The result is represented by the vertical arrow of Figure 30b. There are other ways of removing water, of course, but this is one that we believed (and continue to believe) is within the boundaries of the conditions that not only were on the primitive earth but are here now.

Another kind of problem that arose was also touched on this morning, and that is the one of sequentialization. We weren't prepared to do any experiments until we could visualize how there might be some selection in how amino acids might arrange themselves in polymers or polypeptides. We thought we saw a clue to the answer from studies with enzyme-catalyzed synthesis of anilides in a very artificial system introduced by Bergmann and Fraenkel-Conrat. The results are in Table 4 (Fox et al, 1954). I won't take your time with the operating details of this system, most of which are not germane. If one reacts in an aqueous solution acylamino acids and anilides, uses an enzyme to facilitate the reaction, one then gets a relatively insoluble acylamino acid anilide or an acylpeptide anilide.

What struck us most in the results was that the nature of the synthetic product was a function of the reactant amino acids. In a systematic series like that of benzoylglycine, benzoylalanine, benzoylvaline, benzoylleucine, with glycine anilide under standard conditions, three of these yield benzoylamino acid anilides, but the fourth yields a different kind of product, benzoylglycyl glycine anilide. A couple at the bottom of the table show a difference in product.

Table 4

Selective Influences in the Interaction of Amino Acid Residues[*]

Reactants	Yields
Bz-gly + gly-anilide	Bz-gly-gly-anilide
Bz-ala + gly-anilide	Bz-ala-anilide
Bz-val + gly-anilide	Bz-val-anilide
Bz-leu + gly-anilide	Bz-leu-anilide
Bz-ala + ala-anilide	Bz-ala-anilide
Bz-ala + leu-anilide	Bz-ala-leu-anilide

Key: Bz = benzene; gly = glycine; val = valine; leu = leucine; ala = alanine

[*]By the method of Bergmann and Fraenkel-Conrat, in Fox et al., (1954)

Since these reactions are carried out under standard experimental conditions, the difference is ascribable to the interacting amino acids.

These results led us to believe that maybe there would be some sense to what otherwise seemed quite illogical—the production of protein-like materials by heating amino acids together, inasmuch as we could now visualize the interaction of the amino acids as an internally controlled sequentialization.

I might say, as a footnote, that G. Steinman has published a paper recently (in the *Archives of Biochemistry and Biophysics*) in which he uses the Merrifield system with dicyanamide and also finds in that system a selective synthesis. Steinman infers therefrom that nucleic acid did not, therefore, have to come before the first proteins. This is an inference that we had drawn earlier (Fox, 1965c).

Horowitz: I don't understand what you mean when you say nucleic acids didn't have to come first.

Fox: Nucleic acids are not necessary to bring about a controlled sequentialization of amino acids in any peptides that might form. Figure 31 illustrates another conception that had to be dealt with.

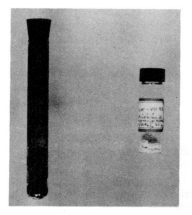

Figure 31. (a) Amino acids heated above the boiling point of water results in tar (b) Amino acids plus aspartic acid and glutamic acid, heated above the boiling point of water, the product of heating twice salted-in and salted-out.

And that was the very widespread knowledge, well documented in the literature, that if one heats amino acids above the boiling point of water, the product will be a dark, tarry mass of forbidding nature, as illustrated in the tube on the left in Figure 31.

As I said Sunday night, from our studies of Darwinian evolution at the molecular level in organisms, we were led to try the experiment of heating, taking into account these factors which I have mentioned and others which I have not mentioned. We were led to test a mixture of all eighteen amino acids common to protein with a sufficient proportion of aspartic acid and glutamic acid. What we get from that is not a dark, unworkable mass, but a light amber polymer (this has been done now in more than ten laboratories that I know of). One doesn't necessarily use all eighteen amino acids, and I don't argue that eighteen were necessary at the primordial event. I believe, however, that the fact that one can accomplish this polymerization with all eighteen shows that the reaction is versatile. It is rugged, particularly in the various ways that we have tested it with added materials. Also, the conceptual possibilities for evolution are greater with a large number of types of amino acid.

Miller: I have always thought the accepted number was twenty, and I am curious why you have omitted two.

Fox: The nineteenth and twentieth, which are assigned by the coding studies, are asparagine and glutamine. When one hydrolyzes asparagine and glutamine one obtains aspartic acid and glutamic acid. Since aspartic acid and glutamic acid are among the eighteen that we start with, these four essentailly resolve to two. Looking at the question from this point of view, and in a primitive context, eighteen is equivalent to twenty. In fact, during this kind of polymerization condensation, amides are formed on aspartic acid and glutamic acid, so at least twenty amino acids occur in the product although we start with eighteen.

Rich: I might say that the structural work on proteins that has come out shows very clearly that the amides (asparagine and glutamine) are distinctly different in the structural role in terms of their role in holding the secondary and tertiary structure together—quite distinct from the acids (glutamic and aspartic). About ten years ago there was a report that the activating enzymes for aspartic acid and asparagine were the same. This was subsequently shown to be erroneous. These different molecules have distinctly different roles in proteins. I recognize that you don't use the amides because they deaminate, but it is important to recognize they are quite different. You can see this clearly around the active site of lysozyme (enzyme used by bacterial virus to lyse the host bacteria) where three asparagines form a whole network of interlaid hydrogen bonds to set up the active surface. They function by virtue of the hydrogen bonding through the amino group.

Fox: I certainly agree with that, except that the amides don't deamidate on heating; the dicarboxylic acids amidate on heating. Nor would I want anyone to draw the inference that in a thermal condensation such as this, asparagine and glutamine cannot be used. These amides have been used, maybe even leading to some difference in the product. There is, indeed, a difference in the rate of reaction, favoring the amides in the kinds of mixtures in which they have been tested.

Kramer: How do you really recover that flaky material? How do you get that?

Fox: The polymer on the right hand side (Fig. 31b) was first prepared by heating one part of aspartic acid, one of glutamic acid, and one part of the sixteen other amino acids—present in that part in equimolar proportions –170° for 6 hours.   This gave a glassy, light amber product. This product is mostly not soluble in water, but it is entirely soluble in aqueous salt solution; it can be salted-in like a globulin and can then be salted-out like a globulin by saturation or half-saturation of the solution with ammonium sulfate.

Kramer: Have you looked at it under the microscope?

Fox: Yes. It appears to be amorphous.

Kramer: No structure of any kind?

Fox: No visible structure of any kind, but as soon as water is introduced into the system, its great propensity to form structures of the kind I showed yesterday afternoon becomes immediately apparent (Figs. 17-19). Not that there isn't some water in the original polymer, but this water is quite tightly bound for the most part, if not entirely. The crucial difference to the reaction is that between a little water and a lot of water. The chemistry and the reaction mechanisms are both, I believe, quite complicated. What is simple, of course, is the operation.

Kramer: And you haven't analyzed this?

Fox: Yes, we have spent many man-hours of effort on characterizing these polymers.

Kramer: Have you all the data on what is on there?

Fox: This (Table 5) is a list of the properties of the thermal polyanhydro-o-amino acids (Fox, 1967b), including the polymers containing eighteen amino acids. These latter are referred to as proteinoids, and have many properties in common with the contemporary proteins. I might at the outset say that the principal property that we are aware of, which is common to many proteins, and which we don't find in these as yet, is antigenicity.

Horowitz: Do they have optical activity?

Fox: Yes, they have optical activity.

Miller: Do you start with the D L or the L ?

Fox: We have examined that question many ways experimentally. If we start with L-amino acids, we find that the majority of the amino acids are substantially racemized but they are not entirely racemized. L-aspartic acid racemizes rapidly. L-glutamic acid does not, and typically under the conditions that I have just cited, the glutamic acid may be 50 to 70 percent racemized.

Table 5

Properties of Thermal Proteinoids

Limited heterogeneity

Qualitative composition

Quantitative composition

Range of molecular weight

Color tests

Solubilities

Inclusion of nonamino acid groups

Optical Activity

Salting-in and salting-out properties

Precipitability by protein reagents

Hypochromicity

Infrared absorption maxima

Recoverability of amino acids on hydrolysis

Susceptibility to proteolytic enzymes

Catalytic activity

Inactivatability of catalysis by heating in aqueous solution

"Nonrandom" (nonuniform) sequential distribution of residues

Nutritive quality

Morphogenicity

Table 6

"Protoenzymic" Activities in Proteinoids

Substrate	Effect
p-Nitrophenyl acetate	Actyptd is greater than Actyhsd; thermal polymers most active; inhibition by organic phosphates; "active site" and inactivation
Glucose	Goes to glucuronic acid and breaks down to CO_2; first natural substrate
ATP	Goes to ADP; energy source "motility"
Pyruvic acid	Goes to acetic acid plus CO_2; L-W intercept
Oxaloacetic acid	Goes to pyruvic acid; some specificities when compared
p-Nitrophenyl phosphate	Goes to second type of phosphate hydrolysis

The neutral amino acids show behavior similar to that of the glutamic acid (Rohlfing, 1964). The product has an α typically -5°.

Ponnamperuma: Did you have to use lower temperatures for that?

Fox: No. These have been carried out at 170 to 195° C.

Horowitz: Do you mean that you start with optically resolved material to get optically active product?

Fox: Yes, in some cases we do. In many cases we use mixtures of DL and L. The results I have cited are for condensation of L-amino acids.

Bada: What kind of catalytic activity do you observe?

Fox: Those data are presented in Table 6. They are from work in several laboratories. The first studies used the model substrate p-nitrophenyl acetate. This has been fully published in two papers (Rohlfing & Fox, 1967a; Rohlfing & Fox, 1967b). This work has identified a kind of "active site" in the proteinoids which consist of histidine and of the imide linkage that is produced from aspartic acid.

McElroy : Is this any faster than you would get with an imidazole?

Fox: Yes, in some proteinoids, over ten times as fast as with histidine. The point of enhanced activity is made particularly by the fact that when the imide linkage—part of the "active site"—is progressively split, the activity is progressively lost (Rohlfing & Fox, 1967b; Usdin et al, 1965).

Orgel: Excuse me, what is the imide linkage?

Fox: The imide linkage is obtained from the side chain of aspartic acid having split out water with the adjacent peptide bond. It is a relatively unstable linkage. Bernhard et al, (1962) implicated the imide linkage as part of the active site of contemporary enzymes, in fact, subsequent to the earliest stage of this work.

Horowitz: How many C terminal and N terminal ends do you find?

Fox: I would like to follow through on this question. Will you ask yours again, Norm (Horowitz), please, later?
Next is the work of Usdin, et al, (1965). They reported that the organic phosphates that function as inhibitors of choline esterase also inhibit this kind of reaction.

With Krampitz I published (Fox & Krampitz, 1964) the accelerated conversion in aqueous solution in the presence of proteinoids of glucose to CO_2 through glucuronic acid, which was identified *per se.*

Orgel: What pH is that?

Fox: The conversion of glucose is now known to be a two-step reaction and possibly only the second step is catalyzed. According to Dr. Hardebeck's (1967) recent studies the optimum of decarboxylation of glucuronic acid is pH 8.

Miller: What was the yield of CO_2 from the glucose?

Fox: It is very small.

Miller: Like what?

Fox: In 24 hours, something less than a percent conversion of glucose.

McElroy: But you do get stoichiometry?

Fox: In one of the fastest reactions, $10\,\mu$ moles of oxaloacetic acid was decarboxylated per μ mole of thermal polymer in less than one hour (Rohlfing, 1967). Conversions were typically 80 to 90 percent complete. In the case of glucose, stoichiometry was not attained.

Miller: Substantially less than one percent or just about a percent?

Fox: In the case of glucose, somewhat less, depending of course on conditions.

Margulis: Do all these proteinoids give you all these activities?

Fox: The proteinoids are varied, depending upon the amino acid content. So I will attempt to approach that question systematically. To answer, I will need to cite other reactions.

The conversion of pyruvic acid to acetic acid and CO_2 was first published by Krampitz and Hardebeck at the University of Bonn in 1966, and has been published in detail (Hardebeck et al, 1967). The Lineweaver-Burk plot has been shown for that reaction both in our laboratory (Durant & Fox, 1966) and in Krampitz' laboratory. Definite evidence of a proteinoid-pyruvic acid interaction as part of the mechanism has thus been obtained.

Miller: And the yield on that reaction?

Fox: In one of these cases (Hardebeck et al, 1967) the pyruvic acid is about 20 percent converted to CO_2.

Horowitz: What time and temperature?

Fox: In the decarboxylation of pyruvic acid, the temperature was 37° C, and the reactions were terminated at 24 hours; for oxaloacetic acid, 30°C, and one to two hours or less.

Orgel: How does the rate compare with that for an unpolymerized mixture at the same pH?

Fox: Roughly twenty times as much in the decarboxylation of pyruvic acid (Durant & Fox, 1966). The upper curve (Fig. 32) shows the effect of a 2:2:1-proteinoid at 37° C. The control is at the bottom, curve ii; the amino acids prior to polymerization are represented by iii; the hydrolyzates fall in these experiments at just about the same relatively low level as in iii.

Rich: When you say "aseptic," what do you mean? How did you do that?

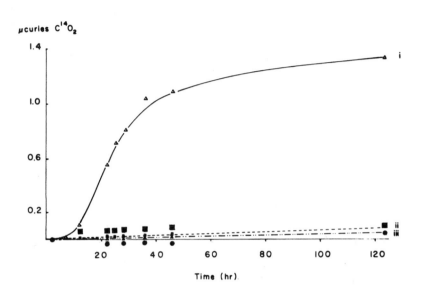

Figure 32. Effect of thermal proteinoid in aqueous solution on decarboxylation of 1-C^{14}-pyruvic acid. (i) Progress curve; (ii) spontaneous control; (iii) mixture of amino acids.

Fox: The amino acids are first tested *per se* to make sure they don't have any activity, or as little as is indicated in Figure 32. Then they are Millipore-filtered and heated at 170° C. They are then dialyzed aseptically to purify them somewhat, or aseptically in any other fractionation. At each stage of the process the presence or absence of microorganisms is monitored, and we are cautious about that possibility despite heating of the amino acids because we have learned in the course of this work that in some cases one can heat proteins to very high temperatures without inactivating them. This is contrary to some of the general understanding of the stability of proteins, but we have found in the literature and in our own studies that some proteins can withstand very high temperatures for quite long times. For example, the α-amylase of *Bacillus stearothermophilus* in aqueous solution loses 29 percent of its activity after 20 hours at 85° C (Manning & Campbell, 1961).

McElroy: Hexokinase.

Fox: Yes, there are others. One needs to be careful about the possibility, not only of keeping out microorganisms, but of being sure that there were no enzymes that might have been introduced along with the amino acids in organisms that didn't survive to be counted. In fact, I think it is fair to say that the results would have come out more rapidly than they did if it were not for these demanding precautions.

Orgel: What buffers are used in this experiment?

Fox: For pyruvate, tris buffer.

Orgel: Why does the reaction stop after one percent of the material is used up?

Fox: Do you mean why does it begin to become asymptotic?

Orgel: It becomes parallel to the control, more or less, after about one percent of the glucose is used up.

McElroy: Is it one percent? I thought the pyruvate was all used up here. Is that not correct?

Fox: Pyruvate was about 20 percent converted to CO_2, but was also converted to other products.

McElroy: Oh, I see, and then the pyruvate is all used up?

Fox: No, we cannot say that.

McElroy: If you take the proteinoid and wash it and start off that way, will it catalyze?

Fox: Yes, many are prepared through a step which involves washing with water. Unfractionated hydrolyzates have little or no activity so contaminants are not responsible.

The decarboxylation of oxaloacetic acid presents the kind of data which indicate that it is truly catalytic. Also, the conversion of oxaloacetic acid to pyruvic acid is favored by proteinoids that are rich in lysine but not by those that are acidic. The reverse is true for the pyruvic acid decarboxylation, so we think we begin to see a gross kind of specificity.

Miller: What is the ratio of the rate not catalyzed by the so-called proteinoid versus that catalyzed with the so-called proteinoid? The ratio or the rates—not yields this time.

Fox: Do you mean K values?

Miller: Yes. Is it a factor of ten, one hundred, a million? I am talking about the oxaloacetic case.

Fox: Ten to fifty.

Orgel: The last observation is particularly interesting, because Westheimer has shown that lysine residues of enzymes are important in decarboxylation reactions.

Sagan: Will you comment on that for those of us who are not familiar with Westheimer's work?

Orgel: Westheimer has shown that enzymatic decarboxylation of a ketoacid proceeds by formation of a Schiff-base with lysine. It is not histidine; it is lysine.

Fox: I think this makes a connected picture between the simple amino acids and polymers of amino acids, in that natural experiments could have led, conceptually, to various polymers of amino acids, some of which would be more active than others.

Kramer: Have you always used the conglomerate proteinoid for this kind of experiment?

Fox: No, in many cases we have used two, three, or five amino acids, et cetera.

Kramer: I mean so far as the overall catalytic activity is concerned, do you take fractions of the proteinoids?

Fox: We have done some fraction work, not published yet. When we look at the fractions, what we find, in general, is a low level of activity, of the order of activity we have been talking about here. This is activity for a number of substrates, and the kind of picture that emerges from this is one which can be applied to proteinoids or to proteins. Both protein and proteinoids increasingly appear to possess a structure that permits an array of specific activities due to a basic chemical polyfunctionality. Both kinds of poly-amino acid have a variety of chemically reactive groups, and the interactions of the individual groups in the macromolecule exponentialize this effect of variety. This is, then, an answer to Lynn's (Margulis) question.

Bada: Have you done any crystallographic studies?

Fox: We have not, no.

Bada: Has anyone?

Rich: On what?

Bada: On the proteinoids.

Rich: You mean powder patterns?

Bada: No, diffraction studies to determine if there is any tertiary structure.

Rich: They are not crystallizable. You are left with only powder patterns.

Fox: Let's not say, Alex, that they are not crystallizable. Let's say that they haven't been crystallized. Attempts have been made and, in essence, what you are saying is correct to date, perhaps.

Rich: If you treat this with pronase, what yield of individual amino acids do you get?

Fox: Dr. Nakashima (Fox & Nakashima, 1967) has been looking at this susceptibility much more closely recently. The yield of the different acids varies with the fractions———

Rich: Excuse me, if you start with DL, not with L alone—or maybe you don't normally start with DL, do you?

Fox: I think from the standpoint of your question, it makes little difference because we get many D residues in the polymer, even if we start with L's. There will be D's. Now you can ask the question, will pronase act on a polymer which has a sprinkling of D-amino acids in it? We know that the proteinoids are split by proteolytic enzymes, such as pepsin. Dr. Nakashima has prepared a simpler copolymer—the thermal copolymer of glutamic acid, glycine, and tyrosine. He has fractionated this polymer on DEAE-cellulose and he has studied its susceptibility to chymotrypsin and pronase. He finds that some fractions are very rapidly split by chymotrypsin, some rapidly by pronase, and other fractions very slowly. This work is in progress now.

Morrison: What is pronase?

Rich: It is a nonspecific proteolytic enzyme that will chew most, but not all, proteins down to amino acids.

Morrison: What is its source?

Rich: I think it comes from a mold.

Fox: Yes, from *Aspergillus.*

Margulis: Will it do this to the D-amino acids?

Rich: No, it won't touch the D-amino acids.

Fox: But evidently the presence in some of these polymers of a substantial proportion of D-amino acids does not interfere with a substantial proteolysis or peptidolysis.

Rich: I doubt if you are cleaving bonds between the D-amino acids. If you start with both D and L residues (half D and half L and they are randomly ordered in the chain) in principle you ought to liberate a quarter of the residues. This is why I asked. It would be nice to know what amino acids and in what proportions you actually liberated.

Horowitz: You'd liberate about one-quarter if all the bonds were peptidic bonds of the residues.

Rich: That is just the point!

Fox: Independent examination suggests that the linkages—nearly all—are peptides, except for imide bonds, which are well known to hydrolyze easily to peptide bonds (Hoagland & Fox, 1967).

If we can return to Table 5, the zinc salt of proteinoids will split ATP and ADP (Fox, 1965b). Various lysine-rich proteinoids have been found to carry out this reaction, but this is the one instance in which we cannot say that all the many preparations that have been examined show this ability (Durant & Fox, 1966).

Another catalysis reported by Dr. Oshima (1967) was the hydrolysis of p-nitrophenyl phosphate. This one is relatively powerful.

McElroy: All your proteinoids don't break down ATP—is that what you are saying?

Fox: No, two types of polymer do facilitate the breakdown of ATP. The transfer of phosphate to molecules other than water has, however, not been demonstrated.

Dr. Krampitz has reported transaminase activity, using α-ketoglutaric acid and urea to yield glutamic acid. When he employs a lysine-rich proteinoid in the presence of sufficient cupric ion, he gets the results but not with cupric ion alone nor with the proteinoid alone (Krampitz, G., 1967, personal communication).

This is our information at the present time on the catalytic activities.

Margulis: Do bugs eat your proteinoids?

Fox: Yes, that is one of the first tests that was made. *Lactobacillus plantarum* (at the time known as *Lactobacillus arabinosus*) used the proteinoids we fed them approximately 60 percent, as well as the metabolized bacterial peptone on which the stock cultures were maintained (Fox & Harada, 1960). At neutrality, "wild" cultures are often seen in the lab in 24 hours.

Figure 33 illustrates the fractionation of an amidated proteinoid on DEAE-cellulose. I am glad Dr. Morrison made the remarks that he did about *random,* because this is a word which can be very time-consuming, so I will just refer to his remarks. The question that arises is whether or not, in a condensation such as this, one gets a wildly disordered polymer. On fractionation on DEAE-cellulose, as shown here, Dr. Nakashima (Fox & Nakashima, 1967) has found that it is not wildly disordered. For *random,* we would expect a medium high horizontal line, and what we see are six major peaks, some of them quite symmetrical.

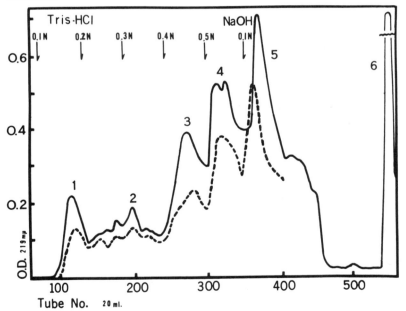

Figure 33. Elution pattern of amidated thermal 1:1:1-proteinoid from DEAE-cellulose.

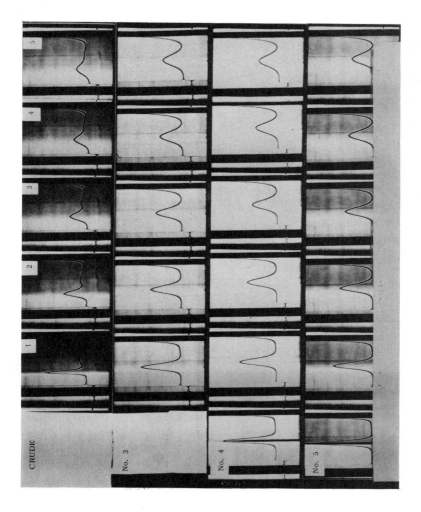

Figure 34. Schlieven patterns from peaks 3, 4, and 5 of Fig. 33 after further purification from Sephadex.

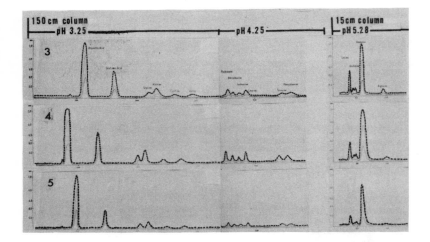

Figure 35a. Chromatograms of total hydrolyzates of peaks 3, 4, 5 of Fig. 33.

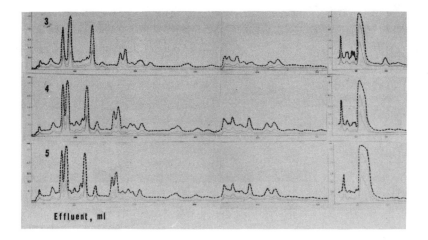

Figure 35b. Chromatograms of partial hydrolyzates of above using 20 times as much sample.

Rich: But this isn't a continuous gradient?

Fox: No, but a continuous gradient gives a similar picture.

Rich: That seems odd, because a discontinuous gradient should give you a new random hump each time you change the gradient, which is what you have, whereas a continuous gradient should not give you the same distribtuion. The two should be really quite different. What you are doing is essentially titrating the protein and pulling off each cluster. You do have a distribution, but it seems more clustered by virtue of using a discontinuous gradient.

Fox: The broken line is the first repetition of the fractionation in this mode and will give you some kind of an idea as to how repeatable this fractionation is on DEAE-cellulose. It has been done seven times.

In Figure 34 we have the Schlieren patterns from peaks 3, 4, and 5 after they have been further purified from Sephadex; the Schlieren patterns are 16 minutes apart, obtained at 47,000 rpm in a Model E ultracentrifuge. The crude fraction is at the top. You can see that there isn't much flattening of the individual peaks in this time. Peaks 3, 4, and 5 represent 37.5 percent of the total polymer.

Figure 35 is for peaks 3, 4, and 5 and presents the analyses graphically. The top three chromatograms are the amino acid analyses from the amino acid analyzer of peaks 3, 4, and 5 from DEAE-cellulose. There are some quantitative differences (which for example you can see in the leucine area), but mostly the differences are much smaller than the similarities we find between each of these fractions. We understand now that the fractionation could occur on the basis of carboxyl and amide content, which is different, but not greatly so (Fox & Nakashima, 1967).

From these analyses, we are led to conclude that the amino acid composition is relatively highly uniform throughout the entire polymer. The pattern obtained from the total hydrolyzate of the crude polymer is quite comparable to any of the three chromatograms at the top.

For fingerprinting, we have used partial hydrolysis and found on 2-dimensional chromatograms that we couldn't distinguish the partial hydrolyzates of peaks 3, 4, and 5 from the DEAE-cellulose column. We find that the amino acid analyzer column is the most sensitive device for distinguishing peptides and for running finger-prints of those available to us. These fingerprints, prepared as in-dicated, are found in the bottom three chromatograms, and they represent, in the original, approximately forty peaks. We can as-cribe fifteen of these to amino acids, leaving about twenty-five which presumably are peptides, with quite a number of amino acids per individual peptide on average. The degree of similarity between fractions 3, 4, and 5 of the original, as obtained from DEAE-cellulose, and as compared in partial hydrolyzates is then evident. This evidence leads to the suggestion that not only the compositions but the se-quences show a relatively high degree of uniformity throughout the entire polymer.

For a rigorous statement on this similarity or difference, we may have to do complete sequences; that kind of work is underway. However, we have one kind of datum in Table 7 which may help to describe the astonishing degree of selectivity indicated in the in-teractions of amino acids.

If we look at the unfractionated proteinoids and compare the total analysis versus the N terminal by the Sanger technique (Fox & Harada, 1960) and versus the G terminal by the Akabori-Bradbury hydrazinolysis technique (Fox & Harada, 1963), we get the kinds of figures represented here. For 2:2:1-proteinoid, if we condense the figures to aspartic acid, glutamic acid, and sixteen other amino acids—which are the basic-neutral and are referred to in Table 7 as BN—we find that the proportions in the total are quite different than they are at either end, which of course represent positions more feasible to analyze than are other positions. If the amino-acid types were randomly distributed, we should expect the composition to be the same in any one position as it is in the total composition. It is not. We explain this and the other results that I have been showing you on the basis that each amino acid, unlike a bead of a different color, has its own shape in space, its own distribution of electric charge, and it is reacting with a growing chain which has its own disbribution of amino acid residues. These are the selective forces that we can visualize at present and which seem to be quite powerful.

Table 7

Total N Terminal and C Terminal Analyses of Two Proteinoids

Substance	N Terminal %	Total %	C Terminal %
	2:2:1—Proteinoid		
Asp	6	71	1
Glu	46	11	8
BN	48	17	91
	2:2:3—Proteinoid		
Asp		50	28
Glu		12	1
BN		38	70

Key

Asp = aspartic acid
Glu = glutamic acid
BN = basic-neutral, or 16 of the amino acids

Burlingame: How big are those peptides in the chromatogram?

Fox: For the peaks from DEAE-cellulose, mean values are 4070, 5160, and 5800 by sedimentation analysis. For fingerprint peptides, I do not know.

Woese: Do you mean to say you don't have any N terminal methionine on these? This is, of course, a provocative question. (N terminal methionine is known to be the last amino acid in the chain coded by AUG in a given nucleic acid sequence, that is, signifying the "periods" in the genetic code.)

Fox: Seriously, we have bought some formylmethionine, and one of the experiments on the agendas in the lab includes use of formylmethionine with the other amino acids.

Miller: It seems to me that all you have established on this is the fact that the N terminal amino acid is frequently aspartic and glutamic.

Orgel: Particularly glutamic.

Miller: Yes, relative to any of the other sixteen amino acids in the mixture. It is not clear why you can then say that there is a substantial amount of nonrandom ordering of amino acids in this peptide chain.

Orgel: We think that glutamic acid undergoes ring closure and this prevents that formation of diketopiperazines, because the terminal carboxyl group ties up the amino group.

Fox: Your suspicion reads on our data. We have done comparative experiments in heating pyroglutamic acid with other amino acids, as compared to control experiments with glutamic acid, and the pyroglutamic acid———

Orgel: What is pyroglutamic?

Fox: α-pyrrolidone carboxylic acid. It reacts much faster than glutamic acid and, for this reason, we believe that part of the reaction mechanism indeed involves the pyroglutamic acid intermediate, a lactam (Fox & Harada, 1958).

Miller: But is there a substantial amount of nonrandomness within the interior of the chain? You showed nonrandomness on the ends, but is there a substantial amount on the interior?

Fox: Yes, I think the fingerprint patterns show that.

Miller: You show just a very small number of peaks. The sizes are very large. You don't know on what basis the peaks come out on the chromatograms at that spot.

Fox: There are about twenty-five peaks.

Miller: It is hard for me to understand how this is really evidence that these peaks represent individual peptides, and that there were substantial regions of nonrandomness within the chain.

Fox: What this does show is that the arrangement of the amino acid residues in the chain tends to be pretty much the same throughout the entire polymer.

Rich: Can you show us one of your fingerprints produced by tryptic breakdown of the polymers?

Fox: No, I don't have that here.

Rich: What copolymer did you use it on?

Fox: It was chymotrypsin, Alex (Rich), and also pronase. The copolymer there is composed of glutamic acid, glycine, and tyrosine, and this you can of course see is the reason for using chymotrypsin.

Rich: Oh, yes, but then even if you have a random mix, you ought to get discrete spots, because the total number of possibilities is small. The real test is to use a larger number of amino acids and see if you get discrete spots—whether, in fact, you get chymotryptic peptides. Instead of using an average of two or three (amino-acid residues) in the length, use, say, five.

Fox: But the size of the fragments obtained by proteolysis is not necessarily 2 or 3.

Rich: No, no, but an average. I am assuming the three amino acids were in equimolar ratios to begin with.

Fox: They were 3:3:1 in one case and in equimolar ratios in another case.

Rich: The point is, they are small; you would get discrete spots.

Fox: They are probably in the range of molecular weight 4000 to 8000, judging from bio-gel solutions.

Rich: No, I mean the chymotryptic peptides would be small. If chymotrypsin cleaves after every phenylalanine, you will produce a small number of molecules, but enough to give you discrete spots.

Fox: Providing there is a regular distribution of the amino residues.

Rich: No, no; assuming a random distribution you are trying to test whether there is an internal ordering. What I am saying is that the real test of that is to begin with a larger number of amino acids and then do a tryptic or chymotryptic digestion and see if you have a small number of spots. Using a large number of amino acids, you will always get a small number of spots, whether it is ordered or random because the enzymes can only break certain of the peptide bonds. Do you follow me?

Fox: Yes, I do follow you.

Rich: That would be a real test. If you still get discrete spots, then you are beginning to get something. This would imply that a large fraction of the polymer is composed of nonrandom peptides that travel together in the chromatogram.

Fox: I agree with you and, in fact, that kind of work is underway.

Orgel: Have you ever rerun the six peaks and seen them come out as single peaks?

Fox: Not on DEAE-cellulose.

Orgel: That would be a very interesting experiment.

Fox: We have done it on Sephadex, not on DEAE-cellulose, and then they come out again as single peaks implying each peak is composed of a relatively homogeneous fraction.

Sulston: Have you looked at the small products of the polymerization?

Fox: Do you mean what passes through the dialysis membrane, the diffusates?

Sulston: Yes.

Fox: There is trouble with that word because some years ago <u>dialysate</u> was used in a sense opposite to that in which it is used now. I wanted to be sure we understood it the same. The answer is essentially no. We have collected some of these fractions, particularly from the synthesis of a radioactive proteinoid, but we haven't untangled them.

Sulston: What are your recent best yields with the polymerization process? What proportion of the amino acids added goes into nondialyzable material?

Fox: I can answer that in a positive rather than negative way: How much polymer do we recover? Typically, under the conditions that we usually use, 10 to 40 percent of amino acids added are converted to polymer. The high yields are obtained when various phosphates, including solid tricalcium phosphate, are added to the reaction mixture.

I might mention one other development. We have been finding within the last year and a half that instead of these relatively high proportions, we can use much smaller proportions of aspartic acid to glutamic and then get yields of polymers which are 3 to 5 percent. We have done this with equimolar proportions of all eighteen amino acids. The product has less than 5 percent aspartic acid, less than 5 percent glutamic acid, less than 10 percent lysine. This composition answers some of the kinds of structural questions that have arisen for some people. These have, however, been answered earlier, but in this case the question doesn't arise. The question of a poly-aspartic acid core, for example, simply doesn't arise with a polymer that has less than 5 percent aspartic acid in it.

The equimolar proteinoids are of particular interest since some of them mimic the composition of histones. We have been studying the binding of polynucleotides with them and learning something about the boundary conditions, or which ones of these will bind with polynucleotides. They have also notable effects with TMV-RNA (Schwartz & Fox, 1967).

Sulston: Have you taken fingerprints of these?

Fox: Not yet.

Non-Nucleic Acid Information Carriers

Horowitz: Alex (Rich), why don't you say something about nucleic acid now?

Rich: All right. Supposing we had to choose a genetic polymer to serve as an information carrier to genetic systems and we chose one at random. What properties would we look for? One property is simply the hydrogen bonding between the nitrogenous bases such as adenine and thymidine which gives rise to complementarity. If you ask, why are adenine (A) and thymidine (T) pairs used, the typical textbook explanation is that they are used because they fit. By this I mean that if you rotate these two bases around the central axis of the helical molecule, the glycosidic bonds fall on top of each other. There is a twofold axis for the glycosidic bonds, which means that the bond can be found on either chain of DNA. Like-wise, the same is true for the guanine (G) and cytosine (C) pair. This has given rise to complementarity, which I call geometric com-plementarity. It permits us to build up a large, regular polynucleo-tide in which specific hydrogen bonds hold these two chains to-gether. The polymer is specific because only with this hydrogen bonding can this geometrical requirement be satisfied. That is our view on DNA. Furthermore, the molecule you build up in this manner is stable because of the base values, and so on. Why does G choose C? If it tried to choose another nitrogenous base, it wouldn't fit into the polynucleotide. Each of the bases has donors of hydrogen bonds and receptors. There is a large number of other possible pairs of hydrogen bonds between pyrimidines and purines, but none of them will grow into the molecule. That has been our view of DNA.

That is only part of the story. About four years ago a student and I directed our attention to the following problem: What can we learn by looking at the association of these molecules in solution, not as polymers where they are constrained by geometry, but as monomers in which they are not stacked? These molecules are flat; they are stabilized. In an aqueous solution, by stacking, we are essentially squeezing out the water between the purines and pyrimidines. However, in a nonaqueous solvent, they do not stack and so we can ask ourselves, "Will they form hydrogen bonds?"

If the pyrimidines and purines are put in a nonaqueous solvent such as chloroform or carbon tetrachloride, the infrared absorption spectrum (unlike that in aqueous solution) allows us to look at the NH stretching vibrations, which tell us something about hydrogen bonding. If we look at these, we get the following (Fig. 36) infrared spectrum of a derivative of adenine.

These spectra show us that at this low concentration there is no evidence of self-association, that is, no evidence of hydrogen bonding between the adenine residues or between the two uracil or thymine residues. Why don't the bases hydrogen bond with each other? They *can* hydrogen bond with each other—and I will shortly show you that they do in solid state. Both the uracil and the thymine residues can hydrogen bond with themselves because each has both a donor and a receptor site but, in fact, they do not. However, when you mix uracil or uracil derivatives and thymine, adenine or their derivatives together in a 1:1 mixture you get this (Fig. 37). The same sort of case may be made for the guanine-cytidine pairs— or their respective derivatives. On this experiment we compared guanosine and cytosine. The observed spectrum of uracil and adenine derivatives is quite different from the calculated (the calculated is

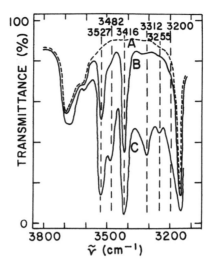

Figure 36. Infrared spectrums of 9-ethyladenine in deuterochloroform from 3100 to 3800 cm^{-1}. Path length of solutions was 1 mm: silica cells used. (A) Solvent spectrum; (B) 9-ethyladenine at a concentration of 0,022M; (C) 9-ethyladenine saturated at 21°C (near 0.1M).

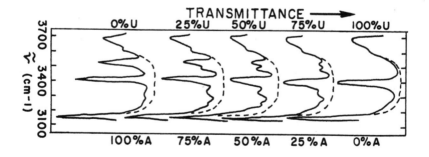

Figure 37. Infrared spectrums of mixtures of 1-cyclohexyluracil and 9-ethyladenine in deuterochloroform solution from 3100 to 3700 cm^{-1}. Path length was 1 mm; silica cells were used. Dashed lines represent solvent and cell background; solid lines represent actual spectrums. Total concentration in all cases was 0.022M but varying ratios (mole percent) of the uracil and adenine derivatives are shown.

simply the sum of the two). There are decreases in the intensities of these bands, and there are increases in the intensity of the other bands. These are typical bands associated with hydrogen bonding.

McElroy: Alex, what temperature were these?

Rich: This is room temperature and quite dilute solution (0.001 M). Let me just say that the reason we looked into these solutions was because in our crystallographic studies of the past five or six years on derivatives of all the four bases (G, C, A, T) we have already studied the peculiar property of co-crystallizing. The bases crystallize together and form hydrogen-bonded dimers in the solid state, many of which are the same as the G-C pairs discussed earlier. We have done structures of five dimers in which the monomers all are held together by three hydrogen bonds, as in the DNA molecule. A large number of adenine-thymine or adenine-uracil residues form not only hydrogen bonds of the Watson-Crick type but also hydrogen bonds involving the imidazole nitrogen, N_7.

Supposing we ask, "What is the association constant in liters per mole at 25°, the enthalpy in kilocalories per mole, and the entropy change for these different reactions?" The adenine-adenine dimerization has an association constant of 3.1; uracil-uracil, 3.6. But adenine-uracil dimerization has an association constant of 100. This association is substantially different. In general, these monomers will associate with each themselves, but they do so weakly. This molecule—the mixed pair of adenine and uracil—will form two hydrogen bonds, but these two are more energetic than those in the self-association, even though these all have a normal geometry. We have a geometric reason for why the association constant is so different in the two types of pairs. It has something to do with the electronic distribution in the molecules themselves. This tells us, then, that adenine and uracil like each other and associate selectively in this way instead of each with itself. We have evidence for this sort of pairing at dilutions of about 5 X 10^{-4} M.

So what we have seen is that the adenine and thymine (or uracil) strongly associate; the guanine and cytosine strongly associate. Since we have data on all these molecules in the same solvent, let's analyze the cross reactions, say guanine with adenine (see right).

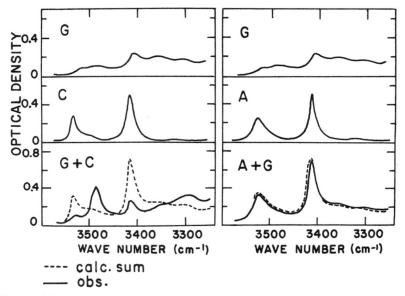

---- calc. sum
—— obs.

Figure 38. Infrared spectra plotted for 2′, 3′-benzylidine-5′-trityl derivatives of guanosine (G) and cytidine (C), and of 9-ethyladenine (A) at a concentration of 0.0009M (path length 2.5 cm.). Dashed line is the calculated spectrum representing the sum of the upper two spectra obtained if the molecules did not interact. The solid line is the observed sum when these two solutes are mixed and in the solution at a concentration of 0.0008M.

Take guanine and adenine, mix them together, and we get no enhancement at all—as if they didn't know the other molecule was there. This is quite different from the observed versus the calculated IR spectra of guanine and cytosine (see left). Each of these has a donor and receptor. They all can form cyclic dimers with hydrogen-bonding, but there is something about the electronic distribution in the individual molecules that tends to form pairs (A + T or A + U and G + C), which gives rise to complementarity of the monomers. I call this an electronic complementarity to distinguish it from the geometric complementarity necessary for building the helices in the nucleic acids.

There is good reason to believe that this kind of interaction can also be experimentally demonstrated in aqueous as well as chloroform solution. For example, if, as Ernst Küchler (Tuppy & Küchler, 1964) has, you fix an adenine derivative to a column and pour a mixture of thymine or uracil and cytosine monomers over it, the cytosine monomer will elute first, the uracil (or thymine) will elute second. If you then fix guanine residues, just the opposite happens: The adenine elutes first. In other words, one can demonstrate with elution off a column in an aqueous solvent specific retention of bases in a way consistent with the previous data.

We have thermodynamic data for the guanine-cytosine series which again give similar enhancement of this type. These data imply, I think, that we should modify our concepts of the kind of requirements needed for being an information carrier in a genetic system. By "information carrier" I mean the ability to store information, replicate the information, and ultimately read it out. As the data I presented shows, these particular molecules—purine and pyrimidine base pairs—are suited to be information carriers not only by virtue of their geometry but also by virtue of their intrinsic properties. My feeling is that this particular set of molecules (nucleic acid derivatives) won out (in the evolutionary scheme). Although they are ubiquitous in terrestrial life I don't believe they are unique. That is, I think other molecules could be used to form other polymers which could be used as information carriers for living systems. I think now we even have a way of looking for them. Using chemical methods, we could make polymers that have a built-in complementarity, both geometric and electronic. Although it is relatively easy to figure out the requirements for geometric complementarity, I think it is rather more difficult to find out what it is that will give rise to electronic complementarity.

This can't really be handled by theoretical chemistry, largely because the incremental energies involved are very small and, therefore, are lost in the approximations used to make calculations of this type. Nonetheless, I think it would be amusing to make a chemical system of complementary polymers based on monomers that are not nucleic acid derivatives, simply to demonstrate that it can be done. That another system is possible might have relevance, if not to biology on this planet then perhaps to another.

Morrison: Aren't you implying sort of a second property of complementarity? The first is the pair-forming with the correct pair. The second is a high ratio of correct pair-forming to self association or to incorrect association. You are talking about this ratio of differences.

Rich: What I am saying is that we see in the actual fact of base-pairing a kind of synergism between two different effects—geometrical and intrinsic—which can be isolated and studied quite separately.

Morrison: But it seems to me that this is requiring too much. This property is certainly desirable for information storage but is by no means necessary.

Rich: That we don't know. I follow your point.

Morrison: Intersymbol reaction only reduces the efficiency of the symbol. In English there is a great deal of redundancy; in Chinese, less; in Greek, still more. G-U (guanine-uracil) is not very efficient here, but it works.

Rich: Aren't you saying that you can build into your information-carrying system a kind of stability by other means? Supposing this property of electronic complementarity did not exist—I presume this would mean that DNA would melt at lower temperatures. Maybe you could compensate for that.

Let me just make a little statement about DNA. Assume it looks like a ladder. It is a molecule in the state of metastable equilibrium. By controlling the ionic environment, one can open or close it. There are adhesive forces—the hydrogen bonding between bases and the stacking interactions which are sort of van der Waals interactions of the entire fit. The H bonds tend to hold the polymer together and the van der Waals interaction is a big force driving it apart.

I think you need just that kind of a balance for a molecule of this type. Failing to have this kind of supplement to the cohesive force, something else would have to achieve this balance. What I am unable to estimate is the magnitude of the electronic contribution relative to that of the other cohesive forces. What you are saying is that if the intrinsic cohesion were not there, and we had only a sort of geometry to go with, we would have to do something else. I don't know to what extent the replacement of the intrinsic cohesion forces by something else might modify the chemistry of the system, but I think it might.

Morrison: I would suggest you would have to have a run of ten A's (adenines) to be a codon instead of———

Rich: That is assuming that each A has an informational contribution. I am not disagreeing with you, I am just unable to assess the magnitude of it.

Morrison: I agree, but looking at information systems, if I am to bring it down to the most efficient phase, then I need every symbol to be there, and it helps very much not to have self-association and to be able to substitute one triplet for the next without worrying about what is next to it. I can get information for every triplet, but if I have to keep saying a long string of letters, then I know that whole long string will not occur even by the local association, because the entropy will beat the energy———

Rich: What you are assuming, then, is that given long strings of A's and U's, you accrue an increment that makes up for this. I can conceive of molecules where you might not. In other words, I can conceive of a molecule where you might have a kind of anticatalysis, about which we talked before, where things would push in the other direction. But I agree with you, one doesn't have to have it as an implicit; after all, we have gone along for a dozen years thinking it wasn't there, and we just found it lately. No hole has been filled.

McElroy: Alex, would you care to comment now on what you think are the selective factors that bring us to this genetic system?

Eglinton: Excuse me, I wonder if I could just take up one point? It concerns selectivity of association and whether systems involving

units other than the purine and pyrimidine bases are possible. We
have done some work in this area. May I draw on the board, and
then we can go back to the genetics?

For a long time, we, too, have been thinking along the lines just
discussed and intended to do similar experiments some years ago
but didn't get around to them. Anet and Muchowski (1962) noted
that *meta*nitrophenol is dimeric in a nonpolar organic solvent (such
as carbon tetrachloride) and that the self-association is remarkably
strong. A 14-membered ring involving twin hydrogen bonds was
postulated. The *meta*methoxycarbonylphenol (Bennet et al, 1967;
Eglinton & Lawrie, 1967) showed similar behavior, and we have encountered (using infrared, ultraviolet, and nuclear magnetic resonance
techniques and also osmometry) the same phenomenon for other
meta-substituted phenols, the substituent group being acetyl (Fig.
39a), methoxyl, or aldehyde. Self-association persists to an unusual
extent in substituted phenols only where closure of a ring of hydrogen bonds is spatially favored. We extended our search to somewhat
bigger molecules. Thus ethyl coumarate (Fig. 39b) displays dimeric
association, presumably involving a 16-membered hydrogen-bonded
ring, down to about 0.3 mM in carbon tetrachloride solution. The
association is a good deal stronger than that of *meta*nitrophenol,
the reason very likely being that the energy gained by electron de-
localization through the system is considerable. I am not proposing
ethyl coumarate as another unit for DNA, but the observations show
what unusual hydrogen bond pairs are possible.

I have in mind, of course, that experiments of this type should be
performed with short lengths of synthetic polymer chains acting as
the "sugar phosphate" backbone to which have been attached units
of phenolic and other types. Interesting self-association phenomena
involving specific pairing, for example, should be observable. Certain
polymers could be expected to associate as double strands held together—as in DNA—by specific hydrogen bonds coded by the placing
of the particular units attached to the backbone.

Rich: Exactly.

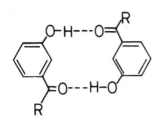

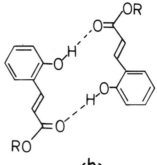

(a)   (b)

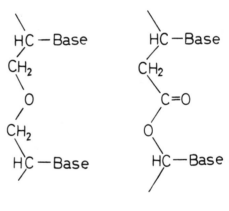

(c)

Figure 39. Hydrogen-bonded dimeric species postulated for solutions of (a) *meta*-hydroxyacetophenone and (b) ethyl coumarate (R=ethyl) in carbon tetrachloride; (c), (d), (e) Sections of single strands of doubly-stranded hypothetical DNA analogues.

Eglinton: Another thing we (Bennet et al, 1967; Eglinton & Lawrie, 1967) have been doing is to look for association that is dependent only on the right stereochemistry, without much regard for the electronic factors. We find this just doesn't work.

Rich: Aha—take note.

Eglinton: We have tried a number of systems, but one of the most suitable for study is a group of polyfunctional steroids. The rigid tetracyclic skeleton (Fig. 40a) provides a molecular framework that is almost ideal for the attachment of functional groups. Specific interactions between molecules can then be studied with some confidence in the relative stereochemical positions of the functional groups. Let us consider two types of functional group: An acidic group, —XH, and a basic group, —B (Eglinton, G., Skovac, F. Lawrie, & M. Martin-Smith, unpublished data). Simple bifunctional steroid molecules may self-associate in solution in a nonpolar solvent, as indicated diagramatically in Figure 40b; since the skeleton is almost rigid, the distances between the atoms of the groups —XH and —B are almost constant, and the molecules may pair precisely where steric factors such as protruding groups do not preclude it. Further, the X atom can be sufficiently based (e.g., oxygen where B becomes X of the XH group) for self-association of *bis* —XH molecules to occur as dimers, as in Figure 40c. This last type of self-association is not particularly effective unless the hydrogen-bonding capabilities of the XH protons can be more fruitfully utilized, for example, by association as oligomers in more concentrated solutions.

The point I wish to make here is that the bifunctional steroids may be constructed with the right geometry for pairing, that is, so that the interacting groups stick out in an appropriate way. However, the rigid hydrocarbon framework does not permit any shift of electrons through it from group —B to group —XH or vice versa. Also the groups can be placed so far apart on the framework that there can be little direct polar effect across the intervening space, except through the intermediacy of solvent cage. More experiments are needed, but it seems that the steric requirements are not the only ones: The concomitant shifting of electronic charge around a fairly

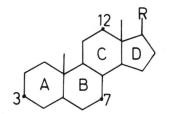

(a)

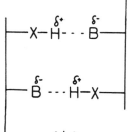

(b)

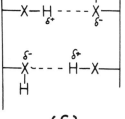

(c)

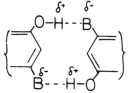

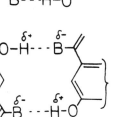

B =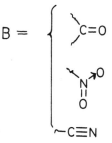

(d)

Figure 40. (a) Sterane skeleton (rings lettered A through D; R=alkyl side chain); (b) and (c) schematic representation of dimeric species (self-pairing). Vertical line represents molecular skeleton: XH, acidic group (proton donor) and B, basic site (proton acceptor); (d) schematic representation of dimeric species formed by certain phenols and enols.

conductive ring of atoms and bonds, as in the phenols already cited, is also important. Other types of compound can be similarly classified (Fig. 40d). Thus dimeric self-association of the nucleic acid bases is of the self-contained, electron-releasing, accepting type, as shown for thymine in Figure 41a.

Mixed association—unsymmetrical pairing—is important in the current theory of DNA coding. Two principal types are shown in simplified diagrams in Figure 41b and c. We have sought without success examples in the steroid series where X and X′ are hydroxyl, and B and B′ are dimethylamino (NMe_2), hydroxyl (OH), and carbonyl (CO), the groups being spaced far enough apart on the skeleton to prevent intramolecular association. However, we did encounter what appeared to be examples of the type in Figure 41b in another series. Thus, perfluoroacetone hydrate in carbon tetrachloride solution shows a marked association with certain diethers which we ascribe to complexes of the type shown in Figure 41d. Again, but-2-yne-1, 4-diol associates more strongly with 1,3-bis-dimethylaminopropane than with other bis-dimethylamino derivatives of the same series; the complex can be tentatively represented as in Figure 41 e. A marked association was also observed with 1,2-bis-(2-pyridyl) ethane.

Mixed pairing between small molecules seems to be rather less common than self-pairing. It is nonetheless very important—witness the mixed pairing of the individual nucleic acid bases—and the factors bringing about preferential mixed pairing merit detailed study. Pairing itself occurs readily between relatively rigid molecules having the right stereochemistry, lone pair orientation, mobility, and polarity. Contrary factors include extensive flexibility, steric hindrance, and the presence of alternative intramolecular hydrogen-bonding possibilities.

We discussed self-association of bile acid derivatives (polyhydroxy compounds such as methyl desoxycholate)based on the skeleton in Figure 40a in addition to the phenolic compounds already mentioned. The derivatives that showed marked association phenomena in carbon tetrachloride solution (Fig. 41) had two, or better three, hydroxyls attached, pointing downward from the lower face of a fused ring system; for example, methyl cholate, i.e., methyl 3α, 7α, 12α—trihydroxycholanate (Fig. 42). The hydroxyls are spaced too far

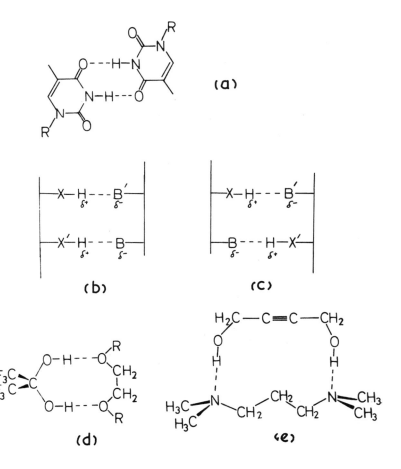

Figure 41. (a) The dimeric species of thymine (N-substituted); (b) and (c) schematic representation of mixed pairing; (b) shows unsymetrical pair—a diacid and a dibase and (c) unsymetrical pair of different monoacid monobases. X and X′ may be the same or different basic sites; (d) and (e) hydrogen-bonded complexes postulated for mixed solutions in carbon tetrachloride of (d) perfluoracetone hydrate and certain ethers, and (e) but-2-yne-1.4-diol and 1,3-bis-dimethylamino-propane.

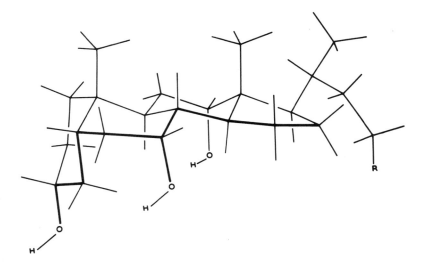

Figure 42. Dreiding model of a molecule of methyl 3, 7, 12 - trihydroxy-cholanate ($R = CO_2$ Me) or 3α, 7α, 12α- trihydroxy - 5β-cholestane ($R=CH_2CHMe_2$). The Carbon-oxygen bonds are in a fixed orientation parallel to one another and perpendicular to the plane through rings B, C, and D.

apart on the carbon skeleton for intramolecular hydrogen bonding to occur. For such compounds, plots of the ratio (M/M) of apparent (M) to true (M) molecular weight against molar concentration (osmometric data) show a steep rise with increasing concentration, leveling off to a value of around 3 or 4. The equilibria are probably not simple, but we suggest that the data can be explained by cluster formation involving about four molecules assembled with the polar (a) faces bearing the rigidly oriented hydroxyl groups facing inward. The ester group in the side chain has little effect. Within such a cluster (Fig. 43a), unstrained arrangement involving energetically favored sequences of interlocked hydrogen bonds are possible, hydroxyls of one molecule alternating with those from another (Fig. 43b). This unusual behavior in nonpolar solvents of the methyl esters of cholic acid, desoxycholic, hyododesoxycholic, et cetera, differs markedly from the helical, polymeric, complex formation described by Blow and Rich (1960). There is a similarity, however, in that both phenomena illustrate the considerable hydrogen-bonding power of this type of molecule.

Rich: Do you know the work on deoxycholate?

Eglinton: That is the next thing I'm coming to.

Rich: Deoxycholate is used by biologists because it pulls off lipid, and in about 1956 I was walking through the lab and a technician had been making deoxycholate solution and he stood there with his mouth open because between two beakers was an enormous thread. That intrigued me. What happens is that the deoxycholate molecules titrate very sharply at about pH 7, add a proton forming a hydrogen bond, and then form a helical complex, 40 Å in diameter and very long. Deoxycholate molecules have the capacity, then, to bind not only with themselves to form a helical array but also to combine with a large number of other molecules.

Eglinton: And to make clathrates.

Rich: Well, they are not clathrates in the normal sense because these other materials are on the outside of the helix. They are not cages.

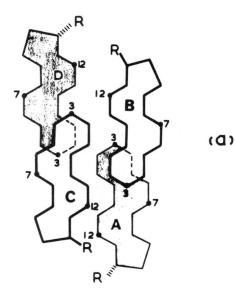

(a)

(b)

Figure 43. Schematic illustration of a cluster of four molecules (A through D) of the compounds illustrated in Fig. 42. The three hydroxyls' positions 3α, 7α, and 12α of each molecule are oriented so that two chains (A7, B7, A3, B12, C3, and D12, and A 12, B3, C12, D3, C7, and D7) of interlocked intermolecular hydrogen bonds are possible. The two hydroxyls at the end of the chains remain free in this tetramer. Larger clusters may be possible. The arrangements shown may be representative of the unusually stable molecular aggregates considered to be present in solutions of steroids possessing the 5β configuration and two or more hydroxyls in positions 3, 7, and 12 on the α face. (Reproduced with permission from *Nature*) (b) Schematic illustration of how the hydroxyls of one molecule could interbond with those of another.

Eglinton: I was referring to the rather insoluble solid clathrate complexes—the choleic acids—which can be made by mixing desoxycholic acid with a wide variety of compounds.

Rich: Yes, indeed.

Eglinton: Returning to our studies of solution of methyl cholate and related compounds in carbon tetrachloride and chloroform, I feel sure that we are not dealing with the high molecular weight, helical polymers of the type you reported for the solutions of desoxycholic acid in water. Our data suggest that not more than about four molecules cluster together.

Rich: Yes, those are different.

Eglinton: Our studies are all in relatively nonpolar solvents such as carbon tetrachloride. What I am trying to bring out is this: A rigid molecule such as 3α, 7α, 12α-trihydroxy-5β-cholestane (see Fig. 42) has hydroxyl groups held in definite positions. This rigid array of hydroxyls brings about strong intermolecular association with a like molecule. An ester group substituent on the side chain, for example, as in methyl cholate has little effect on the association, since it is wiggling about in space and is not held in the right position. If the hydrogen bonds are indeed interlocked as in Figure 43b, then energy may be gained by electron displacement through the array of hydrogen bonds. Mixed pairing of such molecules may be possible, but we have not as yet encountered it.

Returning to the aromatic compounds favored by the electron displacements consequent upon the hydrogen bonding, I subscribe to your (Rich's) points: That other genetic codes are possible, and that the requirements for the operation of such codes are electronic as well as steric. Infrared measurements made in carbon tetrachloride or chloroform solutions are one way to investigate the operation of the potential units. Of course we must still add the proviso that carbon tetrachloride is very different from water!

Rich: Yes, I know, but it is the only place you can do these studies. Also, they are relevant. If you ask, "What is the environment like inside DNA?" the answer is, "It is just like carbon tetrachloride." It is a completely nonaqueous environment full of polyelectrons.

Eglinton: Many biological reactions probably take place in close association with lipid, so that again this is a valid area of work, although it is very difficult to convince an organic chemist of this.

Relationship Between Amino Acid and Nucleic Acid Polymers

McElroy: I am just wondering if Alex (Rich) wants to speculate a little bit on the origin of the first moment of this system. How did selective factors select for the code?

Rich: I am only guessing, of course. My guess is that the simplest idea is that of a singlet code: Two digits, which are plenty. With a singlet code, one could have a high degree of molecular complexity, not life in the full sense. One could consider the change to doublets or triplets to be a kind of large mutational alteration.

I believe the critical step in this is the formation of what was essentially a primitive activating enzyme (some catalyst that adds amino acids to nucleotide polymers; see Fig. 28) rather along the lines that I talked about before. I think that the thing to do chemically is, first of all, to find the conditions for complementary polymerization of polynucleotides. I think it is easy to make polymers of one strand, and I don't think it will be too hard to make them in a complementary fashion.

McElroy: I wouldn't argue about the chemistry. I was wondering what moved things ahead.

Rich: I think I can see a few discontinuous jumps. Forming life is an improbable event, but the only plausible mechanism for getting it to originate is if you don't cluster improbabilities on top of each other. Each event that is improbable must be isolated from the other improbabilities so that you don't have an infinitely small probability.

Let's assume there is a primitive readout system (see Fig. 28). The first improbable event is the formation of a sequence of amino acids, using this statistical readout (whose sequence depends more or less precisely on the nucleotide sequence) which reinforces the predominant reading out. This means, in effect, that if you get, for example, aspartate coupling with UMP, you get an activating enzyme (an amino acid sequence) function (this particular sequence tends to catalyze more or less preferentially the reaction between aspartate and UMP). You are now beginning to translate randomly assembled polynucleotide information into detailed sequences; that is, they are read properly. Most of them are meaningless but the next improbable step, for example, after the activating enzyme, is to make a sort of primitive polymerase.

McElroy: I accept all the chemistry you say and the probability of events, but do you object to the chance occurrence of an important catalytic process which gives you a big jump? Now you associate with the amino acid sequence your polynucleotides.

Rich: I am happy to do it. I am willing to do it with amino acids, providing that the catalytic unit is very small.

McElroy: That is what I am saying.

Rich: If you can show me a dimer or trimer that is catalytically active, splendid, let's use it. If you are going to show me an octamer, then the chances of making very much of it seems rather small.

McElroy: If the sequence is catalytic, you don't need to make much; that is the whole point.

Rich: But you do. It has to be something that is common, because you have no way of replicating it.

McElroy: Let's take that step right there. The way I am going to replicate it is exactly the way you have given it, because as you now have it, the anticodon and the polynucleotides will line up through electronic association. This is exactly the way you argue for the polynucleotides. Now you make a polynucleotide that has the correct sequence already, and that takes off and replicates.

Orgel: This is a theory that has been much discussed. The difficulty is the absence of experimental support. There is no evidence that we know of at the moment for the kind of specific interaction which would permit amino acids to order a nucleotide.

McElroy: Then, would you mind telling me how tRNA recognizes the activating enzyme if it isn't through the anticodon recognition?

Rich: Oh, sure.

Orgel: That (the activating enzyme) is a completely formed enzyme. We are talking about a few amino acids determining the sequence of nucleotides.

McElroy: You mean to say transfer RNA is not recognizing a triplet in the activating enzyme?

Orgel: I don't think so.

Rich: It is doing more than that.

Sulston: Why is the transfer RNA so complicated?

McElroy: I could say why is any enzyme so complicated?

Sulston: It has to recognize the whole chain.

McElroy: I thought Dunnell in his *Nature* paper did some beautiful calculations on the electronic configurations in the anticodon———

Orgel: I am talking about experiments. I know of no case where anyone has demonstrated a specific interaction between amino acids and bases. There are specific interactions between bases and bases but none between amino acids and bases.

McElroy: Bases and polynucleotides.

Orgel: Bases and bases is what Alex (Rich) has been talking about.

McElroy: He has been talking about amino acids and polynucleotides. I can give you references. I was thinking of Dunnell's work.

Rich: These are calculations.

McElroy: He has also done some experiments.

Rich: What were the experiments?

McElroy: Showing how a polyphenylalanine will bind with poly-adenlic acid. You get some specificity.

Rich: I haven't read this.

McElroy: I thought it was in the *Nature* paper. I may have mis-read it.

Rich: If it had calculations in it, I probably turned it over. Leslie (Orgel) can speak to this more authoritatively, but most of the calculations in this field are not worth much.

McElroy: But let me ask you this. How does tRNA recognize an activating enzyme?

Rich: It probably has a recognition site which, I suspect, is distinct from the anticodon site. That is my guess.

McElroy: It is a polynucleotide-amino acid complex.

Rich: Oh, there is no doubt that proteins figuratively read poly-nucleotides. They do it all the time—DPN and God-knows-what.

Orgel: But they don't do it this way.

McElroy: Which way?

Orgel: They don't do it, so far as we know, by a particular amino acid recognizing a particular nucleotide.

Rich: I suspect there is an active site in which a large number of amino acids essentially form an enzymatically active site and nucleo-tides go in. I have tried to build these sites. If you postulate that the polynucleotide coming into an activating enzyme is stacked—which is mainly a poor assumption—but if you postulate that, then you ask yourself,"How many ways in a structural sense are there that a protein can recognize this, and how would you construct the complementary site?" It is a rather interesting nontrivial exercise. At one point, I thought I had a good solution involving the aromatic amino acids: Because they give you that built-in 3.4 Å spacing, I concluded that this was no solution. The aromatic amino acids may still be used but they cannot be the sole reading site for nucleotide polymerization. One has to bring in other residues.

McElroy: I have been impressed with the homogeneity of the tRNA's—of the five examples that we have reasonable data on—except for the anticodon site. I don't see a great many dissimilarities between these five.

Rich: They are very similar. There is no doubt that they are quite similar in structure.

McElroy: Therefore, I am forced to the conclusion that the bases of the anticodon seem to be of primary importance for initial recognition of the activating enzyme for a particular amino acid.

Margulis: That is not so.

Horowitz: There is evidence against that. The activating enzymes for the same amino acid from different species don't always recognize the tRNA's from a given species. [These experiments are based on the idea that the code is universal: The codon-anticodon that determine the amino acid is the same for both species. Thus the code of recognition of the activating enzyme for the different transfer RNA's must lie in some other portion of the molecule, that is, in a portion of the molecule that is different for the different species.]

Margulis: You can change the anticodon and get a different amino acid put in.

Orgel: Repressors are conclusive evidence against this. You take Brenner repressor, which is derived———

Margulis: That is a different set of experiments. You change the anticodon and you get the amino acid put in.

Rich: Oh no, no, no, that is a different experiment. You change the amino acid and show that it is still read. That is a different experiment.

Margulis: But the anticodon is recognizing messenger RNA, and that is not the site involved in amino acid activating enzyme.

Rich: What they did there was change an amino acid after it had been activated, and they showed that it read as it was initially, but that is a different problem. There is no hard proof. People have made oligonucleotides that are complementary to the anticodon and they have asked, "Will they interferé with activation?" These are indirect experiments and their conclusions point to the idea that the activating enzyme reads at a different site, but not in a hard fashion.

Orgel: I think there is one relevant experiment. You take a tRNA which is supposed to accept one amino acid and you modify the anticodon. It continues to accept the original amino acid but puts it in the wrong place. This, unless I am mistaken, is what happens in the case of the tyrosine repressor which Brenner isolated.

Rich: Anyhow, it is not clear.

McElroy: Both things are important. I wouldn't want to argue that, but I am just saying that nucleotides do recognize amino acids.

Rich: There is no doubt of that, and how they do it is an interesting question. However, I don't think that is what happened at the beginning. I think other kinds of interactions went on.

McElroy: I don't know why catalysis impresses me so much, but I have always felt that something could get ahead and away from the crowd if you had catalysis to begin with, and I don't see that you can get that by starting off with a random polynucleotide.

Rich: I think a random polynucleotide will give you selection. If you have a good readout system you will get an activating enzyme. The big question is, "How do you get the readout system?" I don't know the answer to that. These are experiments to be done. I am not against catalysis, and I am not against using common polyamino acids as catalysts. The only trouble is that they have to be widespread. That is why I say a small number, a trimer, a tetramer. If you demand a large specific polymer, then the probability of its being there at the right time and place is small. If it is a small molecule and rather generally distributed, fine.

McElroy: I way trying to find a system that had catalysis and that would immediately give you selection for the right nucleotide sequence, if you see what I mean. There is a big pressure for selecting that way.

Rich: But I thought maybe you were asking a rather more difficult question: "Did the whole system start up with the nucleic acids in the beginning or were there precursors which gave rise to a molecular complexity—not living but a kind of primitive information transfer—and it didn't make the grade before nature fell into this niche and found it was a good thing?" It would be very nice to know about this much more difficult question, but I think we won't know about it for a long time, if ever. I think we may work out a plausible historical sequence for this extant system, and then we may scratch our heads about other possible systems.

McElroy: That is good modern chemistry. I was worrying about how you selected for that right nucleotide sequence.

Rich: I think this might come out experimentally; for example, UMP may prefer glutamate for stereochemical reasons because they form some kind of complex and you get aminoacyl UMP. This is a reason for the selection.

McElroy: I think one could begin to make some arguments that by appropriate subunit associations—by secondary and tertiary structure alterations—one gets several different enzymes from essentially the same amino acid sequence. I think there are some examples of this now. It would be a good possibility that you have six major catalytic types which could be altered by adding tertiary structure to give you specificity. The main thing it seems to me, initially, is to select for that nucleotide sequence, which would give you your duplicating situation for coding these elementary systems, and then evolve the secondary and tertiary structure by adding additional amino acids in a number of ways.

On The Origin Of The Triplet Code

Horowitz: We now have a comment by Carl Sagan.

Sagan: I have only an amateur's interest, but I thought at least I might benefit by your responses; perhaps others here have been thinking along similar lines. I want to talk about the origin of the genetic code.

Alex Rich reiterated today some remarks he made a few years ago, that the present triplet genetic code may have itself evolved from a simpler code. It is certainly clear that the extremely elaborate molecular transcription apparatus of ribosomes, messenger RNA, activating enzymes, and sRNA, could not have arisen *de novo* from the primitive oceans, but must rather be the result of a long evolutionary process. Therefore, some much simpler code had to exist in primitive times—a remark which must hold true even if nucleic acids were not the repository of genetic information in the earliest organisms. It is very important to realize that the earliest transcription apparatus may have been extraordinarily crude. For example, codon degeneracy and ambiguity could have been rampant, so long as some polypeptides tended, in the presence of a given polynucleotide, to be synthesized more frequently than others.

While a typical enzyme may have hundreds of peptide linkages, their active sites may be only a few peptide linkages long. It is clear that enzymatic activity does not in most cases depend upon the entire enzyme—as is apparent from the fact that some enzymes can under-go partial enzymatic hydrolysis without apparent loss of enzymatic activity—from the comparison of enzymes of diverse species, et cetera. Much of the enzyme, apart from the active site, may be involved in regulation of enzymatic activity and in moderating the efficiency of catalysis. It seems likely that at least many bare active sites would have significant catalytic activity, although they might be much less efficient than the full enzyme.

This has interesting implications for the question of the random synthesis of a given catalytic function in primitive times. If we require polypeptides with 100 amino-acid residues constructed of the 20 naturally occurring amino acids, then the probability that a given peptide has the catalytic activity in question is only one in 20^{100}, or roughly one in 10^{130}. The number 10^{130} is larger than the total number of elementary particles in the universe, and it is apparent that if we adopt these numbers, the likelihood of spontaneous origin of any useful catalytic activity from polypeptides is nil. On the other hand, if we only require active sites of, let us say, five amino acids long, then any given active site is produced—assuming only random processes operated—once in every 20^5 cases. This is one in about 3 million, which is not a very large number at all. Active sites usually include amino acid residues with reactive side chains, but such residues can be relatively simple (for example, serine) or may be heterocyclic (for example, cysteine). A nucleotide capable of slightly enhancing the rate of production of a few bare active sites in its vicinity might have extraordinary selective advantage over otherwise equivalent polynucleotides unable to produce such active sites.

In Figure 44 is shown the contemporary triplet code. Twenty amino acids and two or three punctuation marks are being coded by 64 codons. A doublet code with 16 codon assignments would almost be adequate, and the contemporary triplet code in fact shows a fairly large degree of degeneracy. This might suggest that the contemporary triplet code has evolved from a more primitive doublet code, and that the doublet code perhaps evolved from an even more simple singlet code. If this is true—but even if it is not—the full potentialities of the triplet code have not yet been realized and substantial room exists for further evolution of the code. But this immediately raises a serious problem. If at one time in the early history of life on earth a doublet code was utilized, how could an evolution from doublet to triplet ever have occurred without totally losing all the genetic information painfully evolved up to that point in time? If the readout

1st POSITION	2nd POSITION: U	2nd POSITION: C	2nd POSITION: A	2nd POSITION: G	3rd POSITION
U	PHE	SER	TYR	CYS	U
	PHE	SER	TYR	CYS	C
	LEU	SER	*CT-1	*CT-3?	A
	LEU	SER	*CT-2	TRY	G
C	LEU	PRO	HIS	ARG	U
	LEU	PRO	HIS	ARG	C
	LEU	PRO	GLN	ARG	A
	LEU	PRO	GLN	ARG	G
A	ILU	THR	ASN	SER	U
	ILU	THR	ASN	SER	C
	ILU	THR	LYS	ARG	A
	MET	THR	LYS	ARG	G
G	VAL	ALA	ASP	GLY	U
	VAL	ALA	ASP	GLY	C
	VAL	ALA	GLU	GLY	A
	VAL	ALA	GLU	GLY	G

* CT = chain terminator

Figure 44. The contemporary genetic code

instructions changed from reading two nucleotides at a time to reading three nucleotides at a time, the readout mechanism would be out of phase after reading the first codon, regaining phase only every third codon. The only way I can see out of this quandary is to assume that for some reason the primitive code was read three nucleotides at a time, although not all three of the nucleotides may have contained information—one or two of them may simply have been spacers. That is, a doublet code may have involved one nucleotide position which had no significance as far as transcription and which may have been filled by any nucleotide whatever without affecting the readout.

When the potentialities of the doublet code were exhausted, the identity of the third nucleotide might then, for the first time, have had significance for the genetic code.

It is of interest to see if any sign of such an evolution is apparent—fossilized, as it were—in the contemporary code. I am aware that this may not be the case at all and that the contemporary codons might be so selected—for example, to minimize the damage accompanying a single base substitution—as to have no discernible sign of the primitive code. Nevertheless I feel this is an entertaining exercise. Some of the remarks I am about to make are not only obvious but have also occurred to other people, as I discovered in a very interesting discussion I had yesterday with Dr. Woese (Woese, et al, 1966).

The first thing to notice is that with only one or two exceptions it does not matter in the least which of the two purines or which of the two pyrimidines occurs in Position III of the triplet in coding for a particular amino acid. The second thing to notice is that it doesn't much matter which purine *or* pyrimidine exists in Position III. This immediately suggests that Position III was the spacer in a primitive doublet code. In such a code, GU would code for valine, CC for proline, et cetera.

When you reduce the triplet code to a doublet code in this way, it is true that some confusions are made, but by and large these are not very serious confusions. There are confusions with punctuation marks, confusions with the more-difficult-to-produce ring-containing amino acids, confusions between such similar amino acids as aspartic and glutamic acid, and confusion involving sulfur-containing amino acids.

The fundamental role played by the sulfur-containing amino acid, cysteine, appears to be in the tertiary structure of the enzymes, which need not be fundamental for the existence of active sites.

Oró: Not in the case of methionine.

Sagan: With respect to AAX there is a real ambiguity in the hypothetical doublet code but, in any case, as we go further back in time we should expect the coding assignments to be less and less clean.

When we look at the presumed doublet code, the question arises whether it is at all possible to reconstruct a singlet code, because now we have the idea that if a letter could be subtracted from an $(N + 1)$-tuplet code, we can extract the N-tuplet code. First of all, if we look at the four vertical columns in Figure 44 we see certain structural similarities. In Column 1 there is strong valine, leucine, isoleucine similarity. In Column 3 we see aspartic acid and glutamic acid in the same column with asparagine and glutamine. In Column 4 we see arginine in two different rows in the same column. Chemical similarities within a given row are less persuasive. For example, serine is in Column 2 of Row 1, but it is Row 3 of Column 4. This therefore suggests—and Dr. Woese tells me he has independently had the same idea—that it is the first position that was added to make the doublet code and, therefore, that the middle position represents some primitive singlet. This seems to mean, for example, that in primitive times XUY (X and Y are variable nucleotides; U is uracil) coded for a category of amino acids including leucine, isoleucine, and valine. The specificity was probably very crude, so that other amino acids were also occasionally coded by XUY, but a certain statistical preponderance for this group dominated. Similar remarks apply to XCY, XAY and XGY.

When this is done I'm struck by one final item, which is that the sequence of Row 4 involves valine, alanine, aspartic and glutamic acids, and glycine. But these are just about the most abundant amino acids produced in primitive earth simulation experiments by almost all workers, although there is some evidence for serine being produced in greater abundance than valine. At the same time, for the more complex amino acids—those containing rings, those containing sulfur, and the punctuation marks—we should expect each to have had greater difficulty, either in being produced or, in the case of the punctuation marks, in being effective in early times. Therefore as the last step in this speculation there is a suggestion that the singlet code involved U largely for valine, C largely for alanine, A largely for aspartic and glutamic acids, and G largely for glycine.

Rich: You wouldn't have a functional protoprotein.

Sagan: How do you mean?

Rich: You wouldn't have one. You have to have a positive charge if you are going to have a negative charge; you must have both. If you want to make a primitive protein—and I have no objection to it—you can't have only aliphatics, that is, the nonpolar ones. You must have both positive and negative ones. Otherwise, you will get into all kinds of charge troubles. Do you follow me?

Sagan: I understand what you are saying.

Rich: Of course, you might antedate the aspartic and glutamic. That would be a secondary thing. That is not unknown, I should say. We even do it today; we convert our protein to hydroxyprotein after it has been polymerized as protein, e.g., proline and hydroxyproline.

Sagan: In addition, the spacers might have had appropriate polarity. The only remaining point I wish to mention is the work of Eck and Dayhoff (1966) on the structure of ferredoxin. They have looked at the amino acid sequence of this protein and performed a computer reconstruction from the amino-acid statistics to determine what simple amino-acid sequence the evolutionary precursor of this enzyme would have had. They concluded that this precursor protein was a polymer of a tetrapeptide, composed of alanine, aspartic acid, serine, and glycine. This seems to be quite consistent with the idea that a few abundantly produced amino acids were preferentially involved in a very early protein catalysis.

The major reason for bringing up this speculative topic is because if it is right it should be accessible to experimental attack. If there is any even very weak coupling between amino acids and nucleotides or polynucleotides, it may be detectable by column chromatography, or dialysis bags, or something. If any such weak coupling of a specific sort between nucleotides and amino acids were found, it would certainly have profound significance for the origin of life.

Pattee: I would like to go back to this chicken-egg problem that we were talking about, and I won't go very long because, obviously, this problem needs extensive analysis (Pattee, 1967a; Pattee, 1967b), but I just wanted to make a point. When Alex (Rich) got up and talked about the origin of information storage molecules and said they are nucleic acids, I believe this language gets us into difficulty. I think it is certainly meaningful, though perhaps of little significance, to discuss which *substance* came first, polynucleotides or polypeptides. I do not think it is meaningful to discuss the *function* of *information* storage without also defining the *transmission channel,* or code for the way in which this information is transferred. In other words, the very definition of hereditary information in a physical sense requires a prior definition as to what you mean by the transmission channel or the code.

Furthermore, hereditary information transfer itself cannot be meaningfully defined in terms of a static minimum energy structure. Physically, it can only be defined in terms of a specific rate-control process and therefore, in this sense, by a specific catalyst. I am not saying that a polypeptide was necessarily the first rate-controlling process, although it is very likely, because that is what its present function is; but this does imply that the very meaning of the hereditary information-storage device is in a sense defined by the hereditary transmission device. These two cannot be functionally separated and, therefore, although you may use the word *information* roughly, this is still hiding the real chicken-egg problem.

In older biological terms, I think the genotype and phenotype functions are inseparable—neither one alone can be expected to evolve by mutation and natural selection.

Rich: I think you can look at the problem this way. We can make something called "information storage molecule" in the small sense, meaning just a complementary polymer; we can make it easily, I believe, and pushing ahead a few years we can even make it replicate easily, so that it does one function.

Pattee: But the replication does not express anything.

Rich: I agree, that is only one function, and building up the readout system, I think, will take a little more time. In terms of the sequence of events historically, we probably don't know everything that is going on but, in fact, one could have accumulated a fair amount of complementary nucleic acids without any readout system at all, because it is not dependent on it.

Pattee: It is a question of whether you can call this hereditary information.

Rich: I didn't say that. You can accumulate a store of double helical, double stranded nucleic-acid molecules in the absence of any readout systems, I believe.

Pattee: Or, you can accumulate a readout mechanism without a store of random nucleotides.

Rich: You probably could accumulate the components for such a system, but I think I could very well envision a great store of polynucleotides, single and double stranded, and then eventually the development of a class of molecules that act as a primitive readout system.

Pattee: Are you saying the order of these two developments—the storage and readout systems—is crucial with respect to the hereditary process?

Rich: So far, there is nothing hereditary about these molecules.

Pattee: Yes, I agree.

Rich: They only become hereditary once you couple them with a readout system and, in fact, they replicate and produce more such systems. That could have happened much later.

Pattee: I agree, when they are coupled we have a hereditary system. The point I wanted to make was that to say that the information storage molecule came first is not a meaningful statement. You can say the substance—which subsequently, upon the appearance of a code brings out this information—may or may not have been first; but the information transfer idea implies *both* the channel for transmitting it as well as the storage device.

Rich: Maybe we should say a potential information storage molecule.

Pattee: Fine.

Early Replicating Systems

Kramer: Dr. Rich, do you envision duplicating molecules, such as you have spoken about, independent of being confined within a membranous area?

Rich: Sure. There is no limit to the number of ways one can imagine it. You can imagine pools that dry and concentrate, or freeze and concentrate, reactive material. This is an abiotic environment, so such materials won't be consumed. They have to be protected from radiation somewhat in order to accumulate, but this could all go on in the absence of a membrane.

Kramer: You could hardly talk about selection, though.

Rich: There is no selection at that level. The selection process comes later when you begin to make molecules that have some function to read out.

Kramer: When you begin the reading-out process that you talk about, you could then conceive of these systems being confined in a membrane.

Rich: Not necessarily. I think membranes come much later on.

Margulis: Maybe you could clarify it by showing us the simplest replicating system. Use as many organic materials around as you like. What is the minimal replicating system that involves some kind of nucleic acid and proteins (or polypeptides)? Could you show us a model, even if the replication is sloppy?

Pattee: Instead of "replicating," why not say "the simplest hereditary system."

Rich: I will even send you a reprint about it (Rich, 1962). Imagine the following. Let's take an A-T copolymer and let us say that we will ignore the other bases; we are simply replicating, happily. We corrupt the replication process by assembling not simply complementary nucleotides but nucleotides which, say, have amino acyl groups stuck on the hydroxyl group.

Margulis: In other words, first we had a naked gene.

Rich: That is right, but I am corrupting this system. First it's an RNA chain (DNA, I suspect, is a very recent molecule). RNA is the "Ur molecule" because it is involved in both protein synthesis and in replication.

The experiment that I talked about, that didn't work, was an attempt in this direction. That is to say, we have polyuridylic acid with amino acyl groups stuck on the 2' hydroxyl. I wanted to polymerize these in some method. I didn't succeed, but let's assume it can be done. Now we begin to make a polymer of amino acids that is coupled to a complementary polymerization of nucleotides.

Margulis: Somehow this helps you polymerize the same sequence of nucleotides better?

Rich: No. So far nothing has happened. The next step in this process is that you have a bias such that, for chemical reasons, glutamate, say, gets coupled with T and lysine with A. It is only statistical (that is, glutamate goes with T more often than it would if it were a straight function of relative frequency). One of these random polynucleotides then makes a polypeptide chain which reinforces this rough readout. What happened then? Out of a large mass of random polynucleotides you begin to get a rather more faithful translation into polypeptides. The peptide chain reflects—to whatever slight extent—the polynucleotide sequence.

The point is, you have begun to define the system by making a reading out which is straight. The next step (after having made activating enzymes, which is an improbable event, but it is one event) you have to imagine that somewhere in this great class of polynucleotides you produce a polypeptide that has essentially a primitive polymerase activity. I mean it catalyzes the replication of the nucleic acid. At that point selection begins, because here you have a system that has not only the ability to begin to catalyze replication, but it also can catalyze readout. At that stage, things begin to happen in that local area; you have a primitive system for selection to act on.

Morrison: At all stages, you are feeding in some free energy?

Margulis: That's okay, ATP is being made abiogenically.

Rich: I am hardly using ATP, but you are clearly using a pool of molecules that have stored in them anhydrides, or what not—energy fed in, yes, of course.

Fox: Are you proposing that RNA makes the polypeptide or guides the sequence?

Rich: I am saying the sequence of nucleotides in the RNA determines the sequence of amino acid residues in the polypeptide chain. There may be a simple mechanism for doing this. I have looked; I haven't found it, but I will look again.

Kramer: I don't think you can use selective, adaptive language here. You mentioned something about something being "better," which is a way of saying "more adapted." You are talking in evolutionary language—organism language—which means, so far as I can see, that you are talking about membrane———

Margulis: No.

Pattee: Evolution requires a genotype and a phenotype, in biological language.

Kramer: What evidence is there for duplicating, then? How much laboratory or field evidence is there for duplicating systems?

Rich: Duplicating what, polynucleotides?

Kramer: Just duplicating systems, apart from membrane.

Horowitz: That can be done in a homogeneous system. There are no membranes involved.

McElroy: The point is that you do modify the environment and get selection; by modifying the environment, you would get selection with certain types of reactions.

Sagan: It simply reproduces, and it is not an ongoing natural selection. It has to do more than reproduce; it has to have some very weak way in which it influences the surroundings.

Horowitz: It has to be able to mutate and have its mutations be reproduced. Then you begin to get selection and evolution.

Margulis: And you don't need membranes to do that (Spiegelman, 1967).

Kramer: Do you envision this occurring naturally, independent of any membrane separating off this area from an outside environment?

McElroy: Right.

Kramer: I just wanted to get it clear.

Fremont-Smith: But the edges of the pool might act like a membrane, since we think of it as possibly being in an isolated pool.

Sagan: One worldwide organism.

Fox: I think we can't eliminate the possibility that when we know enough, we may find that a membrane is essential to the machinery for synthesizing polynucleotides and polyamino acids together.

Kramer: In other words, it is an assumption, then, that membranes are not essential at this point?

Horowitz: No, it is a fact. In the test tube a membrane is not essential for molecular replication. It is a convenience.

Orgel: The analogy has been made between doodling and writing. Before being able to write in meaningful sentences, it is still possible to put together random sequences. If I understand you right, what you are saying is that there was a long period in which molecules were doodling before they learned to write.

Fremont-Smith: Don't you always have to concede, though, that in a frame of reference they have boundaries. It seems to me this is the kind of thing you are talking about—membrane, perhaps.

Kramer: This is the way I conceive of them.

Fremont-Smith: They are not just out in the total ocean.

Rich: No.

Kramer: Apparently individuals here do not conceive of a bound system.

Margulis: Some primitive replicating system like the one described must have led to a more advanced evolving system in which there was membrane. Any system which could regulate what molecules went in and what went out would have had immediate terrific selective advantage.

Kramer: But what you are saying is that the genetic system came first and the membrane system came later. This is what I am questioning. In other words, you are separating off the controlled environment from the genetic system, and I am wondering whether this is a valid way of approaching the problem. In other words, if you are talking about a controlled environment, and we know that the membrane does function in a sense to control an inner environment and to regulate it, then I am wondering whether what we are saying isn't a sort of double talk.

Pattee: Orgel's analogy can be made just as well another way: We could say that there were molecules that knew how to read but only a very clever one came along and knew how to write a useful message. The point here is that whether a sequence of symbols is "doodling" or "writing" is not an inherent property of the sequence, but depends on what is defined as "reading." The only essential distinction is that the rules of reading must be more permanent than the message itself. This common usage implies that the genetic code must be more stable than genetic messages. It is not reasonable to say that the genetic code evolves faster than the genetic messages.

Kramer: But when you are talking about "a clever molecule," you are talking about some selective advantage. This is the implication that runs through all of this discussion, that there was some selective advantage. I don't think that you can use evolutionary language before you have an organism.

Morrison: The evidence is very clear. The advantage was that such a molecule produces the formation———

Kramer: Advantage for what, a molecule?

Morrison: A site.

Sagan: A molecule is an organism. If it is a molecule it is an organism by any definition, namely, that it is capable of evolution by natural selection; it reproduces itself as an organism. There is no reason why just because membranes are popular today that this fashion was present during the whole history of life. You can see that organisms today live in a much more hostile environment than they probably did in the primitive environment, if the oceans were one percent solution of organic matter, or whatever. So you see, there is another problem of having things the other way around and that is, how do you arrange replication of this membranous coding along with the replication of the genetic material? How do they get together?

On The Evolution Of The Ribosomal System

Rich: Could I raise a point on your next topic on the list, the evolution of the ribosomal mechanism? Since nothing is known about it, I can speak with authority! What is the "Ur" ribosome? There must have been one. Now we are no longer talking about this very early stage but about a fairly sophisticated stage.

If you have two questions, two unknowns, frequently you may join them together and somehow effect a solution. That is really what I am going to do now.

One of the big mysteries of molecular biology is, what is the ribosomal RNA doing, anyhow? The ribosome particle, with a diameter of 200 Å has more than half its mass as RNA. Eighty percent of the RNA of the cell is tied up in ribosomes, these necessary components of an information transfer system. Yet apparently it carries no information in the sense that it is not involved, as far as we know, in the reading and readout process. It is an active organelle but, so far as we know, the detailed sequence of the nucleotides in its RNA does not contain information, say, in the way that either messenger RNA or transfer RNA contains information.

Horowitz: But there are the streptomycin experiments which indicate that the ribosomes do have some role in the accurate———

Rich: Sure. I am not saying they don't have a role. What we don't know is why they contain this great mass of RNA. The ribosome is to the messenger or transfer RNA function what, more or less, an enzyme is to a small molecule substrate. In a sense it is working that way. Most enzymes don't have this massive amount of material and why should the ribosome? That is the problem, and there is no obvious answer.

I make a guess. First of all, if we go from the eukaryotic to the prokaryotic organisms, we find that, for example, mammals have ribosomes with molecular weights of 4.2 to 4.5 million. Bacteria prokaryotes have ribosomes with molecular weights of 2.8 million (Fig. 45). The big difference is in the decrement of protein. There are some differences in the RNA, but they are not very great. They are not as great as the differences in protein.

My speculation is that the first machine for reading out was the RNA alone. A naked RNA, which in the course of evolution has combined with proteins which, in effect, have refined and made more accurate the reading process—hence, the streptomycin business (streptomycin, the potent antibiotic, seems to act by preventing release of newly made protein from the ribosomes of sensitive organisms). But it may be possible to assemble a primitive ribosome-like function, using the ribosomal RNA alone.

We haven't really tried experimentally to find ribosomal functions using RNA alone, but there are suggestions that this might work. The ribosomal RNA is highly folded, lots of secondary structure, and, indeed, one can get systems in which the RNA from the two ribosomal subunits will, in an appropriate environment, associate together independent of the ribosomal protein.

It would be great fun to see if we could get a primitive kind of ribosomal function, because then we'll understand what this is. I think of it as sort of an evolutionary appendix. It represents the evolutionary course of making this very important machine. It was polynucleotide material that was used in the first instance, and it has become modified with time. These might be useful experiments if one could get a set of primitive conditions for carrying out this kind of catalytic function. It is worth looking into.

Woese: Alex (Rich), do you envision this as a tape-reading of the message by the ribosomal RNA?

Rich: The ribosomal RNA with suitable cations serves as an assembly site for pulling together the transfer RNA, activating it, and reacting transfer RNA with its amino-acid residues with messenger RNA. That is clear.

PROKARYOTES   EUKARYOTES

RIBOSOME   RIBOSOME

MW
2.8
million    MW
                                      4.5
                                      million

50S   30S   60S   40S

23S + 16S   28S + 18S
RNA, approx. 27   RNA, many
proteins   proteins

POLYRIBOSOME   MESSENGER
                                RNA

Figure 45.   Ribosomal protein synthesis

Woese: In view of ribosomal reconstitution experiments, the chance of success looks kind of low. By just removing a few proteins, you lose all your capacity to bind messenger RNA. You say you will make this up by adding suitable cations?

Rich: Yes, you have to. The point is, you can get the two ribosomal RNA's, (the 16 and 23 S, Fig. 45) to associate together; it is then moved down a gradient.

McElroy: Alex, what about just the chance consequence that this is the doodling RNA which, for reasons we now know, could very effectively bind proteins? Now this would have tremendous selective advantages in acting as a template for secondary binding of RNA messenger.

Rich: The doodling refers to a messenger-like function (a way of translating a polynucleotide sequence into a polypeptide sequence). The doodling is what might be called "randomized readout." What I am now asking is, what is the system that made this reading out function more efficient? I'm making this sort of far-out suggestion: One bundles up a collection of RNA to make a complex that somehow effects the condensation of these different parts of the system—activated amino acids on transfer RNA coded by some messenger.

Kramer: I don't think you have a right to talk about selective advantage of doodling RNA.

Rich: Ribosomal RNA is a great mystery today. We have gone and looked at all the different kinds of RNA's—transfer, messenger, et cetera—and it is all grand and glorious. But 80 percent ribosomal RNA sits there, and our ignorance is complete.

Margulis: What was the significance of the difference, do you think, between the lower and higher cells?

Rich: As higher cells have evolved, they have added more functions to the ribosome. The mammalian ribosome is very complex. It can do all sorts of subtle things like turn itself on and off in a rather mysterious way.

The bacterial ribosome is simpler from the control point of view. I believe ribosomal machinery functions on the level of translation (of messenger RNA into protein) to bring about these subtle controls. We see elements of it already. We know that there are loosely associated proteins which bind weakly to the ribosome. These bring about the initiation of synthesis and also some of the internal steps needed for translation.

McElroy: Alex (Rich), if you turn it around the other way, what you are really talking about is the multienzyme system, which is really what a ribosome is.

Rich: It is very much like it, yes. One of the reasons I think the control idea may perhaps be a little more plausible than it sounds at first is the fact that the ribosomal proteins aren't built by a simple assembly of subunits the way most viral capsules are built. There are twenty-seven ribosomal proteins; they all appear to be quite different. They are clustered around this RNA core. This is in bacterial cells.

We are just now at the stage where we are beginning to pull off these proteins one by one and ask what functions are lost. The real experiment would be to dissect the ribosome, replace these charges by other cations (whether polyamines or simpler cations) and try to restore the function. Even though we are beginning to disassemble the structure, I suspect rescuing the function by appropriate replacements may be possible.

McElroy: At least in higher cell chromosomes we know roughly the genetic site for the ribosomal synthesis.

Rich: For the ribosomal RNA synthesis, you mean?

McElroy: Yes. How is that finally made into the ribosome? What is the next step? Where is the membrane—the protein material—coming from?

Rich: That's a good question. There are three fragments of RNA in the ribosome. Two big ones and a small one. In the bacteria the large RNA's are molecular weight of about one million and half a million. The small one has molecular weight of about 30,000.

In the case of mammals, the smaller RNA subunit is made. It comes out of the nucleus with a piece of messenger RNA and is clothed with protein rather rapidly. Then it grabs onto the larger subunit.

From some work that has been done with Hela cells, we do know that there is a sequential assembly of the ribosomal proteins. He has not been able to define which proteins, but by doing a general labeled experiment he is able to show a time-dependent sequential assembly process. Some proteins are added first, others are added later.

We don't know yet where the information comes from for making the ribosomal proteins. It is a very interesting subject. At one time it was felt that the information for ribosomal protein must come from the ribosomal RNA. The ribosomal RNA only has enough information for coding about six proteins but there are four or five times that number on the ribosomal coat.

In several labs current work is directed toward the question, "Where is this ribosomal protein being synthesized?" Indeed, there is a graduate student in my laboratory who is making some rather promising headway in this problem. We have some inferential information in the sense that we know the streptomycin locus. We now believe that the receptor for streptomycin sensitivity is one of the ribosomal proteins. In fact, we have very little information on the rest of the ribosomal material.

All one can say in general about the ribosome is that it is a rather complex bit of molecular machinery, and it clearly must have come from something much simpler. What I am suggesting is that the *reductio ad absurdum* in terms of protein content is that one may have had a primitive form of this function—that is, intermediary in the translation of ordered polynucleotide sequences into ordered polypeptide sequences—in the absence of protein to begin with.

Pattee: May I make one comment that is directly related to these models? I don't think that it is legitimate to assume that the storage or readout mechanism can be arbitrarily sloppy to begin with, because this is an information transfer problem, and if the rate of information accumulation through natural selection is lower than the rate of error in the storage and transmission, you obviously won't get anywhere. In a sense there is a reliability threshold which must be achieved before evolution by natural selection can begin.

Rich: Oh, I know, but you can do a lot with poor, noisy translation.

Pattee: Not without redundancy or complicated error-correcting codes, and I don't think these are easy to imagine as spontaneous events.

Rich: Oh, I know you need something. The English language, you know, is about 50 percent redundant. Take out half the letters and you could still read the message.

Pattee: But at the very beginning, there is this crucial reliability threshold that has to be explained.

Horowitz: But at the beginning these processes need not have been very efficient. There wasn't much competition.

Pattee: But they had to be reasonably correct. A more detailed discussion of the reliability problem in hereditary evolution is discussed in the cited reference (Pattee, 1967a & b).

Horowitz: Reasonably, that is right; the mutation rate could have been very high.
    Alex (Rich), what do you think of the speculation that the original polynucleotide itself had a weak catalytic activity in polymerizing amino acids? It may have been exceedingly weak. I realize there is no evidence for this.

Rich: This is the experiment that I described earlier. I am trying to make a template system in which a polynucleotide assembles on its backbone, one by one, sequentially, amino acids which then polymerize.

Horowitz: Polymerize as the result of the catalytic activity of the polynucleotide, or———

Rich: Well, catalytic activity in the following sense: Once you have assembled the polynucleotides in the right order, you then have a configuration in which the bases are not 3.4 Å unfortunately, but a little over 4 Å apart. This is because the polynucleotides are going around a helix, as well. You can imagine that this is a catalytic site in which the polynucleotide comes off and brings the amino acids together, one by one.

McElroy: This is the point I was trying to bring up before, because I think that is right where you get into trouble. You are really talking about a messenger here. Then you don't know of a mechanism by which the individual amino acids now will line up on the polynucleotide.

Rich: I quite agree. I am postulating that we will find one.

McElroy: That is the reason I prefer to put a polypeptide together first. Then you have the code built into the polypeptide as the initial template. You then make your self-replicating unit from that. At least our present knowledge indicates that a messenger is actually being coded by another polynucleotide and not by the amino acids.

Pattee: You have a specific catalyst. That is what a physicist would say is a condition for a "coding process." If you want to make this catalyst out of a polynucleotide, that is one way; or you can make it out of a polypeptide. But one way or the other, it has to be a specific catalyst. Which way is more reasonable?

Rich: What I am saying in this model is that the initial readout mechanism was grossly different from the final readout mechanism, but it had one thing in common, and only one thing: The specificity of the hydrogen bonding; the sequential assembly of nucleotides determined the message. The mechanism *per se* is quite different, and what I am guessing is that once this system began to operate, one could imagine mutational changes which, in effect, modified the mechanism for reading out but still retained this relationship between polynucleotide sequence and polypeptide sequence.

McElroy: I guess I was relying a little too much on thinking that tRNA was the thing you would really make initially.

Rich: You see, I am postulating that the tRNA did not exist *per se* initially. What I am postulating is that simple replication of a polynucleotide brought about a polymerization of an amino acid.

McElroy: But then the whole code would later have to be changed around.

Rich: That is what I am saying.

McElroy: If you start with a polypeptide, then you can make a polynucleotide, just the way we think about how a tRNA works today, all coded. Then you have an RNA all coded and it will begin to replicate itself.

Rich: But it is hard to do in one step.

McElroy: Hard to do what?

Rich: It is hard to see what you need to do. You need to make a class of tRNA's.

McElroy: I will do it the way you are going to do it. I will accept the way you want to make the RNA, but I am saying that the nucleotides will line up on that polypeptide just the way we think they line up with the activating enzyme today.

Rich: What I am really using as my primitive tRNA is one nucleotide; and what I am saying is that later on this became more refined.

McElroy: I would argue, then, that the first little polypeptide of great interest would be one that was an activating enzyme. That would give you some specificity right there for your polynucleotide. From there, I would use whatever mechanism you propose to make polynucleotides. Now, however, the beginning code would be built right into that particular amino acid.

Rich: My feeling is that speculations of this type—I am not disagreeing with you—but speculations of this type are useful only if they, in fact, give you a direction in terms of experiments.

McElroy: I think this will give you some real direction.

Rich: My feeling is that the central problem is a readout mechanism. What we should do, chemically, is to devise any of those experiments that tell us what can happen.

McElroy: I think the interesting experiments today would be to degrade activating enzymes, gradually, and take short polynucleotides of our known code, use the doublet or triplet, see what stage you eventually get to, and see if you get selective binding.

Eglinton: But you may not lose the binding, which is what you want to begin with.

Rich: I think binding experiments with oligonucleotides are very useful to discover the nature of the active site, but I think once you begin to degrade protein, you are in trouble. You lose most of the activity.

McElroy: The enzymatic activity, yes, but the question of whether you have lost binding is, I think, still an experimental problem.

Eglinton: Is the binding site in lysozyme (an enzymatic protein, the detailed structure of which is known) a straight sequence of amino acids?

Rich: No.

Eglinton: Does the site involve portions of chain from different parts of the molecule?

Rich: There are a dozen residues in lysozyme that are in the active site; if you look at them on the chain they are scattered all around, and I suspect this will be true of all proteins. The major reason is that if you look at the detailed geometry of how the groups come in to bind to the substrate, you will find that you can't get that kind of detail with just a single polypeptide chain.

McElroy: What you are saying, then, Alex (Rich), is that late in evolution, you could fold this thing up in a number of ways, but it is interesting that the tRNA's all have adenylic acid as the common acceptor for the activated amino acid.

Rich: Oh, yes, of course; that is very important.

Oro: There is a case of an enzyme said to be quite primitive, the oligopeptides of which are significantly active. They catalyze the same reaction as the protein.

Rich: Let me be clear. I am not at all opposed to an oligopeptide as an enzymatically active unit. All I am saying is that if you want to use it, it has to be small and simple and commonplace if it is not made by polynucleotides. If it is going to be bigger—half a dozen amino acid residues or more—then you have to use a polynucleotide-type system for making it.

McElroy: Alex (Rich), I believe you won't have specificity without the large structure, but you could have catalytic activity. As a matter of fact, I would doubt, with a small polypeptide, that you would have very high catalytic rates.

I am trying to get some way of selecting out this early genetic system in a hurry, you might say. And it seemed to me if you used catalysis, which is the one way to select, and used that to work backward toward the information you need, this would be one way to get the primitive code in a hurry.

Horowitz: I feel, myself, that I have had enough of Genesis. How about Exodus?

EXTRATERRESTRIAL LIFE

EXTRATERRESTRIAL LIFE

SUMMARY OF SESSION

May 24, 1967

On the third day there was an extensive review and discussion of relevant exobiological problems. Since many of these topics have very largely been covered elsewhere, they are only briefly summarized here, with pertinent references listed at the end. The discussion during the previous days of the conference was directed at the production of organic molecules and their interaction and organization in the very early history of the earth, a time so distant that acquiring bona fide uncontaminated samples seems rather unlikely. In addition, as Darwin himself pointed out, with the very occurrence of life, prebiological organic molecules that led to the origin of life would have been destroyed, thereby removing the traces which we would like to have in the experimental investigations. On the other hand, if prebiological organic synthetic processes are very general—that is, not restricted to the earth—then there may very well be on the surfaces of other planets repositories of the very same molecules produced in the early history of the earth. Also, the question of the earliest form of life on earth has similar attendant difficulties, if we are talking about forms of life much simpler than those Barghoorn and Schopf have been discussing. Such very early, and conceivably precellular forms of life may well have developed in some extraterrestrial environment. If, for one reason or another, life ground to a dead halt on such a world, we might be able to find fossil evidence of such earliest life forms. In any case the expected diversity should certainly fulfill the expectations of even the most jaded biologist.

The problems of the early evolution of the solar system and the escape of planetary atmospheres were discussed. It was indicated that we do not know enough to exclude the possibility that atmospheres and prebiological organic processes occurred for considerable periods of time on such bodies as the moon, Mars, and Mercury, which now have little or no atmospheres. It is likely that the primitive atmospheres of all the planets were once reducing.

The physical environment of Venus was described, and the question of the possible existence of complex organic molecules on the surface was discussed. On the basis of the small amount of HCl and HF discovered through groundbased spectroscopy, Fox suggested polyaspartic acid and Oró, halogenated hydrocarbons. Barghoorn suggested coronine, a 7-ring hydrocarbon. Some doubt was expressed, however, about the long-term stability, to say nothing of the biological interest, of such compounds after continued exposure to temperatures of 600° K or higher. In the case that the Venus clouds contain supercooled liquid water, it was debated whether this would provide any useful environment for the propagation of indigenous microorganisms.

The physical environments of the moon and Mars were also discussed. The question of possible sequestered organic matter on these planets was covered, as was the possibility of indigenous organic matter. The idea that subsurface organisms may photosynthesize using infrared protons is a thermodynamic fallacy, unless they can operate with extremely low efficiencies. A fair amount of attention was given to the geological evolution of the terrestrial planets. The present physical environment of Jupiter is so close to that predicted for the early earth, many experiments in prebiological organic chemistry of the earth are also relevant to Jupiter. It is possible that the variegated and striking coloration on the planet and the 2600 Å absorption feature in its ultraviolet spectrum are due to the presence of organic molecules.

Carl Sagan

EXTRATERRESTRIAL LIFE

References

Owen, T., and Greenspan, J.A. 1968. Jovian atmosphere: Near-ultraviolet absorption features. *Science,* 159: 449.

Pittendrigh, C.S., Vishniac, W., and Pearman, J.P.T., (eds.). 1966. Biology and the exploration of Mars. *Nat'l. Acad. Sci., Nat'l. Res. Coun., 1296.* Washington, D.C.

Sagan, C. 1968. Jovian atmosphere: Near-ultraviolet absorption features. *Science,* 159: 448.

_____ 1967. Life on the surface of Venus? *Nature,* 216: 1198.

_____ 1968. Origins of the atmospheres of the earth and planets. In *International Dictionary of Geophysics,* S.K. Runcorn, editor-in-chief, H.C. Urey, section editor. Pergamon Press, London.

Sagan, C., and Morowitz, H. 1967. Life in the clouds of Venus? *Nature,* 215: 1259.

Shklovskii, I.S., and Sagan, C. 1966. *Intelligent Life in the Universe.* Holden-Day Publishing Co., San Francisco.

APPENDIX

APPENDIX

ON THE GEOLOGICAL EVIDENCE FOR THE THERMAL ORIGIN OF LIVING SYSTEMS

COMMENTS BY PROFESSOR GEORGE MUELLER
Submitted by S. W. Fox

The discussion in question centers around the following problem: Did life evolve from a relatively less adapted physiochemical setting, which occupied a relatively high percentage of the surface of the earth, or did it evolve from a more adapted setting, which occupied a relatively smaller percentage of the surface of the earth. An affirmative answer to the first alternative would favor abiogenesis from the oceans or coastal regions, whereas if the balance of our present-day informations tilt toward the second alternative, then, by-and-large a fumarole-hot spring origin of life would be indicated.

In order to approach the problem (at least to the degree of our best present-day abilities) we have to reconstruct: (A) the ratios; ocean, coastal volumes; volumes occupied by fumaroles, hot springs; and, further, the stability of the latter. (B) the "optimum chemical conditions" which are reached in oceans, and so forth, on the one hand, and around fumaroles, and so forth, on the other hand.

(A) At present, hot spring-fumarole areas occupy a relatively small percentage of the surface of our planet, but the increasing proportion of volcanics and also hydrothermal veins in rocks of Precambrian age seem to indicate a trend of general increase of fumarole-hot spring activity. However, it appears from these geological evidences, that ever since the early Precambrian, the fumarole-hot spring areas have been of sporadical distribution, and subordinate relative to the areas occupied by the oceans. Regarding the still earlier

327

history of the Earth, the majority of geologists seem to agree that there was an initial elevated temperature between say 200° C and 800° C on the surface, when conditions must have rather closely resembled those which prevail in our present-day fumaroles and hot springs. The protoorganism could have evolved during this early stage of the history of our planet from the above physicochemical setting, which was optimal from the point of both total volume and potentialities of chemical evolution, as is discussed below. Some factor, such as a too highly reducing atmosphere, for instance, may have prevented the emergence of life at this early stage, and in this case the comparison of presently known "chemical potentialities" of the oceanic and hydrothermal settings may prove of interest, as regards the approach to the problem of the more likely location of the emergence of an organism.

(B)   All the presently known Precambrian sediments consist of a maximum of 5 percent of a carbonaceous complex, which is finely dispersed within 95 percent or more of inorganic minerals. The organic complex in carbonaceous chondrites is generally considered as a direct condensate, without any localized hydrothermal effects, and it shows the same type of distribution, with no microscopically detectable concentrations of carbonaceous matter. It appears, therefore, that in the processes of direct settling of condensates from water or gas, the chemical evolution of organic molecules terminates with the production of a finely dispersed carbonaceous complex in which the biologically significant molecules, such as amino acids, polypeptides, and so on, are greatly diluted with substances which are present only in very small quantities within the modern organisms, such as paraffins, aromatics, and so on. The investigations of the writer seem to demonstrate that the prebiological evolution of the above primary condensates reaches states which are considerably closer to the chemistry of the organism through secondary distillation, polymerization, and other processes by hydrothermal or igneous agencies. The present result of this research is based on bitumens associated with hydrothermal veins in Derbyshire and other locations of the British Isles, in Southwest Africa, Canada, and so forth. The evolutionary advances, above those in the normal sediments, in these "remobilized" carbon-aceous complexes, can be briefly summarized as follows:

(1) Separation of carbonaceous complexes on a microscopical and macroscopical scale, with as little as 0.2 percent inorganic impurities.

(2) Increase of the H/C ratio of the carbonaceous complex from an original 0.4 to 1.7 percent; the H/C of the biologically important molecules is also within the 1.6-2.0 percent region.

(3) Separation of the original hydrothermal distillates into the hitherto observed maximum of six immiscible liquids. The amino acid-rich phase found within the deposits of Derbyshire proved to contain two orders of magnitude more organic acids and well over one order of magnitude more amino acids than the mean for the other five differentiates. It appears that this process of differentiation of carbonaceous complexes through distillation, fractionation, and hydrothermally introduced polymerization would result, in general, in the separation of a phase in which the biologically significant mole-cules would become concentrated.

REFERENCES

REFERENCES

Anet, F.A.L., and Muchowski, J.M. 1962. Fourteen-membered hydrogen-bonded dimers of some meta-substituted phenols. *Proc. Chem. Soc.,* 219.

Bada, J.L., and Miller, S.L. 1968. Ammonium ion concentration in the primitive ocean. *Science,* 159: 423.

Baldwin, A.N., and Berg, P. 1966. *J. Biol. Chem.,* 241: 831.

Ballester, M., and Riera, J. 1964. Perchlorodiphenylmethyl (DDM), a carbon free radical of remarkable stability. *J. Amer. Chem. Soc.,* 86: 4505.

Barghoorn, E.S., and Taylor, S.A. 1965. Microorganisms from the Gunflint chert. *Science,* 147: 563.

Barghoorn, E.S., Meinchein, W.G., and Schopf, J.W. 1965. Paleobiology of Precambrian shale. *Science,* 148: 461.

Barghoorn, E.S., and Schopf, J.W. 1966. Microorganisms three billion years old from the Precambrian of South Africa. *Science,* 152: 758.

Bendoraitis, J.G., Brown B.L., and Hepner, L.S. 1962. Isoprenoid hydrocarbons in petroleum; isolation of 2,6,10,14-tetramethyl-pentadecane by high-temperature gas-liquid chromatography. *Analytical Chem.,* 34: 49.

Bennet, W.S., Eglinton, G., and Kovac, S. 1967. Self-association of phenolics and bile acid derivatives. *Nature,* 214: 776.

Bernal, J.D. 1967. *Origin of Life.* World Book Co., Cleveland.

_____ 1951. *The Physical Basis of Life.* Routledge & Kegan Paul, London.

331

Bernhard, S.A., Berger, A., Carter, J.H., Katchalski, E., Sela, M., and Shalitin, Y. 1962. Co-operative effects of functional groups in peptides. I. Aspartyl-Serine derivatives. *J. Amer. Chem. Soc.,* 84: 2421.

Blankenship, R.R., and Bentall, R. 1965. Thermal springs of the U.S. and other countries of the world—a summary. *Geol. Survey Professional Paper,* 492.

Bloch, K. 1964. *Taxonomic Biochemistry and Serology.* Ronald Press, New York.

Blow, D.M., and Rich, A. 1960. Studies on the formation of helical deoxycholate complexes. *J. Amer. Chem. Soc.,* 82: 3566.

Blumer, M., and Thomas, D.W. 1965."Zamene," isomeric C_{19} monoolefins from marine zooplankton, fishes and mammals. *Science,* 148: 370.

Brand, J.C.D. and Eglinton, G. 1965. *Applications of Spectroscopy to Organic Chemistry.* Oldbourne Press, London.

Breed, R.S., Murray, E.G.D., and Smith, N.R. 1957. *Bergey's Manual of Determinative Bacteriology.* Williams & Wilkins Co., Baltimore.

Bullard, F.M. 1962. *Volcanoes.* University of Texas Press, Austin.

Caress, A., and Rideal, E.K. 1928. *Proc. Roy. Soc. Lon.* 120A: 360.

Clarke, F.W. 1924. *The Data of Geochemistry, 5th ed. Dept. of the Interior, U.S. Geological Survey Bull. 770.* Gov't. Printing Office, Washington, D.C.

Claus, G., and Nagy, B. 1961. A microbiological examination of some carbonaceous chondrites. *Nature,* 192: 594.

Claus, G., Nagy, B., and Europa, D.L. 1963. Further observations on the properties of the "Organized Elements" in carbonaceous chondrites. *Ann. N.Y. Acad. Sci.,* 108: 580.

Croft, W.N., and George, E.A. 1959. Blue-green algae from the middle Devonian of Rhynie, Aberdeenshire. *Bull. British Mus. (Natl. Hist.) Geology,* 3: 339.

Davies, J., Gilbert, W. and Gorini, L. 1964. *Proc. N.Y. Acad. Sci.,* 51: 883.

Dayhoff, M.O., Lippincott, E.R., Eck, R.V., and Nagarajan, G. 1967. Thermodynamic equilibrium in prebiological atmospheres of C, H, O, N, P, S, and Cl. *NASA SP-3040,* Scientific and Technical Information Division, Washington, D.C.

Dixon, M. and Webb, E.C. 1958. *Enzymes.* Academic Press, New York.

Donn, W.L., Donn, B.D. and Valentine, W.G. 1965. On the early history of the earth. *Geol. Soc. Amer. Bull.,* 76: 287.

DuFresne, E.R., and Anders, E. 1962. On the chemical evolution of carbonaceous chondrites. *Geochim Cosmochim Acta,* 26: 1085.

Durant, D.H., and Fox, S.W. 1966. Enhancement of rate of decarboxylation of pyruvic acid and of hydrolysis of adenosine phosphates by thermal poly-anhydro-α-amino acids. *Federation Proc.,* 25: 342.

Eck, R.V. and Dayhoff, M.O. 1966. Evolution of the structure of ferredoxin based on living relics of primitive amino acid sequences. *Science,* 152: 363.

Eglinton, G., Hamilton, R.J., Hodges, R., and Raphael, R.A. 1959. Gas-liquid chromatography of natural products and their derivatives. *Chem. & Ind.,* 955,

Eglinton, G. and Hamilton, R.J. 1967. Leaf epicuticular waxes. *Science,* 156: 1322.

Eglinton, G., and Lawrie, F. 1967. (Paper presented at the International Spectroscopic Meeting, Ottawa, Canada.)

Eugster, Hans. 1967. Hydrous sodium silicates from Lake Magadi, Kenya. *Science,* 158.

Florkin, M., and Mason, H.L. 1960-64. *Comparative Biochemistry, A Comprehensive Treatise,* 7 Vols. Academic Press, New York.

Fox, S.W., Winitz, M., and Pettinga, C.W. 1954. Enzymic synthesis of peptide bonds. VI. The influence of residue type on Papain-catalyzed reactions of some benzoylamino acids with some amino acid anilides. *J. Amer. Chem. Soc.,* 75: 5539.

Fox, S.W., Jonson, J.E., and Middlebrook, M. 1955. Prosynthesis of aspartic acid and alanine from citric acid cycle intermediates. *J. Amer. Chem. Soc.,* 77:1048.

Fox, S.W., Jonson, J.E., and Vegotsky, A. 1956. On biochemical origins and optical activity. *Science,* 446.

Fox, S.W., and Maier, G.D. 1959. A theory of formation of carbon compounds in the primitive earth. *Fifth World Petrol. Congress,* Fordham University, New York.

Fox, S.W., and Harada, K. 1960. The thermal copolymerization of amino acids common to protein. *J. Amer. Chem. Soc.,* 82: 3745.

_____1963. Titration and C-terminal analysis of thermal polyamino acids. *Federation Proc.,* 22: 479.

Fox, S.W., and Yuyama, S. 1963. Abiotic production of primitive protein and formed microparticles. *Ann. N.Y. Acad. Sci.,* 108: 487.

Fox, S.W. 1964a. Experiments in molecular evolution and criteria of extraterrestrial life. *Bioscience,* 14: 13.

_____ 1964b. Thermal polymerization of amino acids and production of formed microparticles on lava. *Nature,* 201: 336.

Fox, S.W., and Krampitz, G., 1964. The catalytic decomposition of glucose in aqueous solutions by thermal proteinoids. *Nature,* 203: 1362.

Fox, S.W., and Yuyama, S. 1964. Dynamic phenomena in microspheres from thermal proteinoid. *Compar. Biochem. & Physiol.,* 11: 317.

Fox, S.W. (ed.). 1965a. *The Origin of Prebiological Systems and Their Molecular Matrices.* Academic Press, New York.

_____ 1965b. Simulated natural experiments in spontaneous organization of morphological units from proteinoid. *The Origin of Prebiological Systems and Their Molecular Matrices.* Academic Press, New York.

_____ 1965c. A theory of macromolecular and cellular origins. *Nature,* 205: 328.

Fox, S.W. 1967a. Comments in *Mathematical Challenges to the Neo-Darwinian Interpretation of Evolution.* Wistar Institute Press, P.S. Moohead and M. Kaplan (eds.). Philadelphia.

_____ 1967b. Radiation and the first bio-polymers. *Radiation Research,* G. Silini (ed.). North Holland, Amsterdam.

Fox, S.W., McCauley, R.J., Fukushima, T., Windsor, C.R., and Montgomery, P. O'B. 1967. Selective action in boundaries of particles of thermal proteinoid. *Federation Proc.,* 26: 749.

Fox, S.W., McCauley, R.J., and Wood, A. 1967. A model of primitive heterotrophic proliferation. *Compar. Biochem. & Physiol.,* 20: 773.

Fox, S.W., and Nakashima, T. 1967. Fractionation and characterization of an amidated thermal 1 : 1 : 1-proteinoid. *Biochim. Biophys. Acta,* 140: 155.

Fox, S.W., Waehneldt, T.V., Windsor, C.R., Ryan, J. and Ferrer, T. 1967. Binding of histone-like thermal proteinoids with polynucleotides. *Abstracts Seventh Int'l. Congress of Biochem.,* Tokyo.

Garrels, R.M. 1965 *Science.* 148: 69.

Garrison, W.M., Morrison, D.H., Hamilton, J.G., Benson, A.A., and Calvin, M. 1951. Reduction of carbon dioxide in aqueous solutions by ionizing radiation. *Science,* 114: 416.

Grunberg-Manago, M., and Michelson, A.M. 1964. *Biochim. Biophys. Acta,* 80:431.

Hamilton, P.B. 1965. Amino acids on hands. *Nature,* 205: 284.

Hamlin, R.M., Lord, R.C., and Rich, A. 1965. Hydrogen-bonded dimers of adenine and uracil derivatives. *Science,* 148: 1734.

Harada, K., and Fox, S.W. 1958. The thermal condensation of glutamic acid and glycine to linear peptides. *J. Amer. Chem. Soc.,* 80: 2694.

Harada, K. 1965. Total optical resolution of free-α-amino acids by the inoculation method. *Nature,* 206: 1354.

_____1967. Formation of amino acids by thermal decomposition of formamide-oligomerization of hydrogen cyanide. *Nature,* 214: 479.

Hardebeck, H.G., Krampitz, G., and Wulf, L. 1967. *Archives Biochem. & Biophys.* (in press).

Havinga, E. 1965. Spontaneous formation of optically active substances. *Biochim. Biophys. Acta,* 13: 171.

Hayatsu, R. 1964. Orgueil meteorite: organic nitrogen contents. *Science,* 146: 1291.

Hayes, J.M., and Biemann, K. 1967. High resolution mass spectrometric investigation of the organic constituents of the Murray and Holbrook chondrites. *Geochim. Cosmochim. Acta* (in press).

Heald, E.F., Naughton, J.J., and Barnes, I.L. 1963. The chemistry of volcanic gases II. Use of equilibrium calculations in the interpretation of volcanic gas samples. *J. Geophys. Res.,* 68:545.

Hoagland, P.D., and Fox, S.W. 1967. Neighboring N-carboxyalkyl group participation in the hydrolysis of phthalimide. *J. Amer. Chem. Soc.,* 89: 1389.

Hoering, T.C. 1962. Annual report of the director of geophysical laboratories, 1961-1962. *Carnegie Institution Yearbook,* 61: 190.

_____ 1967. The organic geochemistry of Precambrian rocks. *Researches in Geochemistry*, Vol. 2, P.H. Abelson (ed.), John Wiley & Sons, Inc. New York. York.

Hoffmann, H.J. 1967. Precambrian fossils near Elliott Lake, Ontario. *Science*, 156: 500.

Holland, H.D. 1965. *Proc. Nat'l. Acad. Sci.*, 53: 1173.

Horowitz, N.H. 1945. On the evolution of biochemical syntheses. *Proc. Nat'l. Acad. Sci.*, 31: 153.

Howard, F.B., Frazier, J., Singer, Maxine F., and Miles, H.T. 1965. Helix formation between polyribonucleotides and purines, purine nucleosides and nucleotides, II. *J. Molec. Biol.*, 16: 415.

Howard, F.B., Frazier, J., and Miles, H.T. 1966. A new polynucleotide complex stabilized by three interbase hydrogen bonds, poly-2-aminoadenylic acid + polyuridylic acid. *J. Biol. Chem.*, 241: 4293.

Huffman, H.M. 1942. The heats of combustion and free energies of some compounds containing the peptide bond. *J. Phys. Chem.*, 46: 885.

Hurley, P.M., Fairbairn, H.W., Pinson, W.H., and Hower, J. 1962. Unmetamorphosed minerals in the Gunflint formation used to test the age of the Animikie. *J. Geol.*, 70: 489.

Hutchinson, G.E. 1954. The biochemistry of the terrestrial atmosphere. In *The Earth as a Planet*, G.P. Kuippr (ed.), University of Chicago Press, Chicago.

Jones, A.S. and Taylor, N. 1967. Synthetic analogues of polynucleotides: Interaction of polymeric adenine derivative with DNA. *Nature*, 215: 505.

Kates, M., Yengoyan, L.S., and Sastry, P.S. 1965. A diether analog of phosphatidyl glycerophosphate in halobacterium cutirubrum. *Biochim. Biophys. Acta*, 98: 252.

Kluyver, A.J., and Van Niel, C.B. 1936. Prospects for a natural system of classification of bacteria. *Zentr. Bakteriol. Parasitenk., II. Abt.*, 94: 369.

Kuznetsov, S.I., Ivanov, M.V., and Lyalikova, N.N. 1963. In *Introduction to Geological Microbiology*. McGraw-Hill Book Co., New York.

Lanphere, M.A., Wasserburg, G., Albee, A.L., and Tilton, G.R. 1964. *Isotropic and Cosmic Chemistry*. H. Craig, S.L. Miller, and G.J. Wasserburg (eds.), North Holland, Amsterdam.

Lipmann, F. 1965. Projecting backward from the present stage of evolution of biosynthesis. *The Origins of Prebiological Systems and their Molecular Matrices,* S.W. Fox (ed.), Academic Press, New York.

Lowe, C.V., Rees, M.W., and Markham, R. 1963. Synthesis of complex organic compounds from simple precursors: Formation of amino acids, amino acid polymers, fatty acids and purines from ammonium cyanide. *Nature,* 199: 219.

MacGregor, A.M. 1940. A Precambrian algal limestone in Southern Rhodesia. *Trans. Geol. Soc. So. Africa,* 43: 9.

Mackenzie, R.T. and Garrels, R.M. 1965. *Amer. J. Science,* 150: 57.

_____ 1966. *Amer. J. Science,* 264: 507.

Manning, G. B. and Campbell, L. 1961. Thermostable-amylase of *bacillus stearothermophilus. J. Biol. Chem.,* 236: 2952.

Marshall, A.L. 1926. *J. Phys. Chem.,* 30: 1078.

Matthews, C.N. and Moser, R.E. 1966. Prebiological protein synthesis. *Proc. Nat'l. Acad. Sci.,* 56: 1087.

Miller, S.L. 1953. A production of amino acids under possible primitive earth conditions. *Science,* 117: 528.

Miller, S.L., and Urey, H.C. 1959. Organic compound synthesis on the primitive earth. *Science,* 130: 245.

Miller, S., and Horowitz, N.H. 1966. *Biology and Exploration of Mars. Nat'l. Acad. of Sci. Publ. 1296,* J.C. Pittendrigh, W. Vishniac, and J.T. Pearman, (eds.)

Morrison, P. 1962. Carbonaceous "snowflakes" and the origin of life. *Science,* 135: 663.

_____ 1964. A thermodynamic characterization of self-reproduction. *Rev. Mod. Phys.,* 36: 517.

Mueller, George. 1954. The theory of genesis of oil through hydrothermal alteration of coal type substances within certain lower carboniferous strata of the British Isles. *Congr. Geol. Int'l. Compt. Rend.,* 12: 279.

Mueller, G., Shaw, R.A., and Ogawa, T. 1965. Interrelations between volatilization curves, elemental composition and total volatiles in carbonaceous chondrites. *Nature,* 206: 23.

Munday, C., Pering, K., and Ponnamperuma, C. 1967. The gamma irradiation of isoprene. Paper presented at the 15th annual meeting, *Radiation Res. Soc.*, San Juan, Puerto Rico.

Murray, R.G.E. 1960. The internal structure of the cell. *The Bacteria, Vol. I: Structure,* I.C. Gunsalus and R.Y. Stanier (eds.), Academic Press, New York.

Nash, H.A., and Bradley, D.F. 1966. Calculation of the lowest energy configurations of nucleotide base pairs on the basis of an electrostatic model. *J. Chem. Phys.*, 45: 1380.

Oparin, A.I. 1938. *The Origin of Life.* The MacMillan Co., New York.

Oró, J. 1963. Studies in experimental organic cosmochemistry. *Ann. N.Y. Acad. Sci.*, 108: 464.

Oró, J., and Skewes, H.B. 1965. Free amino acids on human fingers: The question of contamination in microanalysis. *Nature*, 207: 1042.

Oró, J. 1965. Stages and mechanisms of prebiological organic synthesis. *The Origins of Prebiological Systems,* S.W. Fox (ed.), Academic Press, New York.

Oró, J. and Nooner, D.W. 1967. Aliphatic hydrocarbons in Precambrian rocks. *Nature*, 213: 1082.

Oshima, T. 1967. Catalytic action of proteinoid in the hydrolysis of a phosphate ester. *Federation Proc.*, 26: 451.

Palm, C. and Calvin, M. 1962. Primordial organic chemistry I. Compounds resulting from electron irradiation of $C^{14}H_4$. *J. Amer. Chem. Soc.*, 84: 2115.

Pattee, H.H. 1967a. The physical basis of coding and reliability in biological evolution. *Prolegomena to Theoretical Biology,* C.H. Waddington (ed.), Univ. of Edinburgh Press, Edinburgh (in press).

———— 1967b. Quantum mechanics, heredity, and the origin of life. *J. Theor. Biol.* (in press).

Pavloskaya, T.E., and Pasynski, A.G. 1959. The original formation of amino acids under the action of ultraviolet rays and electric discharges. Proc. Int'l. Sympos. on the *Origins of Life on the Earth,* A.I. Oparin et al (eds.), Pergamon Press, New York.

Pettijohn, F.J. 1943. Archean sedimentation. *Bull. Geol. Soc. Amer.*, 54: 925.

Pirie, N.W. 1952. Vital Blarney. *New Biol.*, 12: 106.

Pitha, J., Jones, R.N., and Pithova, P. 1966. The specificity of hydrogen bond formation between derivatives of nucleic acid bases and some analogues. *Canad. J. Chem.*, 44: 1045

Ponnamperuma, C., Woeller, F., Flores, J., Romiez, M., and Allen, W. 1967. Synthesis of organic compounds by the action of electric discharges in simulated primitive atmospheres. *Advances in Chemistry Series* (in press).

Ramsay, J.G. 1967. Structural relations of the Barberton Mountainland. *Trans. Geol. Soc. So. Africa* (in press).

Rasool, S.J., and McGovern, W.E. 1966. *Nature,* 212: 1225.

Rich, A., and Blow, D.M. 1958. Formation of a helical steroid complex. *Nature,* 182: 423.

Rich, A. 1962. On the origin of informational macromolecules. In *Horizons in Biochemistry,* M. Pullman and B. Pullman (eds.). Academic Press, New York.

Rittmann, A. 1962. *Volcanoes and Their Activity.* John Wiley & Sons, New York.

Rohlfing, D.L. 1964. *The Catalytic Activity and Heat Inactivation of Thermal Poly-α-Amino Acids.* Ph.D. Dissertation, Florida State University.

____ 1967. The Catalytic Decarboxylation of oxaloacetic acid by thermally prepared poly-α-amino acids. *Arch. Biochem. Biophys.,* 119: 468.

Rohlfing, D.L., and Fox, S.W. 1967a. The catalytic activity of thermal polyanhydro-α-amino acids for the hydrolysis of a p-nitrophenyl acetate. *Arch. Biochem. Biophys.,* 116: 122.

____ 1967b. The inactivation of catalytically active thermal polyanhydro-α-amino acids. *Arch. Biochem. Biophys.,* 118: 127.

Rosenfeld, W.D., and Silverman, S.R. 1959. Carbon isotope fractionation in bacterial production of methane. *Science,* 130: 1658.

Rubey, W.W. 1951. Geologic history of sea water. An attempt to state the problem. *Bull. Geol. Soc. Amer.,* 62: 1111.

Ruske, W. 1958-59. Polymere Blaüsaure Wissenschaftliche Zeitschriftder Humboldt. Berlin Univ. *Mathematische-Naturwissenschaftliche Reihe,* 8: 557

Sagan, L. 1967. On the origin of mitosing cells. *J. Theor. Biol.,* 14: 225.

Sanchez, R.A., Ferris, J.P., and Orgel, L.E. 1966. Cyanoacetylene in prebiotic synthesis. *Science,* 154: 784.

_____ 1967. Studies in prebiotic synthesis II. Synthesis of purine precursors and amino acids from aqueous hydrogen cyanide. *J. Mol. Biol.* (in press).

Schopf, J.W., Barghoorn, E.S., Maser, M.D., and Gordon, R.O. 1965. Electron microscopy of fossil bacteria two billion years old. *Science,* 149: 1365.

Schopf, J.W., and Barghoorn, E.S. 1967. Alga-like fossils from the early Precambrian of South Africa. *Science,* 156: 508

Schopf, J.W. 1967. Microflora of the Bitter Springs Formation late Precambrian, Central Australia. *J. Paleon.* (in press).

Schrodinger, E. 1944. *What is Life?* Cambridge University Press, London.

Schwartz, A.W., and Fox, S.W. 1967. Condensation of cyticylic acid in the presence of polyphosphoric acid. *Biochim. Biophys. Acta,* 134: 9.

Shneour, E.A. 1966. Oxidation of graphitic carbon in certain soils. *Science,* 151: 991.

Siegel, S.M., and Giumarro, C. 1966. On the culture of a microorganism similar to the Precambrian microfossil *Kakabekia umbellata* Barghoorn in NH_3-rich atmospheres. *Proc. Nat'l. Acad. Sci.,* 55: 349.

Siegel, S.M., Roberts, K., Nathan, H., and Daly, O. 1967. Living relative of the microfossil *Kakabekia. Science,* 156: 1231.

Sillen, L.G. 1961. *Oceanography.* M. Sears (ed.), Amer. Assoc. Adv. Science, Wash., D.C.

_____ 1965. Oxidation state of earth's ocean and atmosphere. II. The behavior of Fe, S, and Mn in earlier states. Regulating mechanisms for O_2 and N_2. *Arkiv. Kemi.,* 25: 159.

_____ 1967. *Science,* 156: 1189.

Smith, A.E., and Bellware, F.T. 1966. Dehydration and rehydration in a pre-biological system. *Science,* 152: 362.

Sonneborn, T.M. 1965. *Evolving Genes and Proteins*, V. Bryson and H.J. Vogel (eds.), Academic Press, New York.

Spiegelman, S. 1961. Replicating macromolecules. *Amer. Scientist.*

Sullivan, W. 1964. *We Are Not Alone.* McGraw-Hill Book Co., New York.

Taylor, H.S. and Marshall, A.L. 1925. *J. Phys. Chem.*, 29: 1140.

Taylor, H.S. 1926. *Trans. Faraday Soc.* 21: 560.

Tuppy, H., and Küchler, F. 1964. *M. Lefte Chemie*, 95: 1677.

Tyler, S.A. and Barghoorn, E.S. 1954. Occurrence of structurally preserved plants in Precambrian rocks of the Canadian shield. *Science*, 119: 606.

Urey, H.C. 1952a. *Proc. Nat'l. Acad. Sci.*, 38: 351.

_____ 1952b. *The Planets, Their Origin and Development.* Yale University Press, New Haven.

Usdin, V.R., Mitz, M.A., and Killos, P.J. 1965. Inhibition of esterase activity of proteinoids. *Abstr. 150th Meeting Amer. Chem. Soc.*, p. 21 C.

Volker, Th. 1960. Polymere Blausäure. *Angewandte Chemie*, 72: 379.

Von Neumann, J. 1951. The general and logical theory of automata. Cerebral mechanisms. *Behavior*, L.E. Jeffress (ed.). John Wiley & Sons, New York; 1956. Reprinted in *The World of Mathematics*, J.R. Newman (ed.). Simon & Schuster, New York.

Wald, G. 1957. The origin of optical activity. *Ann. N.Y. Acad. Sci.*, 69: 352.

Wigner, E.P. 1961. The probability of the existence of a self-reproducing unit. *The Logic of Personal Knowledge*, Routledge & Kegan Paul, London.

Woese, C.R., Dugres, D.H., Dugres, S.A., Kondo, M., and Saxinger, W.C. 1966. On the fundamental nature and evolution of the genetic code. *Cold Spring Harbor Symposia on Quant. Bio.*

Young, R.S. 1965. Morphology and chemistry of microspheres from proteinoids. *The Origin of Prebiological Systems and Their Molecular Matrices.* Academic Press, New York.

Young, R.S., Ponnamperuma, C., and McCaw, B. 1965. Abiogenic synthesis on Mars. M. Florkin (ed.), *Life Sciences and Space Research*, 3: 127.

Chairman (Acting):
Dr. Norman H. Horowitz
(Biochemical Genetics, Evolution
and Exobiology)
Biology Division
California Institute of Technology
Pasadena, California

Dr. Philip Abelson
(Geochemistry)*
Geophysical Laboratory
Carnegie Institution
Washington, D. C.

Mr. Jeffrey Bada
(Prebiological Organic Synthesis)
Department of Chemistry
University of California
La Jolla, California

Dr. Elso S. Barghoorn
(Precambrian Paleobiology)
Department of Biology
Harvard University
Cambridge, Massachusetts

Dr. A. L. Burlingame
(Organic Geochemistry)
Department of Chemistry
University of California
Berkeley, California

Dr. G. Eglinton
(Organic Geochemistry)
Department of Chemistry
The University of Glasgow
Glasgow, Scotland

*Area of specialization as indicated by participant follows name in parentheses.

Dr. Sidney W. Fox
(Biochemistry)
Institute of Molecular Evolution
Department of Biochemistry
University of Miami
Coral Gables, Florida

Dr. Sol Kramer
(Ethology)
Department of Psychiatry
Division of Behavioral Sciences
University of Florida College of
   Medicine
Gainesville, Florida

Dr. Lynn Margulis—Scientific
   Editor
(Genetics; Microbial Evolution)
Department of Biology
Boston University
Boston, Massachusetts

Dr. W. D. McElroy*
(Biochemistry)
Department of Biology
Johns Hopkins University
Baltimore, Maryland

Dr. Stanley L. Miller
(Prebiological Organic Synthesis)
Department of Chemistry
University of California
La Jolla, California

---

*Present Address

Director
National Science Foundation
Washington, D. C.

Dr. Philip Morrison
(Astronomy; Cosmology)
Department of Physics
Massachusetts Institute of
  Technology
Cambridge, Massachusetts

Dr. N. Henry Moss
(General Surgery; Cancer; Medical
  Education)
Department of Surgery
Temple University Health Sciences
  Center
Albert Einstein Medical Center
Philadelphia, Pennsylvania

Dr. Leslie E. Orgel
(Prebiotic Chemistry)
The Salk Institute for Biological
  Studies
San Diego, California

Dr. Juan Oró
(Biochemistry)
Department of Chemistry
University of Houston
Houston, Texas

Dr. Howard H. Pattee
(Origin of Life)
Biophysics Program
Stanford University
Stanford, California

Dr. Cyril Ponnamperuma
(Chemical Evolution)
Exobiology Division
NASA, Ames Research Center
Moffett Field, California

Dr. Orr E. Reynolds
(Exobiology)
Director, NASA Bioscience Programs
Office of Space Science and Applications
Washington, D. C.

Dr. Alexander Rich
(Nucleic Acid Chemistry)
Department of Biophysics
Massachusetts Institute of Technology
Cambridge, Massachusetts

Dr. Carl Sagan
(Astronomy)
Department of Astronomy
Harvard University and Smithsonian
    Astrophysical Observatory
Cambridge, Massachusetts

Dr. J. William Schopf
(Precambrian Paleobiology)
Department of Biology
Harvard University
Cambridge, Massachusetts

Dr. M. C. Shelesnyak*
(Reproductive Physiology)
Department of Biodynamics
Weizmann Institute of Science
Rehovoth, Israel

---

*Present Address

Director
Interdisciplinary Communications Program
1025 Fifteenth Street, N. W.
Washington, D. C.

Dr. Raymond Siever
(Geochemistry; Geology)
Department of Geological Sciences
Harvard University
Cambridge, Massachusetts

Dr. John Sulston
(Prebiotic Chemistry)
The Salk Institute for Biological
    Studies
San Diego, California

Dr. Carl R. Woese
(Genetic Code)
Department of Microbiology
University of Illinois
Urbana, Illinois

Interdisciplinary Communications Program*
Dr. Frank Fremont-Smith, Director

*As of July 1969

Dr. M. C. Shelesnyak, Director
Interdisciplinary Communications Program
Smithsonian Institution
1025 15th Street, N.W.
Washington, D.C. 20005